A Stanley Gibbons Thematic Catalogue

C000151589

COLLECT
BIRDS ON STAMPS

Jens and Hanne Eriksen

Second Edition 1988

Stanley Gibbons Publications Ltd
London and Ringwood

By Appointment to Her Majesty The Queen
Stanley Gibbons Ltd., London
Philatelists

Published by **Stanley Gibbons Publications Ltd.**
Editorial, Sales Offices and Distribution Centre:
5 Parkside, Christchurch Road, Ringwood,
Hants BH24 3SH

First Edition – June 1983
Second Edition — February 1988

© Stanley Gibbons Publications Ltd 1988

ISBN: 0-85259-182-9

Item No. 2864 (88)

Printed in Great Britain by Whitefriars Press, Tonbridge, Kent

Birds of a Feather

Since the very earliest times mankind has observed, and envied, birds' freedom of flight. Icarus was only one of many imitators and eventual success was only achieved with the help of the aero-engine.

Birds have secured their place in the images of everyday life; Seagulls following the plough, the racket of circling mobs of Starlings preparing to roost in city centres, a flight of Swans rising at sunset, the Robin adorning millions of Christmas cards each year. Virtually every household supplies supplementary feed for the garden birds in winter and the appearance of a rare species results in a virtual stampede of bird watchers to the site. It is, surely, no accident that one of the most successful of the animal charities, the Royal Society for the Protection of Birds, will celebrate its centenary in 1989.

Stamp collectors are no exception to the general trend. In a readers' survey held in 1986 birds was by a considerable margin the most popular theme collected. The first S.G. thematic catalogue, *Collect Birds on Stamps*, was published in 1983 and has been out of print for some time. We received many letters from collectors requesting a second edition, so we are very pleased that Hanne and Jens Eriksen, now based in Oman, have been able to provide one.

You will find all the species which have appeared on stamps here from the awe-inspiring American Bald Eagle to the graceful Greater Flamingo, the solemn Emperor Penguin and, even, the Dodo. Since the last edition there have been over 1800 new bird stamps with over 300 species being illustrated for the first time. All are listed with up-to-date prices and can be identified by the index, including a new version for scientific names, and the species section. In response to requests from readers of the first edition the listings have been extended to cover birds from extinct species.

Although this is the second edition it does also represent a first. This is the first occasion that a Stanley Gibbons catalogue has been produced from personal computer discs. The original data was compiled on disc in Oman, coded and priced at S.G. Publications in Ringwood and printed out through a typesetter at Whitefriars Press, Tonbridge. This is an important development and has considerable implications for catalogue production in the future. We are excited about it and are sure that bird collectors will also be excited by the listings in this new edition of Collect Birds on Stamps.

David J Aggersberg
Pam Basley

About This Book

This catalogue is a listing of stamps depicting birds issued by countries thoughout the world. It is based on the Stanley Gibbons *Stamps of the World Simplified Catalogue*, published annually in two volumes. This second edition contains over 7500 stamps which depict over 1860 different bird species. It has been up-dated so that it includes all bird stamps which have appeared in the *Stamp Monthly* Catalogue Supplements up to and including the October 1987 issue.

What is included
All issues, including overprints and surcharges, depicting wild birds as listed in the *Stamps of the World Catalogue*. Extinct species have been added to this edition and are marked with an asterisk. Miniature sheets which form a natural extension of a stamp series are also included.

What is excluded
All stamp variations of watermark and perforation which are outside the scope of the *Stamps of the World*. The lists also exclude birds forming part of a coat of arms, symbolic birds, poultry and peace doves and those too stylised to be identified. Stamps listed in the Appendix in *Stamps of the World* will be found in similar sections in the countries listing. The birds on these stamps have now been identified.

Countries Section
This section lists in alphabetical order, with prices, the various countries and territories which have issued bird stamps. Within each country or territory the stamps are listed in chronological order with the year of issue and catalogue number taken from the *Stamps of the World Catalogue*.

Each bird has been given a recognised English name (see also under Bird Names) and the listing also includes, in brackets, any other bird name which actually appears on the stamp. The following order of preference has been adopted for quoting these inscriptions: (a) English name, if this differs from that already used; (b) systematic name; (c) local name. The inscriptions are shown exactly as on the stamps. Several designs have appeared with erroneous inscriptions, usually misspellings of the systematic name, but in some instances the inscriptions refer to a completely different bird from that depicted on the stamp. Such instances, Afghanistan Nos. 543/4 for example, are indicated by a !.

Bird Species Section
This section lists all the species which have appeared on stamps in systematic (ornithological) order. Subspecies have not been identified. Under each entry are given, in alphabetical order, the countries and catalogue numbers of the stamps which depict that particular bird.

Bird Names
The recognised English and systematic names follow the order proposed by Richard Howard's and Alick Moore's *A Complete Checklist of the Birds of the World* (Oxford University Press, 1980; 2nd edn, 1984). Extinct species follow the listing in *Extinct and Vanishing Birds of the World* by James C. Greenway (2nd edn, Dover 1967). Many other books have been consulted in the compilation of this catalogue and a selection of the most useful for thematic collecors is given on page v.

Acknowledgments
We would like to thank the many collectors who have responded so positively to the 1st edition of this catalogue. We have seriously listened to their constructive criticism and as a result have changed some identifications of difficult birds as well as included extinct species and birds on coins. Several collectors have asked us to identify the birds in the Appendix sections. This has been achieved in this new edition.

As before we would very much welcome comments and criticism on this edition. Only the users of the catalogue can judge its value.

Hanne and Jens Eriksen
Oman, October 1987

Hanne and Jens Eriksen formerly lived in Aarhus, Denmark. Recently they both took up positions at the new Sultan Qaboos University in the Sultanate of Oman. Hanne (32) is secretary in the Biology Department and Jens (37) is Professor in the Chemistry Department. They are both devoted bird-watchers and wildlife photographers, having travelled in Europe, Asia, Africa and North America in search of birds in their natural habitat.

Books on Birds

A vast number of bird books is available. The following list includes some useful books for the identification of birds, but it is by no means exhaustive.

GENERAL BOOKS

The Birds of the Western Palearctic, Cramp and Simmons, four vols. issued and more to come.

The Birds of Africa, Fry et al., two vols. issued and more to come.

FIELD GUIDES

A Field Guide to the Birds of Britain and Europa, Peterson et al.

A Field Guide to the Birds of East Africa, Williams and Arlott.

A Field Guide to the Brids of West Africa, Serle et al.

Roberts' Birds of South Africa, McLachlan and Liversidge.

The Birds of Seychelles and Outlying Islands, Penny.

The Birds of Oman, Gallagher and Woodcock.

The Birds of the USSR, Flint et al.

A Pictorial Guide to the Birds of the Indian Subcontinent, Ali et al.

The Birds of China, de Schauensee.

A Field Guide to the Birds of Japan.

A Field Guide to the Birds of South-East Asia, King et al.

A Field Guide to the Birds of Australia, Pizzey.

The New Guide to the Birds of New Zealand, Falla et al.

A Field Guide to the Birds of North America, National Geographic Society.

A Field Guide to Mexican Birds, Peterson and Chalif.

Birds of the West Indies, Bond.

A Guide to the Birds of Colombia, Hilty et al.

Guide to the Birds of Venezuela, de Schauensee.

Aves Brasileiras, Frisch.

A Guide to the Birds of South America, de Schauensee.

A Field Guide to the Birds of Galapagos, Harris.

SPECIFIC SPECIES

Seabirds: an identification guide, Harrison.

Herons of the World, Hancock and Elliot.

Waterfowl: Ducks, Geese and Swans of the World, Todd.

Eagles, Hawks and Falcons of the World, Brown and Amadon.

Birds of Prey of Britain and Europa, North Africa and the Middle East, Gensbol.

Pheasants of the World, Delacour.

Rails of the World, Ripley.

Shorebirds: an identification guide to the waders of the world, Hayman et al.

Gulls: a guide to identification, Grant.

Pigeons and Doves of the World, Goodwin.

Parrots of the World, Forshaw and Cooper.

Birds of Paradise and Bowerbirds, Cooper and Forshaw.

Crows of the World, Goodwin.

Societies

Royal Society for the Protection of Birds
The Lodge
Sandy
Beds SG19 2DL

The Bird Stamp Society
Secretary: D. J. Cox
Lynnmoor
Ampney Crucis
Glos GL7 5RY

Stanley Gibbons Ltd

Head Office, Shop and Rare Stamp Departments
399 Strand, London WC2R 0LX.
Offices open Monday – Friday 9.30 a.m. to 5 p.m. and Saturday by appointment only.
Shop open Monday – Friday 9.00 a.m. to 6.00 p.m. and Saturday 10 a.m. to 4.00 p.m.
Telephone 01-836 8444 and Telex 28883 for all departments.

Stanley Gibbons Publications and Promotions
Parkside, Christchurch Road, Ringwood, Hants, BH24 3SH.
Telephone 04254 2363 and Telex 41271.

FILL YOUR GAPS

AT THE WORLD'S LARGEST STAMP SHOP

We hold the largest general stock of British Empire/ Commonwealth stamps in the World and have a comprehensive range of material from many other countries.

We specialise in thematics particularly

BIRDS ON STAMPS

CALL IN – we are open normal shop hours.
OR WRITE – Our efficient mail order service is ready and waiting to fulfil your wants list

Stanley Gibbons Ltd.
399 Strand
London WC2R 0LX
Telephone 01–836 8444

Countries Section

Arrangement

The various countries and territories are listed in the same order as in *Stamps of the World*. Those few which are not in alphabetical order are covered by cross-references. Each entry includes the geographical location and details of the currencies used. The dates quoted against these currencies are those on which they were first used for stamps in this catalogue.

Illustrations

These are three-quarters of actual size. One design from each issue is depicted, but only those overprints and surcharges required for identification are included.

Listings

These are divided into years by dates and into individual issues by the illustrations.

For philatelic details the *Stamps of the World*, or the 22 volume standard catalogue, should be consulted.

A † against the catalogue number indicates an issue where unlisted stamps in the set depict designs other than birds.

Miniature sheets are indicated by a MS prefix.

Prices

Those in the lefthand column are for unused stamps and those in the righthand column are for used.

Issues where all the designs depict birds are priced as sets only; single stamps and those from "broken" sets are priced individually.

Our prices are for stamps in fine average condition, and in issues where condition varies we may ask more for the superb and less for the sub-standard.

The prices of unused stamps are for lightly hinged examples for those issued before 1946, thereafter for examples unmounted mint.

Prices for used stamps refer to postally used examples, though for certain issues it is for cancelled-to-order.

The minimum price quoted is 5p which represents a handling charge rather than a basis for valuing common stamps.

The prices quoted are generally for the cheapest variety of stamps but it is worth noting that differences of watermark, perforation, or other details, outside the scope of this catalogue, may often increase the value of the stamp.

All prices are subject to change without prior notice and we give no guarantee to supply all stamps priced. Prices quoted for albums, publications, etc. advertised in this catalogue are also subject to change without prior notice.

Guarantee

ABU DHABI

Arabian peninsula
1965 100 naye paise = 1 rupee
1966 1000 fils = 1 dinar

1965

12	20np Saker Falcon		
13	40np Saker Falcon		
14	2r Saker Falcon		
		Set of 3	16.00	10.00

1967

35†	200f Lanner Falcon	5.50	2.50

1968

51† 35f Northern Goshawk. 3.00 1.60

1968

629 1a European Black Vulture (*Aegypius monachus*)
630 6a Eagle Owl (*Bubo-bubo*)
631 7a Greater Flamingo (*Phoenicopterus ruber*)

Set of 3 2.00 2.00

ADEN PROTECTORATE STATES
Arabian peninsula
1000 fils = 1 dinar

Seiyun

1967

112† 25f Magpie. 30 25

AFGHANISTAN
Central Asia
100 poul (pul) = 1 afghani (rupee)

1965

543 1a25 Scaly-bellied Green Woodpecker (*Garrulus lanceolatus* !)
544 3a75 Lanceolated Jay (*Chaimarrornis leucocephalus* !)
545 5a Himalayan Monal Pheasant (*Lophophorus impejanus*)

Set of 3 2.00 2.00

1970

692 2a Common Quail (*Coturnix coturnix*)
693 4a Golden Eagle (*Aquila chrysaetos*)
694 6a Ring-necked Pheasant (*Phasianus colchicus*)

Set of 3 2.00 1.75

1972

723† 10a Chukar Partridge (*Alectoris chukar*) .. 1.50 90

1973

751 8a Himalayan Monal Pheasant (*Lophophorus impejanus*)
752 9a Great Crested Grebe (*Podiceps cristatus*)
753 12a Himalayan Snowcock (*Tetraogallus himalayensis*)

Set of 3 2.50 2.00

1974

774 1a Lesser Spotted Eagle (*Aquila pomarina*)
775 6a White-fronted Goose (*Anser albifrons*),
    Ruddy Shelduck (*Casarca ferruginea*),
    Greylag Goose (*Anser anser*)
776 11a Common Coot (*Fulica atra*), Common
    Crane (*Grus grus*)
                   Set of 3 1.75 1.25

1982

886 6a White Stork ('La Cigogne')
887 11a Goldfinch ('Le Rossignol' !)
                   Set of 2   80   60

1985

1062 2a Magpie
1063 4a Green Woodpecker
1064 8a Ring-necked Pheasant
1065 13a Bluethroat, Goldfinch, Hoopoe
1066 18a Peregrine Falcon
1067 25a Chukar Partridge
1068 30a Eastern White Pelican
                   Set of 7 2.75 2.50
MS1069 75a Rose-ringed Parakeet 2.25 2.50

Appendix
The following stamps have either been issued in excess of postal needs, or have not been made available to the public in reasonable quantities at face value. Miniature sheets, imperforate stamps etc. are excluded from this section.

1961
Flora and Fauna. 2p, 175p Chukar Partridge

AITUTAKI
South Pacific
1903 12 pence = 1 shilling,
20 shilling = 1 pound
1967 100 cents = 1 dollar

1903
Nos. 309, 265 and 268a of New Zealand overprinted **AITUTAKI**
and value in native language

5†	3d Huia *	6.50	14.00
6†	6d Brown Kiwi	13.00	25.00
7†	1s Kaka, Kea	65.00	80.00

1973
No. 421 of Cook Islands overprinted **AITUTAKI**

75†	20c White Tern	35	35

1974

121†	50c Huia * (on stamp No. 5)..	75	75

1979

277†	65c Huia * (on stamp No. 5).. .. '. ..	75	75
MS279	30c Huia * (on stamp No. 5)	2.25	2.40

1981

317 1c Gouldian Finch (*Poephila gouldiae*)
318 1c Common Starling (*Sturnus vulgaris*)
319 2c Golden Whistler (*Pachycephala
    pectoralis*)
320 2c Scarlet Robin (*Petroica multicolor*)
321 3c Rufous Fantail (*Rhipidura rufifrous*)
322 3c Peregrine Falcon (*Falco peregrinus*)
323 4c Java Sparrow (*Padda oryzivora*)
324 4c Barn Owl (*Tyto alba*)
325 5c Tahitian Lory (*Vini peruviana*)
326 5c White-breasted Wood Swallow (*Artamus
    leucorhynchus*)
327 6c Purple Swamphen (*Porphyrio porphyrio*)
328 6c Rock Dove (*Columba livia*)

329 10c Chestnut-breasted Mannikin (*Lonchura castaneothorax*)
330 10c Zebra Dove (*Geopelia striata*)
331 12c Eastern Reef Heron (*Egretta sacra*)
332 12c Common Mynah (*Acridotheres tristis*)
333 15c Whimbrel (*Numenius phaeopus*)
334 15c Black-browed Albatross (*Diomeda melanophris*)
335 20c American Golden Plover (*Pluvialis dominica*)
336 20c White Tern (*Gygis alba*)
337 25c Spotbill Duck (*Anas superciliosa*)
338 25c Brown Booby (*Sula leucogaster*)
339 30c Great Frigate Bird (*Fregata minor*)
340 30c Pintail (*Anas acuta*)
341 35c Long-billed Reed Warbler (*Conopoderas caffra caffra*)
342 35c Pomarine Skua (*Stercorarius pomarinus*)
343 40c Banded Rail (*Gallirallus philippensis goodsoni*)
344 40c Spotted Triller (*Lalage maculosa pumila*)
345 50c Royal Albatross (*Diomedea epomophora*)
346 50c Stephen's Lory (*Vini stepheni*)
347 70c Red-headed Parrot Finch (*Erythrura cyaneovirens*)
348 70c Orange Dove (*Ptilinopus victor victor*)
349 $1 Blue-headed Flycatcher (*Myiagra azureocapilla whitneyi*)
350 $2 Red-bellied Flycatcher (*Myiagra vanikorensis rufiventris*)
351 $4 Red Munia (*Amandava amandava*)
352 $5 Flat-billed Kingfisher (*Halcyon recurvirostris*)
Set of 36   17.00   17.00

1983
Nos. 335/48 and 352 surcharged
4471 18c on 20c American Golden Plover
448 18c on 20c White Tern
449 36c on 25c Spotbill Duck
450 36c on 25c Brown Booby
451 36c on 30c Great Frigate Bird
452 36c on 30c Pintail
453 36c on 35c Long-billed Reed Warbler
454 36c on 35c Pomarine Skua
455 48c on 40c Banded Rail
456 48c on 40c Spotted Triller
457 48c on 50c Royal Albatross
458 48c on 50c Stephen's Lory
459 72c on 70c Red-headed Parrot Finch
460 72c on 70c Orange Dove
461 $5.60 on $5 Flat-billed Kingfisher
Set of 15   8.00   8.75

1984

475 2c Gouldian Finch (*Poephila gouldiae*)
476 3c Common Starling (*Sturnus vulgaris*)

477 5c Scarlet Robin (*Petroica multicolor*)
478 10c Golden Whistler (*Pachycephala pectoralis*)
479 12c Rufous Fantail (*Rhipidura rufifrous*)
480 18c Peregrine Falcon (*Falco peregrinus*)
481 24c Barn Owl (*Tyto alba*)
482 30c Java Sparrow (*Padda oryzivora*)
483 36c White-breasted Wood Swallow (*Artamus leucorhynchus*)
484 48c Tahitian Lory (*Vini peruviana*)
485 50c Rock Dove (*Columba livia*)
486 60c Purple Swamphen (*Porphyrio porphyrio*)
487 72c Zebra Dove (*Geopelia striata*)
488 96c Chestnut-breasted Mannikin (*Lonchura castaneothorax*)
489 $1.20 Common Mynah (*Acridotheres tristis*)
490 $2.10 Eastern Reef Heron (*Egretta sacra*)
491 $3 Blue-headed Flycatcher (*Myiagra azureocapilla whitneyi*)
492 $4.20 Red-bellied Flycatcher (*Myiagra vanikorensis rufiventris*)
493 $5.60 Red Munia (*Amandava amandava*)
494 $9.60 Flat-billed Kingfisher (*Halcyon recurvirostris*)
Set of 20   17.00   18.00

506† $1.40 Golden Whistler (on stamp No. 319), Huia * (on stamp No. 121)   1.25   1.40
MS507 $1.40 + 5c Golden Whistler (on stamp No. 319), Huia * (on stamp No. 121) (sheet also contains two other stamps)   2.75   3.00

1985

518 55c Grey Kingbird ('Gray Kingbird')
519 65c Bohemian Waxwing
520 75c Summer Tanager
521 95c Common Cardinal ('Cardinal')
522 $1.15 White-winged Crossbill
Set of 5   3.50   3.50

1986
No. MS507 with 'Ausipex' emblems obliterated in gold
MS549 $1.40 + 5c Golden Whistler (on stamp No. 319), Huia * (on stamp No. 121) (sheet also contains two other stamps)   2.10   2.25

OFFICIAL STAMPS

1985

Nos. 475, 477/88 and 491/4 overprinted or surcharged **O.H.M.S.**

O17	2c Gouldian Finch		
O18	5c Scarlet Robin		
O19	10c Golden Whistler		
O20	12c Rufous Fantail		
O21	18c Peregrine Falcon		
O22	20c on 24c Barn Owl		
O23	30c Java Sparrow		
O24	40c on 36c White-breasted Wood Swallow		
O25	50c Rock Dove		
O26	55c on 48c Tahitian Lory		
O27	60c Purple Swamphen		
O28	65c on 72c Zebra Dove		
O29	80c on 96c Chestnut-breasted Mannikin		
O30	$3 Blue-headed Flycatcher		
O31	$4.20 Red-bellied Flycatcher		
O32	$5.60 Red Munia		
O33	$9.60 Flat-billed Kingfisher		
		Set of 17 15.00 16.00	

AJMAN

Arabian peninsula
1964 100 naye paise = 1 rupee
1967 100 dirhams = 1 riyal

1964

7 †	15np White Stork	25	5
8 †	20np Black-headed Gull	25	8
9 †	30np Lanner Falcon	25	12
16†	3r White Stork	95	95
17†	5r Black-headed Gull	2.50	1.90
18†	10r Lanner Falcon	4.50	3.50

1965

61†	2r White Stork	90	60
62†	3r Black-headed Gull	2.50	1.00
63†	5r Lanner Falcon	3.50	1.40

1967

Nos. 7/9, 16/18 and 61/3 with currency names changed by overprinting **Dh** *or* **Riyals**

105†	15d on 15np White Stork	25	5
106†	20d on 20np Black-headed Gull	25	5
107†	30d on 30np Lanner Falcon	25	5
114†	3r on 3r White Stork	1.25	60
115†	5r on 5r Black-headed Gull	2.00	1.00
116†	10r on 10r Lanner Falcon	6.50	2.00
123†	2r on 2r White Stork (air)	70	60
124†	3r on 3r Black-headed Gull	2.10	70
125†	5r on 5r Lanner Falcon	2.75	1.75

OFFICIAL STAMPS

1965

As Nos. 61/3, additionally inscribed 'ON STATE'S SERVICE'

O70†	2r White Stork	55	25
O71†	3r Black-headed Gull	90	35
O72†	5r Lanner Falcon	3.00	70

1967

Nos. O70/2 with currency names changed by overprinting **Riyals**

O132†	2r on 2r White Stork	65	70
O133†	3r on 3r Black-headed Gull	1.10	1.25
O134†	5r on 5r Lanner Falcon	3.00	2.25

Appendix

The following stamps have either been issued in excess of postal needs, or have not been made available to the public in reasonable quantities at face value. Miniature sheets, imperforate stamps etc. are excluded from this section.

1969

Birds. Air 1r × 11 Secretary Bird, South African Crowned Crane, Whale-headed Stork, Sacred Ibis, Grey Parrot, Sclater's Parrotlet, Muller's Parrot, Moluccan Hanging Parrot, Yellow-crowned Amazon, Wilson's Bird of Paradise, Twelve-wired Bird of Paradise

1971

Tropical Birds. Postage 1d Little Egret (?), 2d Japanese Pheasant, 3d Little Egret (?), 4d Japanese Lesser Sparrow Hawk, 5d White Stork, 10d Golden Pheasant. Air 2r Golden Pheasant, 3r Great-billed Parrot

Tropical Asiatic Birds. Postage 1d Hooded Racquet-tailed Tree Pie, 2d Dusky Broadbill, 3d Red-bearded Bee Eater, 5d Hodgson's Grandala, 7d Red-billed Blue Magpie, 10d Black and Red Broadbill, 12d Whiskered Tree Swift, 15d Magpie, 20d Beautiful Nuthatch, 25d Sultan Tit, 30d Blue-winged Pitta, 40d Brown Eared-Pheasant. Air 50d Yellow-billed Blue Magpie, 80d Scale-feathered Cuckoo, 1r Green Magpie, 3r Silver Pheasant

13th World Scout Jamboree. Japanese Paintings. 20d Manchurian Crane

25th Anniversary of U.N.I.C.E.F. Overprint on 1971 Scout Jamboree issue. 20d Manchurian Crane

---

COLLECT MAMMALS ON STAMPS

The second Stanley Gibbons thematic catalogue — copies are available at £7.50 (p. + p. £1.50) from: Stanley Gibbons Publications Ltd, 5 Parkside, Christchurch Road, Ringwood, Hants BH24 3SH.

ALAND ISLANDS

Baltic
100 penni = 1 markka

1987

25 1m70 Eider (*Somateria mollissima*)
26 2m30 Tufted Duck (*Aythya fuligula*)
27 12m Velvet Scoter (*Melanitta fusca*)

Set of 3	3.75	3.75

ALBANIA

South-east Europe
100 qint = 1 lek

1961

676 1 lek 50 Dalmatian Pelican ('Pelikan')
677 7 lek 50 Grey Heron ('Capke E Murme')
678 11 lek Little Egret ('Capke E Bardhe')

Set of 3	9.00	2.75

1962

728† 1 lek Golden Eagle	25	10
730† 16 lek Golden Eagle	4.50	1.75
(728/30 *Set of* 3)	4.75	2.00

COLLECT RAILWAYS ON STAMPS

1963

748 0 lek 50 Great Crested Grebe (*Podiceps cristatus*)
749 3 lek Golden Eagle (*Aquila chrysaetus*)
750 6 lek 50 Grey Partridge (*Perdix perdix*)
751 11 lek Capercaillie (*Tetrao urogallus*)

Set of 4	9.50	4.50

1964

832 0 lek 50 Winter Wren (*Troglodytes troglodytes*)
833 1 lek Penduline Tit (*Remiz pendulinus*)
834 2 lek 50 Green Woodpecker (*Picus viridis*)
835 3 lek Treecreeper (*Certhia familiaris*)
836 4 lek European Nuthatch (*Sitta europaea*)
837 5 lek Great Tit (*Parus major*)
838 6 lek Goldfinch (*Carduelis garulus*)
839 18 lek Golden Oriole (*Oriolus oriolus*)

Set of 8	9.00	4.50

1965

933 10q White Stork (*Ciconia ciconia*)
934 20q European Cuckoo (*Cuculus canorus*)
935 30q Hoopoe (*Upupa epops*)
936 40q European Bee Eater (*Merops apiaster*)
937 50q European Nightjar (*Caprimulgus europaeus*)
938 1 lek 50 Common Quail (*Coturnix coturnix*)

Set of 6	5.50	3.50

942†	10q Capercaillie	25	10
944†	30q Ring-necked Pheasant	50	40
945†	40q Mallard	75	50

1966

1084 10q Golden Eagle (Aquila chrysaetos)
1085 15q White-tailed Sea Eagle (Haliaetus albicilla)
1086 25q Griffon Vulture (Gyps fulvus)
1087 40q European Sparrow Hawk (Accipiter nisus)
1088 50q Osprey (Pandion haliaetus)
1089 70q Egyptian Vulture (Neophron percnopterus)
1090 90q Common Kestrel (Falco tinnunculus)
Set of 7   7.50   3.75

1967

1098 10q Dalmatian Pelican ('Pelikan')
1099 15q Dalmatian Pelican ('Pelikan')
1100 25q Dalmatian Pelican ('Pelikan')
1101 50q Dalmatian Pelican ('Pelikan')
1102 2 lek Dalmatian Pelican ('Pelikan')
Set of 5   7.00   3.00

1179†	80q Mallard	70	30

1968

1283 15q Bohemian Waxwing (Bombycila garrulus)
1284 20q Rose-coloured Starling (Pastor roseus)
1285 25q Common Kingfisher (Alcedo atthis ispida)
1286 50q Long-tailed Tit (Aegithalus caodatus)
1287 80q Wallcreeper (Tichodroma muraria)
1288 1 lek 10 Bearded Reedling (Panurus biarmicus)
Set of 6   3.50   1.50

1971

1457 5q Crested Tit (Parus cristatus mitratus)
1458 10q Serin (Serinus canaria serinus)
1459 15q Linnet (Acanthis canabina)
1460 25q Firecrest (Regulus regulus !)
1461 45q Rock Thrush (Monticola saxatilis)
1462 60q Blue Tit (Parus coeruleus)
1463 2 lek 40 Chaffinch (Fringilla coelebs)
Set of 7   4.50   2.25

1973

1587 5q Common Tern (Sterna hirundo)
1588 15q White-winged Black Tern (Chlidonias leucoptera)
1589 25q Black-headed Gull (Larus ridibundus)
1590 45q Great Black-headed Gull (Larus argentatus !)
1591 80q Slender-billed Gull (Larus genei)
1592 2 lek 40 Sandwich Tern (Sterna sandvicensis)
Set of 6   3.75   2.00

1974

1683 10q Redwing (*Turdus musicus*)
1684 15q European Robin (*Erithacus rubecula*)
1685 20q Greenfinch (*Chloris chloris*)
1686 25q Bullfinch (*Pyrrhula pyrrhula*)
1687 40q Hawfinch (*Coccothraustes coccothraustes*)
1688 80q Blackcap (*Sylvia atricapilla*)
1689 2 lek 20 Nightingale (*Luscinia megarhyncha*)

Set of 7	3.50	1.75

1975

1761 5q European Wigeon (*Anas penelope*)
1762 10q Red-crested Pochard (*Netta rufina*)
1763 15q White-fronted Goose (*Anser albifrons*)
1764 20q Pintail (*Anas acuta*)
1765 25q Red-breasted Merganser (*Mergus serrator*)
1766 30q Eider (*Somateria mollissima*)
1767 35q Whooper Swan (*Cignus cignus*)
1768 2 lek 70 Common Shoveler (*Spatula clypeata*)

Set of 8	3.00	1.25

ALDERNEY
See under Guernsey

STANLEY GIBBONS
STAMP COLLECTING SERIES
Introductory booklets on *How to Start, How to Identify Stamps* and *Collecting by Theme.* A series of well illustrated guides at a low price. Write for details.

ALGERIA
North Africa
1949 100 centimes = 1 franc
1964 100 centimes = 1 dinar

1949

290†	50f White Stork	..	..	..	..	..	..	2.00	20
292†	200f White Stork	..	..	..	..	..	..	4.50	2.25

1957

374†	15f + 5f White Stork	..	..	..	..	..	3.75	3.75
	(373/4 *Set of 2*)						5.50	5.50

1967

488†	20c Ostrich (*Struthio camelus*)	..	..	..	65	50

1976

689 50c Red-billed Fire Finch (*Lagonosticta senegala senegala*)
690 1d40 Black-headed Bush Shrike (*Tchagra senegala cucullata*)
691 2d Blue Tit (*Parus caeruleus ultramarinus*)
692 2d50 Black-bellied Sandgrouse (*Pterocles orientalis*)

Set of 4	4.00	2.50

1977

722 60c Tristram's Warbler (*Sylvia deserticola*)
723 1d40 Moussier's Redstart (*Phoenicurus moussieri*)
724 2d Temminck's Horned Lark (*Eremophila bilopha*)
725 3d Hoopoe (*Upupa epops*)

Set of 4 3.50 2.75

1979

755 10d White Stork 3.00 1.50

761 1d40 Kabylie Nuthatch (*Sitta ledanti*) 1.25 85

1982

829 50c Waldrapp (*Geronticus eremita*)
830 80c Houbara Bustard (*Chlamydotis undulata*)
831 2d Tawny Eagle (*Aquila rapax*)
832 2d40 Lammergeier (*Gypaetus barbatus*)

Set of 4 2.25 1.50

ANDORRA
Pyrenees Mountains between France and Spain

French Post Offices
100 centimes = 1 franc

1971

F229† 80c Capercaillie ('Coq de Bruyere') 1.50 1.50
(F229/30 Set of 2) 3.25 3.00

1972

F238 60c Golden Eagle ('Aigle Royal') 1.75 1.25

1973

F251 90c Blue Tit ('Mesange Bleue')
F252 1f Lesser Spotted Woodpecker ('Pic Epeichette')

Set of 2 2.00 2.10

1974

F259 60c Citril Finch ('Venturon Montagnard')
F260 80c Bullfinch ('Bouvreuil')

Set of 2 2.75 2.00

1979

F294 1f20 Rock Ptarmigan ('Perdiu Blanca') . .. 75 40

1981

F313 1f20 Bonelli's Warbler (*Phylloscopus bonelli*)
F314 1f40 Wallcreeper (*Tichodroma muraria*)
                       Set of 2   90   50

1985

F368 1f80 Mallard (*Anas platyrhynchos*)
F369 2f20 Goldfinch (*Carduelis carduelis*)
                       Set of 2   85   65

Spanish Post Offices

100 centimos = 1 peseta

EXPRESS LETTER STAMP

1929

E41 20c American Bald Eagle. 6.00 2.75

ANGOLA
South-west Africa
1951 100 centavos = 1 angolar
1977 100 lweis = 1 kwanza

1951

458   5c Dark Chanting Goshawk (*Melierax mechowi*)
459   10c Racquet-tailed Roller (*Coracias spatulatus*)
460   15c Bateleur (*Therathopius ecaudatus*)
461   20c European Bee Eater (*Merops apiaster*)
462   50c Giant Kingfisher (*Ceryle maxima*)
463   1a Yellow-headed Barbet (*Buccanodon anchietae*)
464   1a50 African Open-bill Stork (*Anastomus lamelligerus*)
465   2a Southern Ground Hornbill (*Bucorvus cafer*)
466   2a50 African Skimmer (*Rhynchops flavirostris*)
467   3a Shikra (*Astur polyzonoides*)
468   3a50 Barrow's Bustard (*Otis cafra*)
469   4a African Golden Oriole (*Oriolus notatus*)
470   4a50 Eastern Long-tailed Shrike (*Urolestes melanoleucus*)
471   5a Red-shouldered Glossy Starling (*Lamprocolius phoenicopterus*)
472   6a Sharp-tailed Glossy Starling (*Heteropsar acuticaudus*)
473   7a Fan-tailed Whydah (*Urobrachya bocagei*)
474   10a Half-collared Kingfisher (*Alcedo semitorquata*)
475   12a50 White-crowned Shrike (*Eurocephalus anguitimens*)
476   15a White-winged Starling (*Neocichla gutturalis*)
477   20a Yellow-billed Hornbill (*Laphoceros elegans*)
478   25a Violet Starling (*Cinnyricinclus verreauxi*)
479   30a Sulphur-breasted Bush Shrike (*Chlorophoneus sulfureopectus modestus*)
480   40a Secretary Bird (*Serpentarius serpentarius*)
481   50a Peach-faced Lovebird (*Apapornis roseicollis*)
                       Set of 24   £250   55.00

1984

ANGOLA

827   10k50 Southern Ground Hornbill (*Bucorvos leadbeateri*)
828   14k Palm-nut Vulture (*Gypohierax angolensis*)
829   16k Goliath Heron (*Ardea goliath*)
830   19k50 Eastern White Pelican (*Pelecanus onocrotalus*)
831   22k African Spoonbill (*Platalea alba*)
832   26k South African Crowned Crane (*Balearica pavonina* !)

                          Set of 6   5.50   5.50

ANGUILLA
West Indies
100 cents = 1 West Indian dollar

1967

No. 139 of St. Kitts-Nevis overprinted Independent Anguilla
11†   25c White-crowned Pigeon 60.00   20.00

1968

ANGUILLA

36   10c Purple-throated Carib
37   15c Bananaquit
38   25c Black-necked Stilt
39   40c Royal Tern

                          Set of 4   4.00   2.10

1972

142† $1 Magnificent Frigate Bird ('Man-o'-War')   3.75   3.75
144† $5 Brown Pelican. 8.00   10.00

1976

Nos. 142 and 144 overprinted NEW CONSTITUTION 1976
237† $1 Magnificent Frigate Bird 2.00   2.00
239† $5 Brown Pelican. 4.00   5.50

1977

ANGUILLA

274†   1c Yellow-crowned Night Heron.   10   10
280†   10c American Kestrel ('American Sparrow Hawk')   45   25
289† $10 Red-billed Tropic Bird 5.00   4.25

1979

Nos. 274 and 280 surcharged
349†   38c on 10c American Kestrel   60   40
350†   40c on 1c Yellow-crowned Night Heron   ..   60   40

1980

No. 280 overprinted 50th Anniversary Scouting 1980
403†   10c American Kestrel   10   10

416   5c Brown Pelican ('Pelican')
417   22c Great Blue Heron ('Great Grey Heron')
418   $1.50 Barn Swallow ('Swallow')
419   $3 Ruby-throated Hummingbird ('Humming Bird')

                          Set of 4   2.50   2.10

Nos. 274, 280, 289 and 418/19 overprinted or surcharged
SEPARATION 1980
421†   1c Yellow-crowned Night Heron.   5   5
424†   5c on $1.50 Barn Swallow   15   15
425†   5c on $3 Ruby-throated Hummingbird   15   15
426†   10c American Kestrel   20   20
436†   40c on 1c Yellow-crowned Night Heron   ..   30   30
441† $10 Red-billed Tropic Bird 5.00   3.75

1982

498† $5 Brown Pelican ('Pelicans') 4.25   4.25

No. 498 overprinted COMMONWEALTH GAMES 1982
533† $5 Brown Pelican. 2.75   2.75

1983

No. 498 overprinted **150TH ANNIVERSARY ABOLITION OF SLAVERY ACT**

576†	$5 Brown Pelican	2.50	2.75

1984

No. 498 surcharged

609†	$2.50 on $5 Brown Pelican	1.40	1.50

612†	75c Laughing Kookaburra (on Australia stamp No. 19)	40	40

No. 498 overprinted **U.P.U. CONGRESS HAMBURG 1984**

627†	$5 Brown Pelican	3.00	3.25

1985

![10c Anguilla Barn Swallow]

650	10c Barn Swallow
651	60c American Wood Stork ('Wood Stork')
652	75c Roseate Tern
653	$5 Osprey

		Set of 4	3.50	3.50
MS654	Two sheets (a) $4 Western Tanager; (b) $4 Solitary Vireo ('Solitary Flycatcher')		
		Price for 2 sheets	4.50	5.00

![5c Brown Pelican]

659	5c Brown Pelican
660	10c Mourning Dove ('Turtle Dove')
661	15c Magnificent Frigate Bird ('Man-O-War')
662	20c Antillean Crested Hummingbird
663	25c White-tailed Tropic Bird
664	30c Caribbean Elaenia
665	35c Black-whiskered Vireo
665a	35c Lesser Antillean Bullfinch
666	40c Yellow-crowned Night Heron
667	45c Pearly-eyed Thrasher
668	50c Laughing Gull ('Laughing Bird')
669	65c Brown Booby
670	80c Grey Kingbird
671	$1 Audubon's Shearwater

672	$1.35 Roseate Tern
673	$2.50 Bananaquit
674	$5 Belted Kingfisher
675	$10 Green Heron

	Set of 18	9.50	10.50

No. 498 overprinted **GIRL GUIDES 75TH ANNIVERSARY 1910–1985**

679†	$5 Brown Pelican	2.75	3.00

1986

Nos. 659, 667, 671, 673 and 675 overprinted **AMERIPEX 1986**

715	5c Brown Pelican
716	45c Pearly-eyed Thrasher
717	$1 Audubon's Shearwater
718	$2.50 Bananaquit
719	$10 Green Heron

	Set of 5	6.25	6.75

1987

Nos. 665a, 667, 670 and 675 overprinted **CAPEX'87**

757	35c Lesser Antillean Bullfinch
758	45c Pearly-eyed Thrasher
759	80c Grey Kingbird
760	$10 Green Heron

	Set of 4	5.25	5.50

ANTIGUA
West Indies
100 cents = 1 West Indian dollar

1976

469†	½c Antillean Crested Hummingbird	15	15
470†	1c Imperial Amazon ('Imperial Parrot') . .	15	15
471†	2c Zenaida Dove	15	15
472†	3c Loggerhead Kingbird	15	15
473†	4c Red-necked Pigeon	15	15
474†	5c Rufous-throated Solitaire	15	10

1980

![Ringed Kingfisher ANTIGUA 10c]

666	10c Ringed Kingfisher
667	30c Plain Pigeon
668	$1 Green-throated Carib
669	$2 Black-necked Stilt

	Set of 4	2.50	1.90
MS670	$2.50 Roseate Tern	1.50	1.50

1984

869   40c Rufous-sided Towhee
870   50c Parula Warbler
871   60c House Wren
872   $2 Ruby-crowned Kinglet
873   $3 Common Flicker ('Yellow-shafted Flicker')

		Set of 5	5.00	5.25
MS874	$5 Yellow-breasted Chat		4.00	4.50

1985

924   90c Slavonian Grebe ('Horned Grebe')
925   $1 British Storm Petrel ('Least Petrel')
926   $1.50 Great Blue Heron (white phase)
927   $3 Double-crested Cormorant

		Set of 4	3.50	3.50
MS928	$5 White-tailed Tropic Bird		3.25	3.50

950†	15c Magnificent Frigate Bird	15	10

MS959	$5 Barn Swallow	3.25	3.50

1986

990   60c Mallard
991   90c North American Black Duck ('Dusky Duck')
992   $1.50 Pintail ('Common Pintail')
993   $3 American Wigeon ('Wigeon')

		Set of 4	4.00	4.00
MS994	$5 Eider ('Common Eider')		3.75	4.00

1987

1078†	30c Common Noddy ('Brown Noddy') . ..	15	20
1080†	50c Laughing Gull	25	30
1083†	$2 Royal Tern	1.00	1.10
1084†	$3 Sooty Tern	1.50	1.60
MS1085	Two sheets (b) $5 Brown Booby (other sheet depicts fish)		
	Price for 2 sheets	5.00	5.25

ARGENTINE REPUBLIC
South America
1928 100 centavos = 1 peso
1985 100 centavos = 1 austral

1928

560†	15c Yellow-headed Caracara	2.40	85
562†	20c Yellow-headed Caracara	2.40	85
563†	24c Yellow-headed Caracara	4.25	2.75
566†	35c Andean Condor	4.25	1.00
568†	50c Andean Condor	4.25	50
569†	54c Yellow-headed Caracara	4.25	2.00
570†	72c Yellow-headed Caracara	5.00	2.00
574†	1p26 Andean Condor.	22.00	8.00
575†	1p80 Andean Condor.	22.00	8.00
576†	3p60 Andean Condor.	45.00	20.00

1930

Nos. 562, 568 and 575/6 overprinted **ZEPPELIN 1er VUELO 1930**

587†	20c Yellow-headed Caracara	11.00	6.50
588†	50c Andean Condor	22.00	13.50
585†	1p80 Andean Condor.	60.00	35.00
586†	3p60 Andean Condor.	£170	£100

1931

Nos. 570 and 575/6 overprinted **6 Septiembre 1930–1931**

625†	72c Yellow-headed Caracara	17.00	11.00
627†	1p80 Andean Condor.	35.00	20.00
628†	3p60 Andean Condor.	70.00	40.00

1951

827	20c Andean Condor	25	15

831†	20c Andean Condor	15	8

1960

964	20c + 10c Andean Condor (*Vultur gryphus*)	
965	50c + 20c Fork-tailed Flycatcher (*Muscivora tyrannus*)	
966	1p + 50c Magellanic Woodpecker (*Ipocrantor magellanicus*)	
967	2p + 1p Red-winged Tinamou (*Rhynchotus rufescens*) (air)	
968	3p + 1p50 Greater Rhea (*Rhea americana*)	
	Set of 5	1.25 1.00

1961

1005	4p20 + 2p10 Blue-eyed Cormorant (*Phalacrocorax atriceps atriceps*)	
1006	1p80 + 90c Emperor Penguin (*Aptenodytes forsteri*) (air)	
	Set of 2	1.50 1.10

1962

1076	4p + 2p Chalk-browed Mockingbird (*Mimus saturninus modulator*)	
1077	12p + 6p Rufous-collared Sparrow (*Zonotrichia capensis hypoleuca*)	
	Set of 2	1.50 2.00

1963

1101	4p + 2p Vermilion Flycatcher (*Pyrocephalus rubineus rubineus*)	
1102	11p + 5p Great Kiskadee (*Pitangus sulpharatus bolivianus*) (air)	
	Set of 2	1.10 1.00

COLLECT MAMMALS ON STAMPS

The second Stanley Gibbons thematic catalogue — copies are available at £7.50 (p. + p. £1.50) from: Stanley Gibbons Publications Ltd, 5 Parkside, Christchurch Road, Ringwood, Hants BH24 3SH.

1964

1124 4p + 2p Red-crested Cardinal (*Cardinal paroaria coronata*)

1125 18p + 9p Chilean Swallow (*Iridoprocne leucopyga*) (air)

          Set of 2   1.25   1.00

1965

1127† 4p Chinstrap Penguin   45   25

1966

1165 8p + 4p Chilian Lapwing (*Belonopterus cayennensis lampronotus*)

1166 27p50 + 2p50 Rufous Hornero (*Furnarius rufus rufus*) (air)

          Set of 2   1.50   1.40

1169 12p Magellan Gull   25   25

1967

1191 10p + 5p Scarlet-headed Blackbird (*Amblyramphus holosericeus*)

1192 15p + 7p Blue & Yellow Tanager (*Thraupis bonariensis*) (air)

          Set of 2   1.75   1.50

1214 20p + 10p Amazon Kingfisher (*Chloroceryle amazona*)

1215 26p + 13p Toco Toucan (*Ramphastos toco*) (air)

          Set of 2   75   60

1969

1264 20p + 10p White-faced Whistling Duck (*Dendrocygna viduata*)

1265 26p + 13p Lineated Woodpecker (*Ceophloeus lineatus*) (air)

          Set of 2   80   50

1970

1293 20c + 10c Slender-tailed Woodstar
(*Microstilbon burmeisteri*)

1294 40c + 20c Chilian Flamingo
(*Phoenicopterus rubern chilensis*) (air)
Set of 2 1.25 1.00

1972

1394 25c + 10c Saffron Finch (*Sicalis flaveola
pelzelni*)
1395 65c + 30c Rufous-bellied Thrush (*Turdus
rufiventris*)
Set of 2 1.10 80

1973

1415 50c + 25c Crested Screamer (*Chauna
torquata*)
1416 90c + 45c Saffron-cowled Blackbird
(*Xanthopsar flavus*)
Set of 2 90 85

1422 15c + 15c Golden Pheasant 20 5

1974

1441 70c + 30c Double-collared Seedeater
(*Sphorophila caerulescems*)
1442 1p20 + 60c Hooded Siskin (*Spinus
magellanicus*)
Set of 2 1.00 75

1976

1517† 7p + 3p50 Plush-crested Jay (*Cyanocorax
chrysops*) 25 25
1518† 13p + 6p50 Yellow-collared Macaw (*Ara
auricolis*) 35 25

1978

1591 50p + 50p Hooded Siskin (*Spinus
magellanicus*)
1592 100p + 100p Double-collared Seedeater
(*Sphorophila caerulescems*)
1593 150p + 150p Saffron-cowled Blackbird
(*Xanthopsar flavus*)
1594 200p + 200p Vermilion Flycatcher
(*Pyrocephalus rubineus rubineus*)
1595 500p + 500p Great Kiskadee (*Pitangus
sulpharatus bolivianus*)
Set of 5 14.50 12.50

1979

1665† 500p Ruddy Ground Dove 70 40

1980

MS1687 Two sheets of twelve stamps, one with the centre two stamps depicting South Orkney Naval Station and the other two stamps depicting 'Puerto Soledad, Falkland Islands, 1829'. Other stamps are common to the two sheets (two stamps depict seals):
500p King Penguin (*Aptenodytes patagonica*)
500p Chinstrap Penguin (*Pygoscelis antarcticus*)
500p Adelie Penguin (*Pygoscelis adeliae*)
500p Gentoo Penguin (*Pygoscelis papua*)
500p Giant Petrel (*Macronectes giganteus*)
500p Blue-eyed Cormorant (*Phalacrocorax atriceps*)
500p Snow Petrel (*Pagodroma nivea*)
500p Snowy Sheathbill (*Chiornis alba*)
            Price for 2 sheets   12.00   12.00

1983

MS1858 2p Rockhopper Penguin (*Eudyptes crestatus*); 2p Wandering Albatross (*Diomedea exulans*); 2p Black-browed Albatross (*Diomedea melanophris*); 2p Macaroni Penguin

(*Eudyptes chrysolophus*); 2p Light-mantled Sooty Albatross (*Phoebetria palpebrata*) (sheet also contains seven other stamps) 3.25   3.25

1984

1883† 20p Brazilian Merganser (*Mergus octosetaceus*).. 25   15
1884† 20p Black-fronted Piping Guan (*Aburria jacutinga*) 25   15
1885† 20p Hooded Grebe (*Podiceps gallardoi*) . 25   15

1899† 20p Greater Flamingo 25   20

1985

1967† 10c Magellanic Penguin ('Pinguinera Pta. Tombo') 20   10

1986

1983† 10c Pintado Petrel (*Daption capensis*) .. 15   8
1984† 10c Black-browed Albatross (*Diomedea melanophris*) 15   8

1985†	10c King Penguin (*Aptenodytes patagonica*)	15	8
1986†	10c Giant Petrel (*Macronectes giganteus*)	15	8
1988†	10c Magellanic Penguin (*Spheniscus magellanicus*)	15	8
1989†	10c Paraguayan Snipe (*Gallinago gallinago* !)	15	8

1987

2031†	30c Adelie Penguin..	45	40
	(2030/1 *Set of 2*)	70	60

ARMENIA
Southern Russia
100 kopeks = 1 rouble

1922

Unissued stamps surcharged

187†	1 (k) on 250r Common Crane (red)	1.50	1.50
188†	1 (k) on 250r Common Crane (slate)	3.25	3.25

ARUBA
West Indies
100 cents = 1 gulden

1986

9†	35c Burrowing Owl	55	50

ASCENSION
South Atlantic
1934 12 pence = 1 shilling,
20 shillings = 1 pound
1971 100 pence = 1 pound

1934

28†	1s Sooty Tern ('Wideawake Fair')	12.00	12.00

1956

62†	3d White-tailed Tropic Bird ('Boatswain Bird')..	1.50	1.00
67†	2s6d Sooty Tern ('Wideawake')	17.00	6.50

1963

70	1d Brown Booby
71	1½d White-capped Noddy ('Black Noddy')
72	2d White Tern ('Fairy Tern')
73	3d Red-billed Tropic Bird
74	4½d Common Noddy ('Brown Noddy')
75	6d Sooty Tern ('Wideawake Tern')
76	7d Ascension Frigate Bird ('Frigate-Bird')
77	10d Blue-faced Booby ('White Booby')
78	1s White-tailed Tropic Bird ('Yellow-billed Tropicbird')
79	1s6d Red-billed Tropic Bird
80	2s6d Madeiran Storm Petrel
81	5s Red-footed Booby (brown phase)
82	10s Ascension Frigate Bird ('Frigate-Birds')
83	£1 Red-footed Booby (white phase)

Set of 14   45.00   32.00

1970

133†	2s6d Magpie	2.00	1.75

1976

199 1p Yellow Canary ('Canary')
200 2p White Tern ('Fairy Tern')
201 3p Common Waxbill ('Waxbill')
202 4p White-capped Noddy ('Black Noddy')
203 5p Common Noddy ('Brown Noddy')
204 6p Common Mynah
205 7p Madeiran Storm Petrel
206 8p Sooty Tern
207 9p Blue-faced Booby ('White Booby')
208 10p Red-footed Booby
209 15p Bare-throated Francolin ('Red-throated
     Francolin')
210 18p Brown Booby
211 25p Red-billed Tropic Bird ('Red-billed
     Bo'sun Bird')
212 50p White-tailed Tropic Bird ('Yellow-billed
     Bo'sun Bird')
213 £1 Ascension Frigate Bird
214 £2 White-tailed Tropic Bird, Common
     Waxbill, Ascension Frigate Bird, Sooty
     Tern, Brown Booby, Red-footed Booby,
     Madeiran Storm Petrel

                              Set of 16   16.00   18.00

1984

366† 70p Sooty Tern 1.50   1.50

AUSTRALIA
Oceania
1913 12 pence = 1 shilling,
20 shillings = 1 pound
1966 100 cents = 1 dollar

1913

29a ½d Emu (green)
94   ½d Emu (orange)
30   1d Emu (red)
57   1d Emu (violet)

125 1d Emu (green)
59   1½d Emu (brown)
61   1½d Emu (green)
97   1½d Emu (red)
62   2d Emu (orange)
127 2d Emu (red)
99   2d Emu (brown)
128 3d Emu (blue)
32   4d Emu (orange)
64   4d Emu (violet)
65   4d Emu (blue)
129 4d Emu (olive)
92   4½d Emu (violet)
130 5d Emu (brown)
131 1s4d Emu (blue)

                      Set of 19   £250   40.00

19† 6d Laughing Kookaburra 70.00   38.00

1928

106 3d Laughing Kookaburra 7.00   5.00

1929

116 1½d Black Swan 1.50   1.00

1930
Nos. 97 and 92 surcharged in words
119 2d on 1½d Emu
120 5d on 4½d Emu

                      Set of 2   7.25   7.25

1932

140 1s Superb Lyrebird ('Lyrebird') 60.00   80

1966

146 6d Laughing Kookaburra ('Kookaburra') .. 23.00 55

386†	5c Yellow-tailed Thornbill	35	5
387†	6c Blue-faced Honeyeater	70	50
392†	13c Red-necked Avocet	3.00	40
393†	15c Galah..	4.00	65
394†	20c Golden Whistler	8.00	30
395†	24c Azure Kingfisher	1.40	75
396†	25c Scarlet Robin.	5.50	30
397†	30c Straw-necked Ibis	23.00	45

1937

189a† 6d Laughing Kookaburra ('Kookaburra').. 1.00 5
191 † 1s Superb Lyrebird ('Lyrebird') 1.00 5

1942

1976

617† 18c Galah.. .. .. 35 35

206† 3½d Variegated Wren.. .. .. 20 5
207† 5½d Emu 45 5

1978

1954

669 1c Spotted-sided Finch ('Zebra Finch')
670 2c Crimson Finch
671 5c Hooded Plover ('Hooded Dotterel')
672 15c Forest Kingfisher
673 20c Australian Dabchick ('Little Grebe')
674 20c Eastern Yellow Robin
675 22c White-tailed Kingfisher
676 25c Masked Plover ('Spur-wing Plover')
677a 30c Oystercatcher ('Pied Oystercatcher')
678 40c Variegated Wren ('Lovely Wren')
679 50c Flame Robin
680 55c Comb-crested Jacana ('Lotus-Bird')
                              Set of 12 5.00 2.00

277 3¾d Black Swan 15 5

1964

363 6d Yellow-tailed Thornbill
364 9d Black-backed Magpie
365 1s6d Galah
366 2s Golden Whistler
367 2s5d Blue Wren
368 2s6d Scarlet Robin
369 3s Straw-necked Ibis
                Set of 7 35.00 22.00

694 20c Laughing Kookaburra (on stamp No.
        106) 25 15

1980

AUSTRALIA 10c

Golden Shouldered Parrot

734	10c Golden-shouldered Parrot		
734b	18c Spotted Catbird		
735	28c Australian Bee Eater ('Rainbow Bird')		
736	35c Regent Bowerbird		
737	45c Masked Wood Swallow		
738	60c Australian King Parrot ('King Parrot')		
739	80c Rainbow Pitta		
740	$1 Black-backed Magpie ('Western Magpie')		
	Set of 8	4.50	2.10

1984

AUSTRALIA 45c

903	45c Brown Kiwi, Laughing Kookaburra		
904	45c Raggiana Bird of Paradise (on New Guinea stamps Nos. 180 and 182)		
	Set of 2	1.25	1.25

AUSIPEX 84
AUSTRALIA
30c

MS945	30c Mute Swan (on Western Australia stamp No. 1) (sheet also contains 6 other stamps)	3.00	3.25

Australia 30c

Victoria 150th Anniversary 1984

959†	30c Yellow-tufted Honeyeater	35	40
	(959/60 Set of 2)	70	80

1985

1c   Australia

970	1c Sulphur-crested Cockatoo		
971	33c Sulphur-crested Cockatoo		
	Set of 2	50	65

1986

AUSTRALIA 36c

EMU

1024†	36c Emu	30	35
1026†	36c Laughing Kookaburra ('Kookaburra').	30	35

1987

AUSTRALIA $1
The First Fleet

June 1787 Teneriffe

1066†	$1 Albatross sp...	90	95

OFFICIAL STAMPS

1931

Nos. 94, 125 and 127/30 overprinted **O.S.**

O7†	½d Emu (orange)	8.50	2.00
O8†	1d Emu (green)	4.00	90
O4†	2d Emu (red)..	8.50	70
O10†	3d Emu (blue)	11.00	7.50
O5†	4d Emu (olive)	40.00	6.50
O11†	5d Emu (brown)	60.00	35.00

No. 140 overprinted **O.S.**

O18†	1s Superb Lyrebird	80.00	48.00

STANLEY GIBBONS
STAMP COLLECTING SERIES
Introductory booklets on *How to Start, How to Identify Stamps* and *Collecting by Theme.* A series of well illustrated guides at a low price.
Write for details.

AUSTRALIAN ANTARCTIC TERRITORY
Antarctica
1959 12 pence = 1 shilling,
20 shillings = 1 pound
1966 100 cents = 1 dollar

1959

5†	2s3d Emperor Penguin..	10.00	4.50

1966

9†	2c Emperor Penguin	1.60	40

1973

25†	7c Adelie Penguin..	1.75	40
29†	20c Wandering Albatross ('Albatross')	90	60

1979

43†	20c Adelie Penguin	30	30

STAMP MONTHLY
— finest and most informative magazine for all
collectors. Obtainable from your newsagent or by
postal subscription — details on request.

1983

55†	27c Light-mantled Sooty Albatross	60	60
56†	27c King Cormorant ('Macquarie Island Shag').	60	60
58†	27c Royal Penguin.	60	60
59†	27c Dove Prion ('Antarctic Prion')	60	60
	(55/9 Set of 5)	2.75	2.75

1985

77†	$1 Emperor Penguin	75	80

AUSTRIA
Central Europe
100 groschen = 1 schilling

1925

580†	20g Golden Eagle.	50	5
581†	24g Golden Eagle.	80	30
582†	30g Golden Eagle.	60	5
583†	40g Golden Eagle.	1.25	10
584†	45g Golden Eagle.	1.50	10
585†	50g Golden Eagle.	1.75	12
586†	80g Golden Eagle.	4.25	4.50

620†	10g Common Crane	75	1.60
622†	15g Common Crane	50	75
626†	30g Common Crane	75	1.60
628†	50g Common Crane	75	1.90
631†	1s Common Crane	1.40	3.00

632†	2s Common Crane	1.00	3.00
633†	3s Common Crane	28.00	22.00
634†	5s Common Crane	8.50	14.00
635†	10s Common Crane	6.00	11.00

1950

1215	60g Rook ('Saatkrahe')
1216	1s Barn Swallow ('Rauchschwalben')
1217	2s Black-headed Gull ('Lachmowen')
1218	3s Common Cormorant ('Kormorane')
1219	5s Common Buzzard ('Mausebussard')
1220	10s Grey Heron ('Fischreiher')
1221	20s Golden Eagle ('Steinadler')

	Set of 7	£300	£200

1959

1338†	1s Capercaillie	50	25

1978

1805	6s Black Grouse	60	50

1982

1942†	3s Great Bustard ('Grosstrappe')	25	15
1944†	6s Capercaillie ('Auerhahn')	45	30
	(1942/4 Set of 3)	90	60

1984

2030	4s Mute Swan.	40	15

1986

2094	4s Mute Swan.	40	20

AZORES
Atlantic Ocean
100 centavos = 1 escudo

1986

468	68e50 Bullfinch.	80	45

BAHAMAS
West Indies
1935 12 pence = 1 shilling,
20 shillings = 1 pound
1966 100 cents = 1 dollar

1935

145	8d Greater Flamingo ('Flamingoes in flight')	4.50	4.50

1938

160† 8d Greater Flamingo ('Flamingoes in
flight')   85   90

1942

No. 160 overprinted **1492 LANDFALL OF COLUMBUS 1942**
170† 8d Greater Flamingo..   55   1.00

1965

251† 3d Greater Flamingo ('Flamingo')   40   20

1966

No. 251 surcharged
276† 4c on 3d Greater Flamingo   15   10

1967

As No. 251 but face value in cents
298† 4c Greater Flamingo ('Flamingo')   80   10

1970

352† 3c Greater Flamingo..   10   10

1971

368† 11c Greater Flamingo ('Flamingos')   40   45

1974

429   13c Roseate Spoonbill
430   14c White-crowned Pigeon
431   21c White-tailed Tropic Bird
432   36c Cuban Amazon ('Bahamian Parrot')
                                              Set of 4   4.00   3.50

1981

589   5c Bahama Pintail ('Bahama Duck')
590   20c Reddish Egret
591   25c Brown Booby
592   $1 Black-billed Whistling Duck ('West
        Indian Tree Duck')
                                              Set of 4   2.25   2.40

1982

617   25c Greater Flamingo (*Phoenicopterus
        ruber*, male)
618   25c Greater Flamingo (*Phoenicopterus
        ruber*, female)
619   25c Greater Flamingo (*Phoenicopterus
        ruber*, female with nestling)
620   25c Greater Flamingo (*Phoenicopterus
        ruber*, juvenile)
621   25c Greater Flamingo (*Phoenicopterus
        ruber*, immature)
                                              Set of 5   2.00   2.00

1984

685 31c Bahama Woodstar (*Calliphlox evelynae*)
686 31c Belted Kingfisher (*Megaceryle alcyon*), Greater Flamingo
687 31c Black-necked Stilt (*Himantopus himantopus* !), Greater Flamingo (*Phoenicopterus ruber*)
688 31c Black-necked Stilt, Greater Flamingo
689 31c Osprey (*Pandion haliaetus*), Greater Flamingo

	Set of 5	2.50	2.75

1985

705† 31c Greater Flamingo ('Flamingo')..   50   55

708 5c Killdeer
709 31c Mourning Dove
710 35c Mourning Dove
711 $1 Killdeer

	Set of 4	2.50	2.50

BAHAWALPUR
Indian sub-continent
16 annas = 1 rupee

OFFICIAL STAMP

1945

O4† 4a Eastern White Pelican. 6.00 7.00

BAHRAIN
Arabian peninsula
1000 fils = 1 dinar

1966

148† 200f Lanner Falcon 4.50 90

1980

271 100f Gyrfalcon (Arab with falcon)
272 100f Lanner Falcon (Arab looking at falcon)
273 100f Peregrine Falcon (with outstretched wings)
274 100f Peregrine Falcon (in flight)
275 100f Gyrfalcon (on pillar, facing right)
276 100f Gyrfalcon (on pillar, full face)
277 100f Gyrfalcon (head and breast, facing right)
278 100f Lanner Falcon (head and breast, full face)

	Set of 8	9.00	6.00

BANGLADESH
Indian Subcontinent
100 paisa = 1 taka

1983

204 50p Magpie Robin (*Copsychus saularis*)
205 2t White-breasted Kingfisher (*Halcyon smyrnensis*)
206 3t75 Lesser Golden-backed Woodpecker (*Dinopium benghalense*)
207 5t White-winged Wood Duck (*Cairina scutulata*)

	Set of 4	1.00	1.00

1984

235 1t Sarus Crane
236 2t Common Peafowl ('Peafowl')
Set of 2   15   20

1981

Nos. 630, 632 and 634 surcharged

682 15c on 28c Carib Grackle
683 40c on 45c Zenaida Dove
684 60c on 70c Bananaquit
Set of 3   60   75

1984

762† $1 Ruby-throated Hummingbird 1.00   1.10

BARBADOS
West Indies
100 cents = 1 dollar

1979

622 1c Grassland Yellow Finch ('Grass
     Canary')
623 2c Grey Kingbird ('Rain Bird')
624 5c Lesser Antillean Bullfinch ('Sparrow')
625 8c Magnificent Frigate Bird ('Frigate
     Bird')
626 10c Cattle Egret
627 12c Green Heron ('Green Gaulin')
627a 15c Carib Grackle ('Blackbird')
628 20c Antillean Crested Hummingbird
     ('Hummingbird')
629 25c Scaly-breasted Ground Dove
     ('Ground Dove')
630 28c Carib Grackle ('Blackbird')
631 35c Green-throated Carib
631a 40c Red-necked Pigeon ('Ramier')
632 45c Zenaida Dove ('Wood Dove')
633 50c Red-necked Pigeon ('Ramier')
633a 55c American Golden Plover ('Black
     Breast Plover')
633b 60c Bananaquit ('Yellow Breast')
634 70c Bananaquit ('Yellow Breast')
635 $1 Caribbean Elaenia ('Pee-Whistler')
636 $2.50 American Redstart ('Christmas
     Bird')
637 $5 Belted Kingfisher ('Kingfisher')
638 $10 Moorhen ('Red-Seal Coot')
Set of 21   17.00   19.00

1985

784 45c Peregrine Falcon
785 65c Prairie Warbler
786 75c Great Blue Heron
787 $1 Yellow Warbler
Set of 4   2.50   2.50

1987

836 25c Barn Swallow
837 50c Yellow Warbler
838 65c Audubon's Shearwater
839 75c Black-whiskered Vireo
840 $1 Scarlet Tanager
Set of 5   2.00   2.25

COLLECT MAMMALS ON STAMPS
The second Stanley Gibbons thematic catalogue —
copies are available at £7.50 (p. + p. £1.50) from:
Stanley Gibbons Publications Ltd, 5 Parkside,
Christchurch Road, Ringwood, Hants BH24 3SH.

BARBUDA
West Indies
100 cents = 1 dollar

1974

197†	$5 Magnificent Frigate Bird ('Frigatebird') .	4.00	4.25

1975

No. 197 overprinted **U.S.A.– U.S.S.R. SPACE COOPERATION 1975** *and* **APOLLO** (*No.* 227) *or* **SOYUZ** (*No.* 228)

227	$5 Magnificent Frigate Bird		
228	$5 Magnificent Frigate Bird		
	Set of 2	13.00	18.00

1976

262	35c Bananaquit		
263	50c Blue-hooded Euphonia ('Blue-headed Euphonia')		
264	75c Royal Tern		
265	95c Killdeer		
266	$1.25 Common Cowbird ('Glossy Cowbird')		
267	$2 Purple Gallinule		
	Set of 6	15.00	9.00

1977

Nos. 469/74 of Antigua overprinted **BARBUDA**

305†	½c Antillean Crested Hummingbird	15	15
306†	1c Imperial Amazon ('Imperial Parrot') ..	20	20
307†	2c Zenaida Dove	20	20
308†	3c Loggerhead Kingbird..	20	20
309†	4c Red-necked Pigeon	20	20
310†	5c Rufous-throated Solitaire.	20	20

1980

498†	75c American Bald Eagle	30	30

503	1c American Wigeon ('American Widgeon')	
504	2c Snowy Plover	
505	4c Rose-breasted Grosbeak	
506	6c Mangrove Cuckoo	
507	10c Adelaide's Warbler	
508	15c Scaly-breasted Thrasher	
509	20c Yellow-crowned Night Heron	
510	25c Bridled Quail Dove	
511	35c Carib Grackle	
512	50c Pintail ('Northern Pintail')	
513	75c Black-whiskered Vireo	
514	$1 Blue-winged Teal	
515	$1.50 Green-throated Carib	
516	$2 Red-necked Pigeon	
517	$2.50 Wied's Crested Flycatcher ('Stolid Flycatcher' !)	
518	$5 Yellow-bellied Sapsucker	
519	$7.50 Caribbean Elaenia	
520	$10 Great Egret	

	Set of 18	17.00	16.00

*Nos. 666/*MS*670 of Antigua overprinted* **BARBUDA**

536	10c Ringed Kingfisher		
537	30c Plain Pigeon		
538	$1 Green-throated Carib		
539	$2 Black-necked Stilt		
	Set of 4	2.10	2.10
MS540	$2.50 Roseate Tern	1.40	1.60

1984

*Nos. 869/*MS*874 of Antigua overprinted* **BARBUDA MAIL**

748	40c Rufous-sided Towhee		
749	50c Parula Warbler		
750	60c House Wren		
751	$2 Ruby-crowned Kinglet		
752	$3 Common Flicker ('Yellow-shafted Flicker')		
	Set of 5	4.25	4.75
MS753	$5 Yellow-breasted Chat	3.50	3.75

1985

783	45c Roseate Tern	
784	50c Mangrove Cuckoo	
785	60c Yellow-crowned Night Heron	
786	$5 Brown Pelican	

	Set of 4	3.50	3.75

No. 924/**MS**928 *of Antigua overprinted* **BARBUDA MAIL**
794 90c Slavonian Grebe ('Horned Grebe')
795 $1 British Storm Petrel ('Least Petrel')
796 $1.50 Great Blue Heron (white phase)
797 $3 Double-crested Cormorant

	Set of 4	3.75	3.75
MS798	$5 White-tailed Tropic Bird	3.00	3.25

No. 950 *of Antigua overprinted* **BARBUDA MAIL**

832†	15c Magnificent Frigate Bird	10	10

1986
No. **MS**959 *of Antigua overprinted* **BARBUDA MAIL**

MS850	$5 Barn Swallow	2.50	2.75

BECHUANALAND
Southern Africa
100 cents = 1 rand

1961

168†	1c African Golden Oriole ('Golden Oriole')	15	25
169†	2c Hoopoe ('African Hoopoe')	20	30
170†	2½c Scarlet-chested Sunbird	20	12
171†	3½c Yellow-rumped Bishop ('Cape Widow-Bird')	30	35
172†	5c Swallow-tailed Bee Eater	40	25
173†	7½c African Grey Hornbill ('Grey Hornbill').	40	60
174†	10c Red-headed Weaver.	55	50
175†	12½c Brown-hooded Kingfisher	4.75	2.25

BELGIAN CONGO
Central Africa
100 centimes = 1 franc

1939

226†	1f + 1f Marabou Stork, Ruppell's Griffon ..	5.50	5.50

BELGIUM
Western Europe
100 centimes = 1 franc

1962

1816	40c + 10c Guianan Cock of the Rock ('Coq de Roche, Rotshaan')		
1817	1f + 50c Red Lory ('Rode Lori, Lori Rouge')		
1818	2f + 50c Knysna Turaco ('Touracou du Senegal, Senegal Toerakoe')		
1819	2f50 + 1f Keel-billed Toucan ('Kortbek Toekan, Toucan a Bec Court')		
1820	3f + 1f Greater Bird of Paradise ('Grand Paradisier, Grosse Paradijsvogel')		
1821	6f + 2f Congo Peafowl ('Kongo Pauw, Paon du Congo')		
	Set of 6	7.50	7.00

1966

MS1994	10f + 5f Emperor Penguin	1.25	1.25

1971

2230	10f Adelie Penguin	1.00	80

COLLECT RAILWAYS ON STAMPS
A Stanley Gibbons thematic catalogue on this popular subject. Copies available at £7.50 (p. + p. £1.50) from: Stanley Gibbons Publications Ltd, 5 Parkside, Christchurch Road, Ringwood, Hants BH24 3SH.

1972

2293 2f + 1f Greylag Goose (*Anser anser*)
2294 4f50 + 2f Lapwing (*Vanellus vanellus*)
2295 8f + 4f White Stork (*Ciconia ciconia*)
2296 9f + 4f50 Common Kestrel (*Falco tinnunculus*)

Set of 4   3.25   3.50

1983

2762† 8f Mute Swan   35   10

1985

2845 3f Hawfinch ('Appelvink — Gros Bec')
2846 3f50 European Robin ('Rouge-Gorge — Roodborstje')
2848 8f Common Kingfisher ('Ijsvogel — Martin-Pecheur')
2849 9f Goldfinch ('Chardonneret — Putter')

Set of 4   70   40

1987

2905† 26f + 6f Peregrine Falcon ('Slechtvalk — Faucon Pelerin') 1.25   1.25

BELIZE
Central America
100 cents = 1 dollar

1977

452 8c Red-capped Manakin
453 10c Hooded Oriole
454 25c Blue-crowned Motmot
455 35c Slaty-breasted Tinamou
456 45c Ocellated Turkey
457 $1 White Hawk

Set of 6   3.75   4.00

1978

467 10c White-capped Parrot ('White-crowned Parrot')
468 25c Crimson-collared Tanager
469 35c Citreoline Trogon
470 45c American Finfoot ('Sungrebe')
471 50c Moscovy Duck
472 $1 King Vulture

Set of 6   4.25   4.75

1979

488 10c Boat-billed Heron
489 25c Grey-necked Wood Rail
490 35c Lineated Woodpecker
491 45c Blue-grey Tanager
492 50c Laughing Falcon
493 $1 Long-tailed Hermit

Set of 6   2.50   2.25

1980

560 10c Jabiru
561 25c Barred Antshrike
562 35c Northern Royal Flycatcher ('Royal
     Flycatcher')
563 45c White-necked Puffbird
564 50c Ornate Hawk Eagle
565 $1 Golden-masked Tanager

Set of 6	7.00	6.00
MS566 $2 Jabiru; $3 Golden-masked Tanager ..	7.50	6.50

Nos. 560/5 overprinted or surcharged **BELIZE ESPAMER'80**
MADRID 3–12 OCT. 1980

577 10c Jabiru
578 25c Barred Antshrike
579 35c Northern Royal Flycatcher
580 40c on 45c White-necked Puffbird
581 40c on 50c Ornate Hawk Eagle
582 40c on $1 Golden-masked Tanager

Set of 6	2.50	2.50

1981

662†	$2 Keel-billed Toucan	1.40	1.40

1982

No. 662 surcharged **ESSEN 82**

678†	$1 on $2 Keel-billed Toucan.	1.00	65

1983

No. 662 surcharged

743†	$1.25 on $2 Keel-billed Toucan..	2.00	2.25

1984

806	$1 White-fronted Amazon ('White-fronted Parrot')		
807	$1 White-capped Parrot		
808	$1 Mealy Amazon ('Mealy Parrot')		
809	$1 Red-lored Amazon ('Red-lored Parrot')		
	Set of 4	2.50	3.00
MS810	$3 Scarlet Macaw	2.10	2.50

1985

823	10c White-tailed Kite		
824	15c Ruby-crowned Kinglet ('Cuvier's Kinglet')		
825	25c Painted Bunting		
826	75c Belted Kingfisher		
827	$1 Common Cardinal ('Northern Cardinal')		
828	$3 Long-billed Curlew		
	Set of 6	3.25	3.50

1986

963†	10c Keel-billed Toucan	8	10
965†	25c Collared Aracari..	15	20
967†	$1 Emerald Toucanet.	65	70
968†	$1.25 Crimson-rumped Toucanet ('Crimson-rumped Toucan')	80	85

BENIN
West Africa
100 centimes = 1 franc

1978

729 100f Red-breasted Merganser
730 100f African Pygmy Goose (on Dahomey
        stamp No. 250)

Set of 2 2.50 1.75

1979

752† 15f Fiery-breasted Bush Shrike
       (*Malaconotus cruentus*) 25 20

1982

861 5f Laughing Kookaburra ('Dacelo Gigas')
862 10f Bluethroat ('La Gorge Bleue')
863 15f Barn Swallow ('L'Hirondelle')
864 20f Woodland Kingfisher ('Martin-
        Pecheur'), Village Weaver ('Tisserin')
865 30f Reed Warbler ('La Rousserolle')
866 60f Warbler sp ('Fauvette Commune')
867 80f Eagle Owl ('Hibou Grand Doc')
868 100f Sulphur-crested Cockatoo ('Cacatoes')

Set of 8 1.60 90

1985

995 150f Arctic Skua ('Labbe Parasite')
996 300f Oystercatcher ('Huitrier Pie')

Set of 2 1.90 1.60

Nos. 251/2 and 271/2 of Dahomey surcharged **Republique**
Populaire du Benin

1007† 75f on 100f Fiery-breasted Bush Shrike
        (*Malaconotus cruentus*) 35 30
1008† 75f on 200f Broad-billed Roller
        (*Eurystomus glaucurus*) 35 30
1009† 90f on 250f African Emerald Cuckoo
        (*Chrysococcyx cupreus*) 40 35
1011† 150f on 500f Iris Glossy Starling
        (*Coccyolius iris*) 65 60

BERMUDA
North Atlantic Ocean
1938 12 pence = 1 shilling,
20 shillings = 1 pound
1970 100 cents = 1 dollar

1938

114b† 7½d White-tailed Tropic Bird 2.50 1.75

1953

143† 6d White-tailed Tropic Bird (*Phaeton
        flavirostris*).. .. .. 80 50
143a† 8d White-tailed Tropic Bird (*Phaeton
        flavirostris*) 1.25 45

As No. 143 but inscribed 'ROYAL VISIT 1953'
151 6d White-tailed Tropic Bird 20 20

1956

No. 143a *overprinted* **50th ANNIVERSARY US–BERMUDA OCEAN RACE 1956**

154† 8d White-tailed Tropic Bird   15   15

1978

387†	3c White-tailed Tropic Bird	15	5
388†	4c White-eyed Vireo	10	5
389†	5c Eastern Bluebird	10	5
391†	8c Common Cardinal ('Cardinal (Redbird)')	10	10
403†	$5 Cahow	6.50	7.00

1985

490   12c Osprey
491   30c Yellow-crowned Night Heron
492   40c Great Egret
493   $1.50 Eastern Bluebird ('Bluebird')

                  Set of 4   3.75   3.75

BHUTAN
Central Asia
100 chetrum = 1 ngultrum

1968

187   2c Red-faced Liocichla ('Crimson-winged Laughing Thrush')
188   3c Ward's Trogon
189   4c Burmese Peacock-Pheasant ('Grey Peacock-Pheasant')

190   5c Rufous-necked Hornbill
191   15c Fire-tailed Myzornis ('Myzornis')
192   20c Red-faced Liocichla ('Crimson-winged Laughing Thrush')
193   30c Ward's Trogon
194   50c Burmese Peacock-Pheasant ('Grey Peacock-Pheasant')
195   1n25 Rufous-necked Hornbill
196   2n Fire-tailed Myzornis ('Myzornis')

197   1n50 Red-faced Liocichla ('Crimson-winged Laughing Thrush') (air)
198   2n50 Ward's Trogon
199   4n Burmese Peacock-Pheasant ('Grey Peacock-Pheasant')
200   5n Rufous-necked Hornbill
201   10n Fire-tailed Myzornis ('Myzornis')

                  Set of 15   7.50   6.00

1970

Various stamps surcharged **20 CH**

214†	20c on 4n Sclater's Monal Pheasant (*Lophophorus sclareti*) (Appendix)	90	90
218†	20c on 2n Fire-tailed Myzornis (No. 196) ..	70	70
219†	20c on 2n50 Ward's Trogon (No. 198)	90	90
220†	20c on 4n Burmese Peacock-Pheasant (No. 199) ..	90	90
221†	20c on 5n Rufous-necked Hornbill (No. 200)	85	85
222†	20c on 10n Fire-tailed Myzornis (No. 201) ..	85	85

Various stamps surcharged **20 CH**

231†	20c on 2n Satyr Tragopan (*Tragopan satyra*) (Appendix)..	1.50	1.50
232†	20c on 7n Kalij Pheasant (*Lophura leucomelana hamiltoni*) (Appendix)	1.50	1.50
239†	20c on 30c Ward's Trogon (No. 193)	1.50	1.50
240†	20c on 50c Burmese Peacock-Pheasant (No. 194) ..	1.50	1.50
241†	20c on 1n25 Rufous-necked Hornbill (No. 195)	1.50	1.50
242†	20c on 1n50 Red-faced Liocichla (No. 197).	1.60	1.60

1971

Various stamps surcharged

258†	55c on 5n Himalayan Monal Pheasant (*Lophophorus impeyanus*) (Appendix) ..	50	50
259†	90c on 9n White Eared-Pheasant (*Crossoptilon crossoptilon drouyni*) (Appendix)	75	75
262†	90c on 2n Fire-tailed Myzornis (No. 196) ..	75	75

1982

445   2n Orange-bellied Leafbird ('Orange-bellied Chloropsis')
446   3n Himalayan Monal Pheasant ('Monal Pheasant')

447 5n Ward's Trogon
448 10n Mrs Gould's Sunbird

| | | Set of 4 | 4.00 | 4.00 |
| MS449 | 25n Maroon Oriole. | | 5.50 | 5.50 |

1985

624 50c Mallard ('Brewers Duck')
625 1n Willow/Red Grouse ('Willow Ptarmigan')
626 2n Mountain Plover
627 3n Red-throated Diver ('Red-throated Loon')
628 4n Spruce Grouse
629 5n Hooded Merganser
630 15n Whooper Swan ('Trumpeter Swan')
631 20n Goldeneye ('Common Goldeneye')

		Set of 8	5.50	5.50
MS632	25n Sharp-shinned Hawk..		3.25	3.25
MS633	25n Tufted Titmouse ..		3.25	3.25

Appendix

The following stamps have either been issued in excess of postal needs, or have not been made available to the public in reasonable quantities at face value. Miniature sheets, imperforate stamps etc. are excluded from this section.

1968

Pheasants. 1c, 2n Satyr Tragopan; 2c, 4n Sclater's Monal Pheasant; 4c, 5n Himalayan Monal Pheasant; 8c, 7n Kalij Pheasant; 15c, 9n White Eared-Pheasant

1969

Birds (plastic-surfaced). Postage 15c Tawny Owl, 50c Red Munia, 1n25 Northern Goshawk, 2n Humboldt Penguin. Air 3n Chattering Lory and Eclectus Parrot, 4n Greater Bird of Paradise, 5n Mandarin, 6n Ring-necked Pheasant

1970

Animals (plastic-surfaced). 85c Satyr Tragopan

BIAFRA
West Africa
12 pence = 1 shilling,
20 shillings = 1 pound

1968

Nos. 174/5, 178/81 and 185 of Nigeria overprinted **SOVEREIGN BIAFRA** *and arms*

6 †	1½d Splendid Sunbird ..	2.00	3.50
7 †	2d Village Weaver, Red-headed Malimbe ('Weavers') ..	16.00	25.00
9 †	6d Saddle-bill Stork ..	2.50	3.00
10†	9d Grey Parrot..	75	1.10
11†	1s Blue-breasted Kingfisher ('Kingfishers').	48.00	70.00
12†	1s3d Crowned Crane ('Crown Bird') .	32.00	45.00
16†	£1 Cattle Egret..	10.00	20.00

BOLIVIA
South America
1925 100 centavos = 1 boliviano
1963 100 centavos = 1 peso boliviano

1925

| 187† | 25c Andean Condor .. | 1.50 | 50 |

1928

| 221† | 5c Andean Condor .. | 1.00 | 25 |

1939

354†	40c Cocoi Heron ('Garza') ..	1.40	50
355†	45c Cocoi Heron ('Garza') ..	1.40	50
358†	90c Toco Toucan ('Tucan') ..	3.50	75
359†	1b Toco Toucan ('Tucan') ..	3.50	75
360†	2b Andean Condor ('Condor') ..	3.75	75
361†	3b Andean Condor ('Condor') ..	4.50	1.00

1941

| 382† | 50b Andean Condor .. | 10.00 | 1.25 |
| 383† | 100b Andean Condor. | 23.00 | 4.00 |

STANLEY GIBBONS
STAMP COLLECTING SERIES
Introductory booklets on *How to Start, How to Identify Stamps* and *Collecting by Theme.* A series of well illustrated guides at a low price.
Write for details.

1963

759† 1p40 Andean Condor. 1.00 70

1981

1053 4p Scarlet Macaw (*Ara macao*)
1054 7p Green-winged Macaw (*Ara chloroptera*)
1055 8p Blue and Yellow Macaw (*Ara ararauna*)
1056 9p Red-fronted Macaw (*Ara rubrogenys*)
1057 10p Yellow-collared Macaw (*Ara auricollis*)
1058 12p Hyacinth Macaw (*Anodorynchus hyacinthinus*)
1059 15p Military Macaw (*Ara militaris*)
1060 20p Chestnut-fronted Macaw (*Ara severa*)
Set of 8 9.50 4.50

1985

1106† 25000p Andean Condor (*Sarcorhamphus gryphus*) 10 5

BOPHUTHATSWANA
Southern Africa
100 cents = 1 rand

1980

60 5c Pied Babbler
61 10c Carmine Bee Eater
62 15c Shaft-tailed Whydah
63 20c Meyer's Parrot
Set of 4 1.10 1.25

1983

112 10c Kori Bustard
113 20c Little Black Bustard ('Black Korhaan')
114 25c Crested Bustard ('Red-crested Korhaan')
115 40c Barrow's Bustard ('Stanley Bustard')
Set of 4 1.10 1.00

1985

166† 30c Mariqua Sunbird. 15 12

BOTSWANA

Southern Africa
1966 100 cents = 1 rand
1976 100 thebe = 1 pula

1966

Nos. 168/75 of Bechuanaland overprinted **REPUBLIC OF BOTSWANA**

206†	1c African Golden Oriole ('Golden Oriole')	15	5
207†	2c Hoopoe ('African Hoopoe')	20	5
208†	2½c Scarlet-chested Sunbird	25	5
209†	3½c Yellow-rumped Bishop ('Cape Widow-Bird')	30	15
210†	5c Swallow-tailed Bee Eater	30	20
211†	7½c African Grey Hornbill ('Grey Hornbill').	30	30
212†	10c Red-headed Weaver.	60	20
213†	12½c Brown-hooded Kingfisher	1.25	75

1967

220	1c Golden Oriole	
221	2c Hoopoe ('African Hoopoe')	
222	3c Groundscraper Thrush	
223	4c Cordon-bleu ('Blue Waxbill')	
224	5c Secretary Bird	
225	7c Yellow-billed Hornbill	
226	10c Burchell's Gonolek ('Crimson-breasted Shrike')	
227	15c Malachite Kingfisher	
228	20c African Fish Eagle ('Fish Eagle')	
229	25c Go-away Bird ('Grey Loerie')	
230	35c Scimitar-bill	
231	50c Comb Duck ('Knob-billed Duck')	
232	1r Levaillant's Barbet ('Crested Barbet')	
233	2r Didric Cuckoo ('Diederick Cuckoo')	

Set of 14 27.00 17.00

1975

346†	4c Ostrich	25	5

COLLECT MAMMALS ON STAMPS

The second Stanley Gibbons thematic catalogue —
copies are available at £7.50 (p. + p. £1.50) from:
Stanley Gibbons Publications Ltd, 5 Parkside,
Christchurch Road, Ringwood, Hants BH24 3SH.

1978

411	1t Little Black Bustard ('Black Korhaan')	
412	2t Marabou Stork	
413	3t Green Wood Hoopoe ('Red-billed Hoopoe')	
414	4t Carmine Bee Eater	
415	5t African Jacana	
416	7t African Paradise Flycatcher ('Paradise Flycatcher')	
417	10t Bennett's Woodpecker	
418	15t Red Bishop	
419	20t Crowned Plover	
420	25t Giant Kingfisher	
421	30t White-faced Whistling Duck ('White-faced Duck')	
422	35t Green Heron ('Green-backed Heron')	
423	45t Black-headed Heron	
424	50t Spotted Eagle Owl	
425	1p Gabar Goshawk	
426	2p Martial Eagle	
427	5p Saddle-bill Stork	

Set of 17 14.00 14.00

1979

451†	45t Hoopoe (on stamp No. 221)	45	55

1981

Nos. 417 and 422 surcharged

497	25t on 35t Green Heron	
498	30t on 10t Bennett's Woodpecker	

Set of 2 90 1.00

1982

515	1t African Masked Weaver ('Masked Weaver')
516	2t Lesser Double-collared Sunbird

517 3t Red-throated Bee Eater ('White-fronted
    Bee-Eater')
518 4t Ostrich
519 5t Grey-headed Gull
520 6t African Pygmy Goose ('Pygmy Goose')
521 7t Cattle Egret
522 8t Lanner Falcon
523 10t Yellow-billed Stork
524 15t Red-billed Pintail ('Red-billed Teal')
525 20t Barn Owl
526 25t Hammerkop ('Hamerkop')
527 30t South African Stilt ('Stilt')
528 35t Blacksmith Plover
529 45t Senegal Wattled Plover ('Wattled
    Plover')
530 50t Helmet Guineafowl ('Crowned Guinea-
    fowl')
531 1p Cape Vulture
532 2p Augur Buzzard

Set of 18   3.75   4.25

1218 10c Red-crested Cardinal (*Paroaria
    coronata*)
1219 20c Quadrille Wren (*Leucolepis
    modulator*)
1220 50c Amazonian Royal Flycatcher
    (*Onychorhynchus swainsoni*)

Set of 3   1.25   35

1983

541† 7t Wattled Crane ('Wattle Crane')   15   8

1973

1434 20c Swallow-tailed Manakin (*Chiroxiphia
    caudata*)
1435 20c Troupial (*Icterus jamacaii*)
1436 20c Brazilian Ruby (*Clytolaema
    rubricauda*)

Set of 3   95   55

1478† 40c Scarlet Ibis (*Eudocimus ruber*)   65   15
1480† 1cr Scarlet Macaw (*Ara macau*) 2.75   15
1481† 2cr Greater Rhea (*Rhea americana*) 4.50   2.00
    (1478/81 *Set of 4*)   8.50   3.00

BRAZIL
South America
1968 100 centavos = 1 cruzeiro
1986 100 centavos = 1 cruzado

1968

1215 20c Harpy Eagle (*Harpia harpya*)   55   15

1978

1710 7cr50 Saffron Finch (*Sicalis flaveola*)
1711 8cr50 Banded Cotinga (*Cotinga maculata*)
1712 9cr50 Seven-coloured Tanager (*Tangara
    fastuosa*)

Set of 3   2.50   1.10

1980

1866 5cr Vinaceous Amazon (*Amazona
      vinacea*)
1867 5cr Red-tailed Amazon (*Amazona
      brasiliensis*)
1868 28cr Red-spectacled Amazon (*Amazona
      pretrei*)
1869 28cr Brown-backed Parrotlet (*Touit
      melanonota*)

Set of 4   5.00   2.25

1981

1895 7cr Ruby-Topaz Hummingbird
      (*Chrysolampis mosquitos*)
1896 7cr Horned Sungem (*Heliactin cornuta*)
1897 7cr Frilled Coquette (*Lophornis magnifica*)
1898 7cr Planalto Hermit (*Phaethornis pretrei*)

Set of 4   70   45

1983

2003 150cr Adelie Penguin   40   20

2015 30cr Toco Toucan (*Ramphastos toco*)
2016 185cr Cuvier's Toucan (*Ramphastos t.
      tucanus*)

2017 205cr Red-breasted Toucan (*Ramphastos
      dicolorus*)
2018 215cr Channel-billed Toucan (*Ramphastos
      v. vitellinus*)

Set of 4   1.50   1.00

1984

2083 65cr Great Egret
2084 65cr Roseate Spoonbill
2085 80cr Jabiru, Red-cowled Cardinal

Set of 3   65   25

2086 65cr Scarlet Macaw, Glaucous Macaw.   ..   15   5

2091† 65cr American Wood Stork, Great Egret ..   20   8
2092† 65cr American Wood Stork, Roseate
       Spoonbill   20   8
                    (2091/3 *Set of 3*)   25   8

2121† 120cr Scarlet Macaw   15   10

STAMP MONTHLY
— finest and most informative magazine for all
collectors. Obtainable from your newsagent or by
postal subscription — details on request.

1985

2168   220cr Common Noddy (*Anous stolidus*)
2169   220cr Magnificent Frigate Bird (*Fregata magnificens*), Blue-faced Booby
2170   220cr Blue-faced Booby (*Sula dactylatra*), Red-billed Tropic Bird
2171   2000cr Grey Plover (*Pluvialis squatarola*)

Set of 4   55   35

1986

2257   6cz50 European Bee Eater, Crested Tit, ? .   60   55
(2256/8 *Set of* 3)   1.25   1.10
Nos. 2256 and 2258 depict unidentifiable birds.

1987

2269   1cz Adelie Penguin   15   8

1971

39†   4p Snow Petrel. 7.00   3.50
41†   10p Adelie Penguin 9.50   5.00

1972

42   5p Emperor Penguin
43   10p Emperor Penguin
Set of 2   6.00   3.00

1978

88†   25p Emperor Penguin..   ..   ..   1.00   85

BRITISH ANTARCTIC TERRITORY
Antarctica
1969 12 pence = 1 shilling,
20 shillings = 1 pound
1971 100 pence = 1 pound

1969

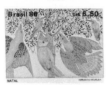

20†   3½d Adelie Penguin 3.25   2.00

1979

89   3p Macaroni Penguin
90   8p Gentoo Penguin
91   11p Adelie Penguin
92   25p Emperor Penguin
Set of 4   14.00   6.00

1981

| 100† | 13p Adelie Penguin | .. .. | 35 | 45 |

1982

| 108† | 26p Adelie Penguin | .. .. | 50 | 60 |

1983

| 113† | 5p Chinstrap Penguin | .. .. | 10 | 15 |

1985

| 143† | 7p McCormick's Skua (*Catharacta skua maccormicki*) | .. .. | 15 | 12 |

BRITISH COMMONWEALTH OCCUPATION FORCE (JAPAN)

1946

Nos. 189a *and* 191 *of Australia overprinted* **B.C.O.F. JAPAN 1946**
| B4† | 6d Laughing Kookaburra.. .. .. | 9.00 | 6.50 |
| B5† | 1s Superb Lyrebird | .. .. | 10.00 | 10.00 |

BRITISH GUIANA
South America
100 cents = 1 dollar

1938

| 319† | $3 Wattled Jacana | .. .. | 18.00 | 18.00 |

1954

| 333† | 3c Wattled Jacana | .. .. | 40 | 5 |
| 343† | $1 Channel-billed Toucan ('Toucan') | .. .. | 4.25 | 80 |

BRITISH HONDURAS
Central America
100 cents = 1 dollar

1962

202	1c Great Curassow
203	2c Red-legged Honeycreeper
204	3c Northern Jacana ('American Jacana')
205	4c Great Kiskadee
206	5c Scarlet-rumped Tanager
207	10c Scarlet Macaw
208	15c Slaty-tailed Trogon ('Massena Trogon')
209	25c Red-footed Booby
210	50c Keel-billed Toucan
211	$1 Magnificent Frigate Bird
212	$2 Rufous-tailed Jacamar
213	$5 Montezuma Oropendola

Set of 12   28.00   18.00

1964

Nos. 202, 204/5, 207 *and* 209 *overprinted* **SELF GOVERNMENT 1964**
217	1c Great Curassow
218	3c Northern Jacana
219	4c Great Kiskadee
220	10c Scarlet Macaw
221	25c Red-footed Booby

Set of 5   20   25

1966

Nos. 202, 204/5, 207 and 209 overprinted **DEDICATION OF SITE NEW CAPITAL 9th OCTOBER 1965**

230	1c Great Curassow		
231	3c Northern Jacana		
232	4c Great Kiskadee		
233	10c Scarlet Macaw		
234	25c Red-footed Booby		
	Set of 5	20	25

40	3r50 White-throated Rail ('Flightless Rail') ..	8.00	10.00

BRITISH INDIAN OCEAN TERRITORY
Indian Ocean
100 cents = 1 rupee

1968

No. 196 of Seychelles overprinted **B.I.O.T.**

1†	5c Black Parrot	10	10

29†	5r Great Frigate Bird	6.50	8.00

1969

31	2r25 Sacred Ibis.	1.50	80

1971

39†	1r50 Western Reef Heron ('Dimorphic Egrets')	6.00	6.00

1972

45	95c White-throated Rail, Sacred Ibis		
46	1r50 White-throated Rail, Sacred Ibis		
	Set of 2	1.40	1.25

1975

62	5c Aldabra Drongo		
63	10c Black Coucal ('Malgasy Coucal')		
64	20c Mascarene Fody ('Red-headed Forest Fody')		
65	25c White Tern ('Fairy Tern')		
66	30c Crested Tern		
67	40c Brown Booby		
68	50c Common Noddy ('Noddy Tern')		
69	60c Grey Heron		
70	65c Blue-faced Booby		
71	95c Madagascar White Eye ('Malagasy White-Eye')		
72	1r Green Heron ('Green Backed Heron')		
73	1r75 Lesser Frigate Bird		
74	3r50 White-tailed Tropic Bird		
75	5r Souimanga Sunbird		
76	10r Madagascar Turtle Dove ('Malagasy Turtle Dove')		
	Set of 15	21.00	28.00

1980

78† 65c Sacred Ibis. 40 60

439	20c Brown Booby	
440	25c Magnificent Frigate Bird	
441	50c White-tailed Tropic Bird	
442	75c Brown Pelican	
	Set of 4	1.25 1.25

BRITISH VIRGIN ISLANDS
West Indies
100 cents = 1 dollar

1982

1956

160† $2.40 Brown Pelican.. .. .. 10.00 11.00
161† $4.80 Magnificent Frigate Bird ('Man-o'-War Bird') 16.00 17.00

479 15c Green-throated Carib
480 30c Green-throated Carib
481 35c Antillean Crested Hummingbird
482 $1.25 Antillean Crested Hummingbird
Set of 4 3.25 3.25

1962
Nos. 160/1 surcharged
172† $1.40 on $2.40 Brown Pelican 4.00 5.00
173† $2.80 on $4.80 Magnificent Frigate Bird .. 5.50 6.00

1985

1964

180† 3c Brown Pelican. 20 5

560 1c Red-billed Tropic Bird ('Boatswain Bird')
561 2c Yellow-crowned Night Heron ('Night Gaulin')

1973

289 1c Green-throated Carib, Antillean Crested Hummingbird
290 5c Zenaida Dove
291 10c Ringed Kingfisher
292 25c Mangrove Cuckoo
293 50c Brown Pelican
294 $1 Magnificent Frigate Bird
Set of 6 3.00 3.75

562 5c Mangrove Cuckoo ('Rain Bird')
563 8c Northern Mockingbird ('Mockingbird')
564 10c Grey Kingbird ('Chinchary')
565 12c Red-necked Pigeon ('Wild Pigeon')
566 15c Least Bittern ('Bittlin')
567 18c Smooth-billed Ani ('Black Witch')
568 20c Clapper Rail ('Pond Shakey')
569 25c American Kestrel ('Killy-killy')
570 30c Pearly-eyed Thrasher ('Thrushie')
571 35c Bridled Quail Dove ('Marmi Dove')
572 40c Green Heron ('Little Gaulin')
573 50c Scaly-breasted Ground Dove ('Ground Dove')
574 60c Little Blue Heron ('Blue Gaulin')
575 $1 Audubon's Shearwater ('Pimleco')

576 $2 Blue-faced Booby ('White Booby')
577 $3 Cattle Egret ('Cow Bird')
578 $5 Zenaida Dove ('Turtle Dove')

Set of 19   15.00   17.00

588 5c Seaside Sparrow
589 30c Passenger Pigeon *
590 50c Yellow-breasted Chat
591 $1 American Kestrel

Set of 4   3.00   3.00

OFFICIAL STAMPS

1986

Nos. 560/78 overprinted **OFFICIAL**

O16 1c Red-billed Tropic Bird
O17 2c Yellow-crowned Night Heron
O18 5c Mangrove Cuckoo
O19 8c Northern Mockingbird
O20 10c Grey Kingbird
O21 12c Red-necked Pigeon
O22 15c Least Bittern
O23 18c Smooth-billed Ani
O24 20c Clapper Rail
O25 25c American Kestrel
O26 30c Pearly-eyed Thrasher
O27 35c Bridled Quail Dove
O28 40c Green Heron
O29 50c Scaly-breasted Ground Dove
O30 60c Little Blue Heron
O31 $1 Audubon's Shearwater
O32 $2 Blue-faced Booby
O33 $3 Cattle Egret
O34 $5 Zenaida Dove

Set of 19   8.50   9.25

BRUNEI
South-east Asia
100 cents = 1 dollar

1984

352 $1 Great Argus Pheasant, Crested Wood
     Partridge, Helmeted Hornbill   75   80

BULGARIA
South-east Europe
100 stotinki = 1 lev

1959

1140 2s Great Tit
1141 8s Hoopoe
1142 16s Great Spotted Woodpecker
1143 45s Grey Partridge
1144 60s Rock Partridge
1145 80s European Cuckoo

Set of 6   3.25   1.25

1961

1236 2s Capercaillie (*Tetrao urogallus*)
1237 4s Dalmatian Pelican (*Pelecanus crispus*)
1238 16s Ring-necked Pheasant (*Phasianus colchicus*)
1239 80s Great Bustard (*Otis tarda*)
1240 1lev Lammergeier (*Gypaetus barbatus*)
1241 2lev Hazel Grouse (*Tetrastes bonasia*)

Set of 6   3.50   1.50

1965

1517 1s Bullfinch (*Pyrrhula pyrrhula*)
1518 2s Golden Oriole (*Oriolus oriolus*)
1519 3s Rock Thrush (*Monticola saxatilis*)
1520 5s Barn Swallow (*Hirundo rustica*)
1521 8s Common Roller (*Coracias garrulus*)
1522 10s Goldfinch (*Carduelis carduelis*)
1523 13s Rose-coloured Starling (*Pastor roseus*)
1524 20s Nightingale (*Luscinia megarhynchos*)

Set of 8   7.50   2.25

1967

1682†	1s Ring-necked Pheasant	25	5
1683†	2s Rock Partridge	25	5
1684†	3s Grey Partridge	25	5

1968

1813†	1s European Black Vulture	25	10
1814†	2s South African Crowned Crane	25	10

1832	1s Dalmatian Pelican (*Pelecanus crispus*)
1833	2s Little Egret (*Egretta garzetta*)
1834	3s Great Crested Grebe (*Podiceps cristatus*)
1835	5s Common Tern (*Sterna hirundo*)
1836	13s White Spoonbill (*Platalea leucorodia*)
1837	20s Glossy Ibis (*Plegadis falcinellus*)

Set of 6　2.50　1.25

1976

2455	1s Mute Swan (*Cygnus olor*)
2456	2s Ruddy Shelduck (*Tadorna ferruginea*)
2457	3s Common Shelduck (*Tadorna tadorna*)
2458	5s Garganey (*Anas querquedula*)
2459	13s Mallard (*Anas platyrhynchos*)
2460	18s Red-crested Pochard (*Netta rufina*)

Set of 6　2.25　75

1978

2680	1s Black Woodpecker (*Dryocopus martius*)
2681	2s Syrian Woodpecker (*Dendrocopos syriacus*)
2682	3s Three-toed Woodpecker (*Picoides tridactylus*)
2683	13s Middle Spotted Woodpecker (*Dendrocopos medius*)
2684	23s Lesser Spotted Woodpecker (*Dendrocopos minor*)
2685	43s Green Woodpecker (*Picus viridis*)

Set of 6　2.00　1.10

1981

2930	5s Squacco Heron (*Ardeola ralloides*)
2931	8s Eurasian Bittern (*Botaurus stellaris*)
2932	13s Cattle Egret (*Ardeola ibis*)
2933	25s Great Egret (*Casmerodius albus*)
2934	53s Black Stork (*Ciconia nigra*)

Set of 5　2.25　85

1984

3154	5s Rock Dove (*Columba livia*)
3155	13s Stock Dove (*Columba oenas*)
3156	20s Wood Pigeon (*Columba palumbus*)
3157	30s Turtle Dove (*Streptopelia turtur*)
3158	42s Domestic Pigeon (*Columba var. domestica*)

Set of 5　2.00　85

3183 5s Dalmatian Pelican (*Pelecanus crispus*)
3184 13s Dalmatian Pelican (*Pelecanus crispus*)
3185 20s Dalmatian Pelican (*Pelecanus crispus*)
3186 32s Dalmatian Pelican (*Pelecanus crispus*)

		Set of 4	1.40	65

1985

3306†	5s Chukar Partridge.	10	5
3307†	8s European Pochard	15	5
3308†	13s Mallard	25	10
3309†	20s Woodcock	40	15

BURKINA FASO
West Africa
100 centimes = 1 franc

1985

789 60f Wood Duck (*Aix sponsa*)
790 100f Northern Mockingbird (*Mimus polyglotos*)
791 300f Northern Oriole (*Icterus galbula*)
792 400f White-breasted Nuthatch (*Sitta carolinensis*)
793 500f Common Flicker (*Asyndesmus lewis* !) (air)
794 600f Rough-legged Buzzard (*Buteo cagopus*)

		Set of 6	7.50	6.25
MS795	1000f White-crowned Pigeon (*Columba leucocephala*)	4.50	3.75

BURMA
South-east Asia
100 pyas = 1 kyat

1964

174 1p White-browed Fantail (25x21 mm)
175 2p White-browed Fantail (25x21 mm)
176 3p White-browed Fantail (25x21 mm)
177 5p Indian Roller (22x26 mm)
178 10p Indian Roller (22x26 mm)
179 15p Indian Roller (22x26 mm)
180 20p Red-whiskered Bulbul (35x25 mm)
181 25p Crested Serpent Eagle (27x37 mm)
182 50p Sarus Crane (27x37 mm)
183 1k Indian Pied Hornbill (27x37 mm)
184 2k Kalij Pheasant (37x27 mm)
185 5k Green Peafowl (27x37 mm)

Set of 12	12.00	5.50

1968

195 1p White-browed Fantail (21x17 mm)
196 2p White-browed Fantail (21x17 mm)
197 3p White-browed Fantail (21x17 mm)
198 5p Indian Roller (23x28 mm)
199 10p Indian Roller (23x28 mm)
200 15p Indian Roller (23x28 mm)
201 20p Red-whiskered Bulbul (39x21 mm)
202 25p Crested Serpent Eagle (21x39 mm)
203 50p Sarus Crane (21x39 mm)
204 1k Indian Pied Hornbill (21x39 mm)
205 2k Kalij Pheasant (39x21 mm)
206 5k Green Peafowl (21x39 mm)

Set of 12	10.00	4.25

OFFICIAL STAMPS

1965

Nos. 175/7, 179 and 181 overprinted with Burmese letters (11½ mm long)

O186 2p White-browed Fantail
O187 3p White-browed Fantail
O188 5p Indian Roller
O189 15p Indian Roller
O190 25p Crested Serpent Eagle

Set of 5	30	30

1966

Nos. 174/6 and 179 overprinted with Burmese letters (15 mm long on Nos. O192/4, 12 mm long on No. O195)

O192 1p White-browed Fantail
O193 2p White-browed Fantail
O194 3p White-browed Fantail
O195 15p Indian Roller

Set of 4	20	20

Nos. 174/7 and 179/85 overprinted with Burmese letters (14½ mm long)

O196	1p White-browed Fantail		
O197	2p White-browed Fantail		
O198	3p White-browed Fantail		
O199	5p Indian Roller		
O200	15p Indian Roller		
O201	20p Red-whiskered Bulbul		
O202	25p Crested Serpent Eagle		
O203	50p Sarus Crane		
O204	1k Indian Pied Hornbill		
O205	2k Kalij Pheasant		
O206	5k Green Peafowl		
		Set of 11 11.00	9.50

1968

Nos. 195/8 and 200/6 overprinted with Burmese letters

O207	1p White-browed Fantail		
O208	2p White-browed Fantail		
O209	3p White-browed Fantail		
O210	5p Indian Roller		
O211	15p Indian Roller		
O212	20p Red-whiskered Bulbul		
O213	25p Crested Serpent Eagle		
O214	50p Sarus Crane		
O215	1k Indian Pied Hornbill		
O216	2k Kalij Pheasant		
O217	5k Green Peafowl		
		Set of 11 10.00	8.00

BURUNDI
Central Africa
100 centimes = 1 franc

1965

127	50c Purple Swamphen (*Porphyrio alba*)
128	1f Little Bee Eater (*Melittophagus pusillus*)
129	1f50 Secretary Bird (*Sagittarius serpentarius*)
130	2f Yellow-billed Stork (*Ibis ibis*)
131	3f Congo Peafowl (*Afropavo congensis*)
132	3f50 African Darter (*Anhinga rufa*)
133	4f Purple Swamphen (*Porphyrio alba*)
134	5f Little Bee Eater (*Melittophagus pusillus*)
135	6f50 Secretary Bird (*Sagittarius serpentarius*)
136	8f Yellow-billed Stork (*Ibis ibis*)
137	10f Congo Peafowl (*Afropavo congensis*)
138	15f African Darter (*Anhinga rufa*)
139	20f Saddle-bill Stork (*Ephippiorhynchus senegalensis*)
140	50f Abyssinian Ground Hornbill (*Buceros abyssinicus*)
141	100f South African Crowned Crane (*Balearica pavonina* !)

142	6f Secretary Bird (*Sagittarius serpentarius*) (air)		
143	8f African Darter (*Anhinga rufa*)		
144	10f Congo Peafowl (*Afropavo congensis*)		
145	14f Little Bee Eater (*Melittophagus pusillus*)		
146	15f Yellow-billed Stork (*Ibis ibis*)		
147	20f Saddle-bill Stork (*Ephippiorhynchus senegalensis*)		
148	50f Abyssinian Ground Hornbill (*Buceros abyssinicus*)		
149	75f Martial Eagle (*Polemaetus bellicosus*)		
150	130f Lesser Flamingo (*Phoeniconais minor*)		
		Set of 24 18.00	7.50

1967

Nos. 127, 129, 132 and 134/50 overprinted **REPUBLIQUE DU BURUNDI**

221	50c Purple Swamphen
222	1f50 Secretary Bird
223	3f50 African Darter
224	5f Little Bee Eater
225	6f50 Secretary Bird
226	8f Yellow-billed Stork
227	10f Congo Peafowl
228	15f African Darter
229	20f Saddle-bill Stork
230	50f Abyssinian Ground Hornbill
231	100f South African Crowned Crane
232	6f Secretary Bird (air)
233	8f African Darter
234	10f Congo Peafowl
235	14f Little Bee Eater
236	15f Yellow-billed Stork
237	20f Saddle-bill Stork
238	50f Abyssinian Ground Hornbill
239	75f Martial Eagle
240	130f Lesser Flamingo
	Set of 20 38.00 18.00

1970

534	7f South African Crowned Crane.	50	25
534	7f Secretary Bird	50	25
535	14f South African Crowned Crane (air)	50	30
535	14f Secretary Bird..	50	30

Nos. 534 and 535 each cover 18 different designs forming a map of the Nile.

STANLEY GIBBONS
STAMP COLLECTING SERIES
Introductory booklets on *How to Start, How to Identify Stamps* and *Collecting by Theme*. A series of well illustrated guides at a low price.
Write for details.

536	2f Great Grey Shrike (*Lanius excubitor*)
537	2f Common Starling (*Sturnus vulgaris*)
538	2f Yellow Wagtail (*Motacilla flava*)
539	2f Sand Martin (*Riparia riparia*)
540	3f Winter Wren (*Troglodytes troglodytes*)
541	3f Firecrest (*Regulus ignicapillus*)
542	3f Sky Lark (*Alauda arvensis*)
543	3f Crested Lark (*Galerida cristata*)
544	3f50 Woodchat Shrike (*Lanius senator*)
545	3f50 Rock Thrush (*Monticola saxatilis*)
546	3f50 Black Redstart (*Phoenicurus ochruros*)
547	3f50 Ring Ousel (*Turdus torquatus*)
548	4f Redstart (*Phoenicurus phoenicurus*)
549	4f Dunnock (*Prunella modularis*)
550	4f Grey Wagtail (*Motacilla cinerea*)
551	4f Meadow Pipit (*Anthus pratensis*)
552	5f Hoopoe (*Upupa epops*)
553	5f Pied Flycatcher (*Ficecula hypoleuca*)
554	5f Great Reed Warbler (*Acrocephalus arundinaceus*)
555	5f Common Kingfisher (*Alcedo atthis*)
556	6f50 House Martin (*Delichon urbica*)
557	6f50 Sedge Warbler (*Acrocephalus schoenobaenus*)
558	6f50 Fieldfare (*Turdus pilaris*)
559	6f50 Golden Oriole (*Oriolus oriolus*)
560	8f Great Grey Shrike (*Lanius excubitor*) (air)
561	8f Common Starling (*Sturnus vulgaris*)
562	8f Yellow Wagtail (*Motacilla flava*)
563	8f Sand Martin (*Riparia riparia*)
564	10f Winter Wren (*Troglodytes troglodytes*)
565	10f Firecrest (*Regulus ignicapillus*)
566	10f Sky Lark (*Alauda arvensis*)
567	10f Crested Lark (*Galerida cristata*)
568	14f Woodchat Shrike (*Lanius senator*)
569	14f Rock Thrush (*Monticola saxatilis*)
570	14f Black Redstart (*Phoenicurus ochruros*)
571	14f Ring Ousel (*Turdus torquatus*)
572	20f Redstart (*Phoenicurus phoenicurus*)
573	20f Dunnock (*Prunella modularis*)
574	20f Grey Wagtail (*Motacilla cinerea*)
575	20f Meadow Pipit (*Anthus pratensis*)
576	30f Hoopoe (*Upupa epops*)
577	30f Pied Flycatcher (*Ficecula hypoleuca*)
578	30f Great Reed Warbler (*Acrocephalus arundinaceus*)
579	30f Common Kingfisher (*Alcedo atthis*)
580	50f House Martin (*Delichon urbica*)
581	50f Sedge Warbler (*Acrocephalus schoenobaenus*)
582	50f Fieldfare (*Turdus pilaris*)
583	50f Golden Oriole (*Oriolus oriolus*)

Set of 48 24.00 12.50

STAMP MONTHLY

— finest and most informative magazine for all collectors. Obtainable from your newsagent or by postal subscription — details on request.

1971

623†	3f African White-backed Vulture (*Gyps africanus*)	25	25
635†	11f Ostrich (*Struthio camelus*)	70	30
647†	17f African White-backed Vulture (*Gyps africanus*) (air)..	70	30
659†	31f Ostrich (*Struthio camelus*)	1.25	50

No. 647 surcharged **AIDE INTERNATIONALE AUX REFUGIES**, emblem and premium

678†	17f + 1f African White-backed Vulture	50	25

No. 659 surcharged **JEUX PRE-OLYMPIQUES MUNICH 1972**, rings and premium

686†	31f + 1f Ostrich	1.75	1.00

1977

1179†	2f Marabou Stork (*Leptoptilos crumeniferus*)..	25	25
1183†	5f Whale-headed Stork (*Balaeniceps rex*)	30	25
1186†	8f Greater Flamingo (*Phoenicopterus ruber roseus*)..	35	25
1193†	11f Verreaux's Eagle (*Aquila verreauxii*)	40	30
1196†	21f Secretary Bird (*Sagittarius serpentarius*)	50	40
1200†	27f Vulturine Guineafowl (*Acryllium vulturinum*)	70	45
1203†	9f Marabou Stork (*Leptoptilos crumeniferus*) (air)	30	25
1207†	13f Whale-headed Stork (*Balaeniceps rex*)..	50	30
1210†	30f Greater Flamingo (*Phoenicopterus ruber roseus*)..	75	50
1217†	35f Verreaux's Eagle (*Aquila verreauxii*)	85	60
1220†	54f Secretary Bird (*Sagittarius serpentarius*)	1.10	75
1224†	70f Vulturine Guineafowl (*Acryllium vulturinum*)	1.75	90

1979

1318   1f Abyssinian Ground Hornbill (*Buceros abyssinicus*)
1319   2f African Darter (*Anhinga rufa*)
1320   3f Little Bee Eater (*Melittophagus pusillus*)
1321   5f Lesser Flamingo (*Fhoeniconais minor*)
1322   8f Congo Peafowl (*Afropavo congensis*)
1323   10f Purple Swamphen (*Porphyrio alba*)
1324   20f Martial Eagle (*Polemaethus bellicosus*)
1325   27f Yellow-billed Stork (*Ibis ibis*)
1326   50f Saddle-bill Stork (*Ephippiorhynchus senegalensis*)

1327   6f Abyssinian Ground Hornbill (*Buceros abyssinicus*) (air)
1328   13f African Darter (*Anhinga rufa*)
1329   18f Little Bee Eater (*Melittophagus pusillus*)
1330   26f Lesser Flamingo (*Fhoeniconais minor*)
1331   31f Congo Peafowl (*Afropavo congensis*)
1332   36f Purple Swamphen (*Porphyrio alba*)
1333   40f Martial Eagle (*Polemaethus bellicosus*)
1334   54f Yellow-billed Stork (*Ibis ibis*)
1335   70f Saddle-bill Stork (*Ephippiorhynchus senegalensis*)

Set of 18	11.00	10.00

CAICOS ISLANDS
West Indies
100 cents = 1 dollar

1985

68   20c Thick-billed Vireo
69   35c Black-faced Grassquit
70   50c Pearly-eyed Thrasher
71   $1 Greater Antillean Bullfinch

Set of 4	3.00	3.25
MS72 $2 Stripe-headed Tanager	3.25	3.50

CAMBODIA
South-east Asia
100 cents = 1 riel

1964

162   3r Magpie
163   6r Common Kingfisher
164   12r Grey Heron

Set of 3	1.40	1.25

CAMEROUN
West Africa
100 centimes = 1 franc

1953

263 15f Sacred Ibis	1.50	75

1962

326† 200f Ostrich ('Autruches')	4.25	1.25

1971

600† 10f Crowned Crane 25 20

1972

663 10f Great Blue Turaco (*Corytheola cristata*)
664 45f Red-faced Lovebird (*Agapornis pullaria guineesis*)

                   Set of 2 90 45

1977

786 30f Ostrich
787 50f Crowned Crane ('Crown-Cranes')

                   Set of 2 1.25 50

1979

859† 100f Cattle Egret 1.00 75

1982

941 10f Cameroun Mountain Francolin ('Perdrix')
942 15f Red-eyed Dove ('Tourterelle')
943 20f Barn Swallow ('Hirondelle')

                   Set of 3 30 30

See also No. 1071.

1983

967 25f Martial Eagle ('L'Aigle Martial')
968 30f Rufous-breasted Sparrow Hawk ('L'Epervier')
969 50f Purple Heron ('Le Heron Pourpre')

                   Set of 3 65 30

1984

1021 60f Nightingale ('Le Rossignol')
1022 60f Ruppell's Griffon ('Le Vautour')

                   Set of 2 70 45

1985

1061† 140f Yellow-casqued Hornbill ('Le Toucan') 55 40
1063† 200f European Robin ('Le Rouge-Gorge').   70 55
(1061/3 *Set of* 3)   1.60 1.25

1986

As No. 941 *but inscribed* 'REPUBLIQUE DU CAMEROUN REPUBLIC OF CAMEROON'
1071† 10f Cameroun Mountain Francolin ('Perdrix') 5 5
(1070/1 *Set of* 2)   10 10

CANADA
North America
100 cents = 1 dollar

1946

407 7c Canada Goose 1.50 5

1952

443 7c Canada Goose 25 5

1954

474 15c Northern Gannet 65 5

1955

479† 5c Whooping Crane 25 5
(478/9 *Set of* 2)   40 10

1957

495 5c White-billed Diver 20 5

1963

539 15c Canada Goose. 2.00 5

1968

620 5c Grey Jay. 25 10

1969

638 6c White-throated Sparrow
639 10c Savannah Sparrow ('Ipswich Sparrow')
640 25c Hermit Thrush
Set of 3   2.50 3.00

1978

906   12c Peregrine Falcon (*Falco peregrinus*) ..   20   15

1980

977† 17c Prairie Chicken (*Tympanuchus cupido*
      pinnatus)   20   15
      (976/7 Set of 2)   40   30

1986

1189 34c Great Blue Heron
1190 34c Snow Goose
1191 34c Great Horned Owl
1192 34c Spruce Grouse
                        Set of 4   1.40   1.40

OFFICIAL STAMPS

1946

No. 407 overprinted **O.H.M.S.**
O10† 7c Canada Goose 6.00   2.50

1950

Nos. 407 and 443 overprinted **G**
O29† 7c Canada Goose (No. 407). 8.00   7.50
O32† 7c Canada Goose (No. 443). 1.00   75

CAPE JUBY
North-west Africa
100 centimos = 1 peseta

1938

Nos. 204 and 210 of Spanish Morocco overprinted **CABO JUBY**
96†   10c White Stork   50   25
102† 1p50 White Stork 1.75   75

1944

Nos. 269 and 276 of Spanish Morocco overprinted **CABO JUBY**
130† 1c Cattle Egret   25   25
137† 30c Cattle Egret   25   25

CAPE VERDE ISLANDS
Atlantic
100 centavos = 1 escudo

1981

512   1e Little Egret (*Egretta garzetta*)
513   4e50 Barn Owl (*Tyto alba*)
514   8e Grey-headed Kingfisher (*Halcyon
      leucocephala*)
515   10e Moorhen (*Gallinula chloropus*)
516   12e Helmet Guineafowl (*Numida
      meleagris*)
                        Set of 5   1.25   70
MS517 50e Raza Island Lark (*Alauda razae*) ..   2.00   2.00

CAYES OF BELIZE
Central America
100 cents = 1 dollar

Appendix

The following stamps have either been issued in excess of
postal needs, or have not been made available to the public in
reasonable quantities at face value. Miniature sheets,
imperforate stamps etc. are excluded from this section.

1984

Marine Life, Map and Views. 5c Red-faced Booby, 10c Brown
Pelican

1985

Birth Bicentenary of John J. Audubon. 25c Blue-winged Teal,
75c Semipalmated Sandpiper, $1 Yellow-crowned Night
Heron, $3 Moorhen

CAYMAN ISLANDS
West Indies
1935 12 pence = 1 shilling,
20 shillings = 1 pound
1969 100 cents = 1 Jamaican dollar

1935

102† 1d Red-footed Booby ('Booby Birds') 2.50   60
109† 2s Red-footed Booby ('Booby Birds') 30.00   30.00

1962

165† ¼d Cuban Amazon ('Cayman Parrot')   15   20

1969

222† ¼d Grand Cayman Thrush ('Cayman Thrush')   5   5

No. 222 surcharged
238† ½c on ¼d Grand Cayman Thrush   5   10

1970

273† ½c Grand Cayman Thrush ('Cayman Thrush')   10   5

1973

319† 3c Grand Cayman Thrush   10   10

STANLEY GIBBONS
STAMP COLLECTING SERIES
Introductory booklets on *How to Start, How to Identify Stamps* and *Collecting by Theme*. A series of well illustrated guides at a low price.
Write for details.

1974

337   3c White-winged Dove
338   10c Vitelline Warbler
339   12c Antillean Grackle ('Greater Antillean Grackle')
340   20c West Indian Red-bellied Woodpecker
341   30c Stripe-headed Tanager
342   50c Yucatan Vireo
             Set of 6   15.00   8.50

1975

383   3c Common Flicker ('Yellow-shafted Flicker')
384   10c Black-billed Whistling Duck ('West Indian Tree Duck')
385   12c Yellow Warbler
386   20c White-bellied Dove
387   30c Magnificent Frigate Bird
388   50c Cuban Amazon ('Cayman Amazon')
             Set of 6   6.50   6.25

1978

470† 30c Screech Owl   30   45

1980

519†	20c Louisiana Heron ('Tricoloured Heron')	60	35
523†	$1 Black-crowned Night Heron	2.50	2.50

1983

576†	20c Magnificent Frigate Bird	30	35

1984

592	5c Snowy Egret		
593	10c Bananaquit		
594	35c Belted Kingfisher ('Kingfisher')		
595	$1 Brown Booby		
		Set of 4 3.50	3.50

1986

627	10c Magnificent Frigate Bird		
628	25c Black-billed Whistling Duck ('West Indian Whistling Duck')		
629	35c La Sagra's Flycatcher		
630	40c Yellow-faced Grassquit		
		Set of 4 2.00	2.25

CENTRAL AFRICAN EMPIRE
Central Africa
100 centimes = 1 franc

1978

596	100f Red Crossbill		
597	100f African Fish Eagle (on Central African Republic stamp No. 16)		
		Set of 2 2.25	1.40

CENTRAL AFRICAN REPUBLIC
Central Africa
100 centimes = 1 franc

1960

12	50f Great Blue Turaco (*Corytheola cristata*)		
13	100f Abyssinian Roller (*Coracias abyssinica*)		
14	200f Knysna Turaco (*Turacus persea*)		
15	250f Red-faced Lovebird (*Agapornis pullaria pullaria*)		
16	500f African Fish Eagle (*Concuma vocifer clamans*)		
		Set of 5 23.00	9.25

1960

No. 276 of French Equatorial Africa surcharged **XVIIe OLYMPIADE 1960 REPUBLIQUE CENTRAFRICAINE 250F** *and Olympic rings*

18	250f on 500f African Darter.	7.00	7.00

1971

229†	5f + 5f Helmet Guineafowl ('La Pintade'), Scaly Francolin ('La Perdrix').	2.25	1.75
232†	30f + 10f Senegal Coucal ('La Tortue et le Coucou')	5.50	5.50

1981

803 50f Plumed Guineafowl ('Komba')
804 90f Schlegel's Francolin ('Dodoro')
805 140f Black-headed Bunting, Ortolan
     Bunting ('Kaya')
                   Set of 3   1.75   65

1983

972† 40f Cattle Egret   20   12
974† 180f Yellow-billed Oxpecker 1.10 55

975† 400f Cuban Macaw * (air) 2.25 1.25
976† 500f Grey Parrot 2.75 1.75

1985

1076 60f Screech Owl (Otus asio)
1077 110f Mangrove Cuckoo (Coccizus minor)
1078 200f Mourning Dove (Zenaidura
     macroura)
1079 500f Wood Duck (Aix sponsa)
                   Set of 4   3.25 2.75

COLLECT RAILWAYS ON STAMPS
A Stanley Gibbons thematic catalogue on this
popular subject. Copies available at £7.50 (p. + p.
£1.50) from: Stanley Gibbons Publications Ltd, 5
Parkside, Christchurch Road, Ringwood, Hants
BH24 3SH.

1099 40f Blue Jay (Cyanocitta cristata)
1100 80f Chuck Will's Widow (Caprimulgus
     carolinensis)
1101 130f Ivory-billed Woodpecker
     (Campephilus principales)
1102 250f Collie's Magpie-Jay (Calocitta
     formosa !)
1103 300f Mangrove Cuckoo (Coccizus minor)
     (air)
1104 500f Barn Swallow (Hirundo rustica)
                  Set of 6 5.00 4.50
MS1105 600f Pileated Woodpecker (Dryocopus
     pileatus). 2.50 2.50

Appendix
The following stamps have either been issued in excess of
postal needs, or have not been made available to the public in
reasonable quantities at face value. Miniature sheets,
imperforate stamps etc. are excluded from this section.

1982
Animals and Rotary International. Air 1500f Secretary Bird

CEYLON
Indian Ocean
100 cents = 1 rupee

1964

485† 5c Hill Myna ('Grackle')   5   5
488† 15c Common Peafowl ('Peacock')   70   5
494† 60c Ceylon Junglefowl   70   5
495† 75c Asian Black-headed Oriole ('Oriole') ..   70   5

CHAD
Central Africa
100 centimes = 1 franc

1960

No. 276 of French Equatorial Africa surcharged **XVIIe OLYMPIADE 1960 REPUBLIQUE DU TCHAD 250F** and Olympic rings

65	250f on 500f African Darter.	7.00	7.00

1961

82	50f Red Bishop (*Euplectes oryx*)
83	100f Scarlet-chested Sunbird (*Chalcomitra senegalensis*)
84	200f African Paradise Flycatcher (*Tchitrea viridis*)
85	250f Malachite Kingfisher (*Corythornis cristata*)
86	500f Carmine Bee Eater (*Merops nubicus*)

		Set of 5	26.00	9.75

1966

163	50f Greater Blue-eared Glossy Starling (*Lamprocolius chalybaeus hartlaubi*)
164	100f White-throated Bee Eater (*Merops albicollis*)
165	200f African Pygmy Kingfisher (*Ispidina picta*)
166	250f Red-throated Bee Eater (*Melittophagus bullocki bullocki*)
167	500f Little Green Bee Eater (*Merops orientalis*)

		Set of 5	17.00	6.50

1970

Nos. 164/6 surcharged with new value and various space flight inscriptions and diagrams

305	50f on 100f White-throated Bee Eater
306	100f on 200f African Pygmy Kingfisher
307	125f on 250f Red-throated Bee Eater

		Set of 3	3.00	2.00

1971

336	1000f Great Egret (*Egretta alba*)..	17.00	9.00

1978

535	100f Grey Heron
536	100f Carmine Bee Eater (on stamp No. 86)

		Set of 2	2.50	1.75

1985

REPUBLIQUE DU TCHAD

794	70f Saddle-bill Stork ('Jabiru')
795	110f Ostrich ('Autruche')
796	150f Marabou Stork ('Marabout')
797	200f Secretary Bird ('Messager Serpentaire')

		Set of 4	2.10	1.90
MS798	500f Secretary Bird ('Messager Serpentaire')	2.50	2.50

Appendix

The following stamps have either been issued in excess of postal needs, or have not been made available to the public in reasonable quantities at face value. Miniature sheets, imperforate stamps etc. are excluded from this section.

1972

13th World Scout Jamboree, Asagiri, Japan (1971). Postage 70f White-tailed Sea Eagle (?)

CHILE
South America
100 centavos = 1 peso

1931

223†	5c Andean Condor	25	25
224†	10c Andean Condor	25	25
225†	20c Andean Condor	25	12

1940

No. 225 surcharged Cts. 80 and winged device

282†	80c on 20c Andean Condor	40	25

1948

381c†	60c Chilean Pigeon (*Columba araucana*) .	40	25
381h†	60c Emperor Penguin ('Pinguino Imperial')	40	25
381o†	60c Common Caracara (*Caracara vulgaris*)	40	25
381q†	60c Red-gartered Coot (*Fulica chilensis*) .	40	25
381x†	60c Torrent Duck (*Raphipterus chilensis*)	40	25
382c†	2p60 Chilean Pigeon (*Columba araucana*)	60	30
382h†	2p60 Emperor Penguin ('Pinguino Imperial')	60	30
382o†	2p60 Common Caracara (*Caracara vulgaris*)	60	30
382q†	2p60 Red-gartered Coot (*Fulica chilensis*)	60	30
382x†	2p60 Torrent Duck (*Raphipterus chilensis*)	60	30
383c†	3p Chilean Pigeon (*Columba araucana*) (air)	60	60
383h†	3p Emperor Penguin ('Pinguino Imperial')	60	60
383o†	3p Common Caracara (*Caracara vulgaris*)	60	60
383q†	3p Red-gartered Coot (*Fulica chilensis*) ..	60	60
383x†	3p Torrent Duck (*Raphipterus chilensis*) ..	60	60

1980

855	3p50 Andean Condor	20	10

1981

870†	10p50 Gentoo Penguin	55	45

1984

971†	15p Chinstrap Penguin	40	20

988†	9p Chinstrap Penguin	25	12

1985

1002†	10p Black-tailed Stilt (*Himantopus himantopus* !)	40	20
1005†	10p Patagonian Conure (*Psittacus cyanalysios*)	40	20
1008†	10p Common Diuca Finch (*Diuca diuca*) ..	40	20
1011†	10p Ferruginous Pygmy Owl (*Glaucidium nanum*).	40	20

1019†	20p James's Flamingo (*Phoenicoparrus jamesi*)	25	12
1020†	20p Giant Coot (*Fulica gigantea*)	25	12

1986

1066 40p Swallow-tailed Tern (*Sterna vittata*)
1067 40p Blue-eyed Cormorant (*Phalacrocorax atriceps*)
1068 40p Emperor Penguin (*Aptenodytes forsteri*)
1069 40p Great Skua (*Catharacta lonnberg*)

Set of 4	1.40	1.10

CHINA
Eastern Asia
100 cents = 1 dollar (yuan)

Chinese Empire

1897

105†	$1 Bean Goose	40.00	35.00
106†	$2 Bean Goose	£200	£220
107†	$5 Bean Goose	£120	£250

1898

131†	$1 Bean Goose	20.00	1.75
132†	$2 Bean Goose	40.00	7.50
133†	$5 Bean Goose	75.00	25.00

Chinese Republic

1912

Nos. 131/3 *overprinted with four Chinese characters signifying* Republic of China

204	$1 Bean Goose.	17.00	2.25
205	$2 Bean Goose.	35.00	7.50
232	$5 Bean Goose.	90.00	£110

1949

1344 $1 Whistling Swan
1345 $2 Whistling Swan
1346 $5 Whistling Swan
1347 $10 Whistling Swan

	Set of 4	26.00	38.00

Manchuria
100 fen = 1 yuan

1940

127 2f Manchurian Crane
128 4f Manchurian Crane

	Set of 2	1.00	1.00

Chinese People's Republic
1949 100 cents = 1 dollar
1955 100 fen = 1 yuan

REGIONAL ISSUES FOR EAST CHINA

PARCEL POST STAMPS

1949

紙印裹包 圓其壹

政郵東華

圓其壹 紙印裹包

No. 1347 *surcharged*

ECP383	$200 on $10 Whistling Swan	
ECP384	$500 on $10 Whistling Swan	
ECP385	$1000 on $10 Whistling Swan	
ECP386	$2000 on $10 Whistling Swan	
ECP387	$5000 on $10 Whistling Swan	
ECP388	$10000 on $10 Whistling Swan	

	Set of 6	£100	40.00

1950

Nos. 1344/6 and unissued 10c surcharged

ECP403	$5000 on 10c Whistling Swan	
ECP404	$10000 on $1 Whistling Swan	
ECP405	$20000 on $2 Whistling Swan	
ECP406	$50000 on $5 Whistling Swan	

Set of 4   £200   £100

GENERAL ISSUES

1950

中國人民郵政

壹佰圓

★★

Nos. 1344/7 and unissued stamps surcharged

1450	$50 on 10c Whistling Swan
1451	$100 on 16c Whistling Swan
1452	$100 on 50c Whistling Swan
1453	$200 on $1 Whistling Swan
1453a	$200 on $2 Whistling Swan
1454	$400 on $5 Whistling Swan
1455	$400 on $10 Whistling Swan
1455a	$400 on $20 Whistling Swan

Set of 8   2.50   3.00

Nos. 1451/2 are imperforate.

1958

1767	4f Whistling Swan
1768	8f Whistling Swan

Set of 2   15.00   1.10

1962

2029	8f Manchurian Crane
2030	10f Manchurian Crane
2031	20f Manchurian Crane

Set of 3   9.50   2.25

1979

2847	4f Golden Pheasant
2848	8f Golden Pheasant
2849	45f Golden Pheasant

Set of 3   1.25   75

1980

2946† 8f Common Kingfisher   25   15

3015† 8f Black-naped Oriole   25   25

1982

3194†   70f Masked Hawfinch   65   35
Nos. 3190/1 depict unidentifiable birds.

3202   8f Hoopoe (*Upupa epops*)
3203   8f Barn Swallow (*Hirundo rustica*)
3204   8f Black-naped Oriole (*Oriolus chinensis*)
3205   20f Great Tit (*Parus major*)
3206   70f Great Spotted Woodpecker
          (*Dendrocopos major*)
                            Set of 6   1.10   70
MS3207   2y Ashy   Minivet,   Magpie   Robin,
          Daurian   Redstart,   Red-flanked
          Bluetail, Little Cuckoo (*Cuculidae,*
          Campephagidae, Turnidae) 2.50   2.50

1983

3283   8f Mute Swan (*Cygnus olor*) (one swan)
3284   8f Mute Swan (*Cygnus olor*) (two swans)
3285   10f Whistling Swan (*Cygnus colnmbianus*)
3286   80f Whooper Swan (*Cygnus cygnus*)
                            Set of 4   1.10   55

1984

3301†   10f Manchurian Crane   10   8
3302†   70f Manchurian Crane   80   50
                      (3300/2 *Set of 3*)   90   55
MS3303   2y Manchurian Crane 2.25   2.25

3311   8f Japanese Crested Ibis (*Nipponia*
          nippon) (flying)
3312   8f Japanese Crested Ibis (*Nipponia*
          nippon) (standing)
3313   80f Japanese Crested Ibis (*Nipponia*
          nippon)
                            Set of 3   1.00   55

3342†   80f Manchurian Crane   80   40

3347†   20f Manchurian Crane   25   12

1986

3450   8f Great White Crane (*Grus leucogeranus*)
3451   10f Great White Crane (*Grus*
          leucogeranus)
3452   70f Great White Crane (*Grus*
          leucogeranus)
                            Set of 3   40   20
MS3453   2y Great White Crane (*Grus*
          leucogeranus)   90   50

Taiwan

100 cents = 1 new Taiwan yuan

1950

壹　臺

圓　幣

100

As No. 1347 of China, but without value, surcharged
100   $1 on (-) Whistling Swan
101   $2 on (-) Whistling Swan
102   $5 on (-) Whistling Swan
103   $10 on (-) Whistling Swan
104   $20 on (-) Whistling Swan

Set of 5   £800   £250

1951

伍　臺

圓　幣

5.00

As No. 1347 of China, but without value, surcharged
129   $5 on (-) Whistling Swan
130   $10 on (-) Whistling Swan
131   $20 on (-) Whistling Swan
132   $50 on (-) Whistling Swan

Set of 4   £300   45.00

1952

臺弍拾圓

20.00

As No. 1347 of China, but without value, surcharged
148   $10 on (-) Whistling Swan
149   $20 on (-) Whistling Swan
150   $50 on (-) Whistling Swan

Set of 3   £400   £150

1959

321   $8 Slaty-backed Gull 1.25   25

1960

360† $1.60 Red-billed Blue Magpie   70   30
361† $2 Green-winged Teal 1.25   70

1963

466   80c Barn Swallow
467   $2 Northern Gannet
468   $6 Manchurian Crane

Set of 3   6.50   1.90

1966

580† $5 Magpie..   ..   ..   1.40   35

588   $3.50 Bean Goose
589   $4 Bean Goose
590   $4.50 Bean Goose

591 $5 Bean Goose
592 $5.50 Bean Goose
593 $6 Bean Goose
594 $6.50 Bean Goose
595 $7 Bean Goose
596 $8 Bean Goose

                                  Set of 9   7.50   1.75

1967

618 $1 Muller's Barbet (*Megalaema oorti nuchalis*)
619 $2 Maroon Oriole (*Oriolus trailli ardens*)
620 $2.50 White-bellied Wedge-tailed Green Pigeon (*Sphenurus sieboldii sororia*)
621 $3 Formosan Blue Magpie (*Urocissa caerulea*)
622 $5 Crested Serpent Eagle (*Spilornis cheela hoya*)
623 $8 Mikado Pheasant (*Syrmaticus mikado*)

                                  Set of 6   6.50   1.75

1968

643   $1 Bean Goose (red)   30   15
MS644 $1 Bean Goose (green, imperforate). ..   50   60

1969

709 $2.50 Bean Goose
710 $5 Bean Goose
711 $8 Bean Goose

                                  Set of 3   3.00   75

716 $1 Ring-necked Pheasant
717 $2.50 Ring-necked Pheasant
718 $5 Chinese Jungle Mynah, Magpie Robin, Black-naped Oriole
719 $8 Manchurian Crane

                             Set of 4   2.50   90

1973

938† $1 Green Peafowl.   5   5

1974

1011† $8 Narcissus Flycatcher 1.10   30

1975

1071† $8 Tree Sparrow. 1.00 25

1976

1118† $10 Japanese Quail 1.00 45

1977

1134 $2 Black-naped Oriole
1135 $8 Common Kingfisher
1136 $10 Pheasant-tailed Jacana
                                          Set of 3 1.75 90

1979

1264 $2 Swinhoe's Pheasant
1265 $8 Steere's Liocichla
1266 $10 Formosan Yuhina
                                          Set of 3 2.00 95

1983

1504 $2 Brown Shrike
1505 $18 Grey-faced Buzzard-Eagle
                                     Set of 2 70 50

1984

1524† $2 Mandarin.. .. .. 15 5
1527† $18 Japanese Pheasant 90 40

1986

1663 $2 Green-winged Macaw 15 5

CHRISTMAS ISLAND
Indian Ocean
100 cents = 1 dollar

1963

19† 50c Christmas Island Frigate Bird ('Frigate
     Bird').. .. .. 2.75 1.00
20† $1 White-tailed Tropic Bird ('Golden Bo'sun
     Bird').. .. .. 5.50 2.25

1977

78†	45c Christmas Island Frigate Bird (*Fregata andrewsi*)	85	45
79†	50c Christmas Island Imperial Pigeon (*Ducula whartoni*)	95	60

84†	10c Rock Partridge ('A partridge in a pear tree')	15	20
85†	10c Turtle Dove ('Two turtle doves')	15	20
87†	10c Black-browed Albatross ('Four calling birds').	15	20
89†	10c Cereopsis Goose ('Six geese a-laying')	15	20
90†	10c Black Swan ('Seven swans a-swimming')	15	20

1978

98†	45c Abbott's Booby	60	75

1982

152	1c Eastern Reef Heron ('Reef Heron')	
153	2c Common Noddy ('Noddy')	
154	3c White-bellied Swiftlet ('Glossy Swiftlet')	
155	4c Christmas Island Imperial Pigeon ('Imperial Pigeon')	
156	5c Christmas Island White Eye ('Silvereye')	
157	10c Island Thrush ('Thrush')	
158	25c Red-tailed Tropic Bird ('Silver Bosunbird')	

159	30c Emerald Dove	
160	40c Brown Booby	
161	50c Red-footed Booby	
162	65c Christmas Island Frigate Bird ('Frigatebird')	
163	75c White-tailed Tropic Bird ('Golden Bosunbird')	
164	80c Australian Kestrel ('Nankeen Kestrel')	
165	$1 Indonesian Hawk Owl ('Hawk-Owl')	
166	$2 Australian Goshawk ('Goshawk')	
167	$4 Abbott's Booby	
	Set of 16 7.50 8.25	

1983

175†	24c White-tailed Tropic Bird	20	20

1987

236†	36c Indonesian Hawk Owl ('Hawk Owl') ..	25	30

CISKEI
Southern Africa
100 cents = 1 rand

1981

5	1c Knysna Turaco (*Tauraco corythaix*)	
6	2c Cape Wagtail (*Motacilla capensis*)	
7	3c White-browed Coucal (*Centropus superciliosus*)	
8	4c Yellow-tufted Malachite Sunbird (*Nectarinia famosa*)	
9	5c Stanley Crane (*Anthropoides paradisea*)	
10	6c African Red-winged Starling (*Onychognathus morio*)	
11	7c Giant Kingfisher (*Ceryle maxima*)	
12	8c Hadada Ibis (*Bostrychia hagedash*)	
13	9c Black Cuckoo (*Cuculus clamosus*)	
14	10c Black-collared Barbet (*Lybius torquatus*)	
14a	11c African Black-headed Oriole (*Oriolus larvatus*)	

14b 12c Malachite Kingfisher (*Alcedo cristata*)
14c 14c Hoopoe (*Upupa epops*)
15   15c African Fish Eagle (*Haliaeetus vocifer*)
15a 16c Cape Puff-back Flycatcher (*Batis capensis*)
16   20c Cape Longclaw (*Macronyx capensis*)
17   25c Cape Dikkop (*Burhinus capensis*)
18   30c African Green Pigeon (*Treron calva*)
19   50c Cape Parrot (*Poicephalus robustus*)
20   1r Narina Trogon (*Apaloderma narina*)
21   2r Cape Eagle Owl (*Bubo capensis*)

Set of 21 5.25 5.25

1984

60   11c Banded Sand Martin
61   25c House Martin
62   30c Greater Striped Swallow
63   45c Barn Swallow ('European Swallow')

Set of 4 1.00 1.00

1976

20† 1c Brown Booby 12 12
31† $1 Sooty Tern 2.25 2.00

1979

48† 25c Sooty Tern.. .. .. 25 35
(48/9 Set of 2) 75 1.00

COCOS (KEELING) ISLANDS
Indian Ocean
1963 12 pence = 1 shilling,
20 shillings = 1 pound
1969 100 cents = 1 dollar

1963

6† 2s3d White Tern 35.00 11.00

1969

14† 10c Banded Rail (*Rallus philippensis*) 1.50 70
15† 15c Java Sparrow (*Padda oryzivora*) 1.25 45
16† 20c Red-tailed Tropic Bird (*Phaethon rubricauda*) 1.25 45
17† 30c Sooty Tern (*Sterna fuscata*) 1.50 50
18† 50c Eastern Reef Heron (*Demigretta sacra*) 2.25 70
19† $1 Great Frigate Bird (*Frigata minor*) 3.50 2.50

1985

131† 80c Sooty Tern 75 75

132 33c Red-footed Booby
133 60c Rufous Night Heron ('Nankeen Night Heron')
134 $1 Banded Rail ('Buff-banded Rail')

Set of 3 1.75 2.00

1986

154† $1 Silver Gull.. .. .. 90 95

COLOMBIA
South America
100 centavos = 1 peso

1876

84a† 5c Andean Condor 2.00 50

1935

476† 10p Andean Condor £425 £350

1966

1175† 50c Red-billed Tropic Bird.. .. .. 45 25

STANLEY GIBBONS
STAMP COLLECTING SERIES
Introductory booklets on *How to Start, How to Identify Stamps* and *Collecting by Theme*. A series of well illustrated guides at a low price.
Write for details.

1974

1363 1p White-tailed Trogon (*Trogon viridis*)
1364 1p30 Keel-billed Toucan (*Ramphastos sulfuratus brevicarinatus*)
1365 2p Andean Cock of the Rock (*Rupicola peruviana sanguinolenta*)
1366 2p50 Scarlet Macaw (*Ara macao*)
                                     Set of 4   80   50

1975

1372† 2p Golden Pheasant 40 25
1373† 3p Blue and Yellow Macaw 45 25

1977

1421 10p Wattled Jacana (*Jacana jacana*)
1422 20p Plum-throated Cotinga (*Cotinga maynana*)
1423 5p Crimson-mantled Woodpecker (*Piculus rivolii*) (air)
1424 5p Purple Gallinule (*Porphyrula martinica*)
1425 10p Pompadour Cotinga (*Xipholaena punicea*)
1426 10p Northern Royal Flycatcher (*Onychorhynchus coronatus* !)
                                     Set of 6   4.50   1.10

No. 1364 surcharged
1438 2p on 1p30 Keel-billed Toucan 25 25

1979

1485† 7p Scarlet Ibis, Louisiana Heron 60 25

1980

1505† 4p Andean Condor ('Condor').. .. .. .. 25 10
1509† 4p Greater Flamingo ('Flamenco'). 25 10
1522† 4p Resplendent Quetzal ('Quetzal') 25 10
1528† 4p Scarlet Macaw ('W'). 25 10
Stylised birds are depicted on Nos. 1503, 1510, 1517, 1521 and 1526.

1533 12p Blue and Yellow Macaw 75 30

1982

1671 30p Scarlet Macaw 75 15

COLLECT RAILWAYS ON STAMPS
A Stanley Gibbons thematic catalogue on this popular subject. Copies available at £7.50 (p. + p. £1.50) from: Stanley Gibbons Publications Ltd, 5 Parkside, Christchurch Road, Ringwood, Hants BH24 3SH.

1983

1698 20p Andean Condor

1699 30p Andean Condor (air)
Set of 2 1.25 40

1985

1721† 14p Lineated Woodpecker (*Dryocopus lineatus nuperus*) 20 5
(1720/1 Set of 2) 30 10

1727 20p Straight-billed Woodcreeper (*Xiphorhynchus picus*)
1728 50p Coppery-bellied Puffleg (*Eriocnemis cupreoventris*)
1729 55p Blue-crowned Motmot (*Momotus momota*)
Set of 3 1.40 65

1986

1762 20p Andean Condor 20 8

COMORO ISLANDS
Indian Ocean
100 centimes = 1 franc

1967

60 2f Anjouan Sunbird (*Nectarinia comorensis*)
61 10f Malachite Kingfisher (*Alcedo vintsidides johannae*)
62 15f Mascarene Fody (*Foudia eminentissima*)
63 30f Courol (*Leptosomus discolor gracilis*)

64 75f Madagascar Paradise Flycatcher (*Terpsiphone mutata comorensis*) (air)
65 100f Blue-cheeked Bee Eater (*Merops superciliosus*)
                                            Set of 6   22.00   15.00

1971

94 5f Great Egret (*Egretta alba melanorhynchos*)
95 10f Comoro Olive Pigeon (*Columba polleni*)
96 15f Green Heron (*Butorides striatus rhizophorae*)
97 25f Comoro Blue Pigeon (*Alectroenas sganzini*)
98 35f Humblot's Flycatcher (*Humblotia flavirostris*)
99 40f Allen's Gallinule (*Porphyrula alleni*)
                                            Set of 6   6.50   3.50

1976

207† 15f Andean Condor ('Condor')   50   20

1977

219† 400f Galapagos Penguin ('Manchot des Galapagos'). 4.00   1.50

1978

271 15f Allen's Gallinule (*Porphyrula alleni*)
272 20f Blue-cheeked Bee Eater (*Merops supercimosus*)
273 35f Malachite Kingfisher (*Alcedo vintsioides johannae*)
274 40f Madagascar Paradise Flycatcher (*Terpsiphone*)
275 75f Anjouan Sunbird (*Nectarinia comorensis*)

276 400f Great Egret (*Egretta alba*) (air)
                                            Set of 6   5.50   2.50
MS277 500f Mascarene Fody (*Foudia eminentissima*) 3.50   1.25

1979

337† 50f Courol (*Leptosomus discolor*)   50   20
338† 75f Blue-cheeked Bee Eater (*Merops superciliosus*)   75   35
                                (336/8 Set of 3)   1.25   55

Nos. 271/5 *overprinted or surcharged* **Republique Federale Islamique des Comores**
339   15f Allen's Gallinule
340   30f on 35f Malachite Kingfisher
341   50f on 20f Blue-cheeked Bee Eater
342   50f on 40f Madagascar Paradise Flycatcher
343   200f on 75f Anjouan Sunbird
Set of 5   3.00   3.00

1981
No. 338 *surcharged* **60F**
434†   60f on 75f Blue-cheeked Bee Eater.   50   40

1985

550   100f Barn Swallow (*Hirundo rustica*)
551   125f Northern Oriole (*Icterus galbula*)
552   150f Red-shouldered Hawk (*Buteo lineatus*)
553   500f Red-breasted Sapsucker (*Sphyropieus varius* !)
Set of 4   3.50   3.25

Appendix
The following stamps have either been issued in excess of postal needs, or have not been made available to the public in reasonable quantities at face value. Miniature sheets, imperforate stamps etc. are excluded from this section.

1975
Various stamps overprinted or surcharged **ETAT COMORIEN.** 10f on 2f Anjouan Sunbird (No. 60), 40f Allen's Gallinule (No. 99)

CONGO (BRAZZAVILLE)
Central Africa
100 centimes = 1 franc

1960
No. 276 *of French Equatorial Africa surcharged* **XVIIe OLYMPIADE 1960 REPUBLIQUE DU CONGO 250F** *and Olympic rings*
3   250f on 500f African Darter 6.00   6.00

STAMP MONTHLY
— finest and most informative magazine for all collectors. Obtainable from your newsagent or by postal subscription — details on request.

1967

113   50f Sociable Weaver (*Philaeterus socius*)
114   75f European Bee Eater (*Merops apiaster*)
115   100f Lilac-breasted Roller (*Coracias caudatus*)
116   150f Regal Sunbird (*Cinnyris regius*)
117   200f South African Crowned Crane (*Balearica pavonina* !)
118   250f Secretary Bird (*Sagittarius serpentarius*)
119   300f Knysna Turaco (*Tauraco corythaix*)
Set of 7   27.00   11.00

1976

534   5f Saddle-bill Stork ('Jabirus')
535   10f Shining-blue Kingfisher ('Martin-Pecheur')
536   20f Crowned Crane ('Grues Couronnees')
Set of 3   65   55

1978

616   65f Mallard (*Anas platyrhynchos*)
617   75f Purple Heron (*Ardea purpurea*)
618   150f Great Reed Warbler (*Acrocephalus arundinaceus*)
619   240f Hoopoe (*Upupa epops*)
Set of 4   5.50   2.50

643   100f Peregrine Falcon
644   100f Hoopoe (on stamp No. 619)

Set of 2   2.40   1.75

1980

761† 45f Olive-bellied Sunbird ('Souimanga
        olivatre')   50   40
762† 75f Red-crowned Bishop ('Travailleur a
        tete rouge')..   75   45
763† 90f Moorhen ('Poule d'eau africaine')   85   50
764† 150f African Pied Wagtail ('Alouette
        canelle'). 1.50   70
765† 200f Yellow-mantled Whydah
        (Coliuspasser macrourus). 2.00   90
                    (761/6 Set of 6)   7.00   3.50
No.766 (250f) depicts a stylised combination of a bee eater and
a roller.

1982

886†   40f Grey Parrot   30   10

BIRDS   BIRDS   BIRDS

1985

985   100f Black-headed Grosbeak
        (Passeriformes fringillidae)
986   150f Scarlet Ibis (juvenile) (Eudocimus
        ruber)
987   200f Red-tailed Hawk (Buteo jamaicensis)
988   350f Labrador Duck * (Camptorhynchus
        labradorius)
                    Set of 4   3.25   2.75

CONGO (KINSHASA)
Central Africa
100 centimes = 1 franc

1963

468   10c Eastern White Pelican ('Pelicans')
469   20c Crested Guineafowl ('Pintades de
        Schouteden')
470   30c African Open-bill Stork ('Bec-Ouvert')
471   40c Abdim's Stork ('Cigognes a Ventre
        Blanc')
472   1f Whale-headed Stork ('Bec-en Sabot')
473   2f Marabou Stork ('Marabout')
474   3f Greater Flamingo ('Flamants Roses')
475   4f Congo Peafowl ('Paon Congolais')
476   5f Hartlaub's Duck ('Canards de Hartlaub')
477   6f Secretary Bird ('Serpentaire')
478   7f Black-casqued Hornbill ('Calaos')
479   8f Sacred Ibis ('Ibis Sacre')
480   10f South African Crowned Crane ('Grue
        Couronnee')
481   20f Saddle-bill Stork ('Jabiru d'Afrique')
                    Set of 14   6.00   2.50

COOK ISLANDS

South Pacific

1893 12 pence = 1 shilling,
20 shillings = 1 pound

1967 100 cents = 1 dollar ·

1893

11†	½d White Tern (blue)	3.50	4.75
28†	½d White Tern (green)	1.40	2.50
15a†	2d White Tern	3.75	6.50
18a†	6d White Tern	13.00	19.00
46†	1s White Tern	20.00	32.00

1949

151†	1d Red-tailed Tropic Bird	1.25	85

1963

166†	5d White Tern ('Love Tern')..	1.60	35

1967

No. 166 surcharged

210†	4c on 5d White Tern	80	25

1973

421†	20c White Tern	35	20

1974

496†	25c White Tern (on stamp No. 15a)	40	40

1976

563	$1 Mangaia Kingfisher	3.25	2.25

1977

583	$1 Cook Islands Swiftlet	3.50	2.00

1978

617	$1 Pitcairn Warbler	1.75	1.00

1979

653†	30c American Bald Eagle	30	35

658   $1 Rarotongan Fruit Dove. 1.75   1.75

1985

1015   30c Downy Woodpecker
1016   55c Black-throated Blue Warbler
1017   65c Yellow-throated Warbler
1018   75c Chestnut-sided Warbler
1019   95c Dickcissel
1020 $1.15 White-crowned Sparrow
                                    Set of 6   3.25   3.25
MS1021 Three sheets. (a) $1.30 Red-cockaded Woodpecker; (b)
   $2.80 Seaside Sparrow; (c) $5.30 Zenaida Dove
                              Price for 3 sheets   7.25   7.50

1980

1209†   2col10 Harpy Eagle (*Harpia harpyja*)   35   25
1210†   2col50 Scarlet Macaw (*Ara macao*)   45   30

1984

1332   10c Resplendent Quetzal ('Quetzal')
1333   50c Red-legged Honeycreeper ('Mielero
          Patirrojo')
1334   1col Clay-coloured Thrush ('Mirlo Pardo')
1335   1col50 Blue-crowned Motmot ('Momoto de
          Diadema Azul')
1336   3col Green Violetear ('Colibri
          orejiviolaceo verde')
1337   10col Blue and White Swallow
          ('Golondrina Azul y Blanca')
                                    Set of 6   1.40   70

COSTA RICA
Central America
100 centimos = 1 colon

1979

1132   1col Songbird sp
1133   2col Songbird sp
1134   20col Songbird sp
                                    Set of 3   3.75   2.50

COLLECT MAMMALS ON STAMPS
The second Stanley Gibbons thematic catalogue —
copies are available at £7.50 (p.+p. £1.50) from:
Stanley Gibbons Publications Ltd, 5 Parkside,
Christchurch Road, Ringwood, Hants BH24 3SH.

CUBA
West Indies
100 centavos = 1 peso

1956

772   8c Wood Duck
773   12c Plain Pigeon (grey)
783   12c Plain Pigeon (green)
774   14c Gundlach's Hawk
775   19c Herring Gull
776   24c American White Pelican
777   29c Goosander
778   30c Bobwhite
779   50c Great Blue Heron (two phases)
780   1p Common Caracara (red)
784   1p Common Caracara (blue)
781   2p Northern Jacana (purple)

785 2p Northern Jacana (red)
782 5p Ivory-billed Woodpecker (red)
786 5p Ivory-billed Woodpecker (purple)
                                    Set of 15   75.00   27.00

No. 776, but colour changed, surcharged **Inauguracion Edificio**
Club Filatelico de la Republica de Cuba Julio 13 de 1956 8c
8c on 24c American White Pelican 1.75   75

As No. 781 but colour changed, surcharged **SOCIEDAD**
INTERAMERICANA DE PRENSA XII ASAMBLEA – LA HABANA
1956 12c *and emblem*
794 12c on 2p Northern Jacana 1.75   80

1959
As No. 780, but colour changed, surcharged **CONVENCION ASTA**
OCTUBRE 17 1959 12c.
910 12c on 1p Common Caracara 1.90   1.00

1960
As Nos. 772/3, but colours changed, overprinted with Stamp Day
emblem
951 8c Wood Duck
952 12c Plain Pigeon
                                    Set of 2   1.90   85

1961

1000† 2c Cuban Grasquit (*Tiaris canora*)   50   25
1003a† 2c Cuban Macaw * (*Ara tricolor*)   50   25
1003b† 2c Cuban Trogon (*Priotelus temnurus*) ..   50   25
1003c† 2c Bee Hummingbird (*Mellisuga*
        helenae)   50   25
1003d† 2c Ivory-billed Woodpecker
        (*Campephilus principalis bairdii*) . ..   50   25

1965

1287 3c Northern Oriole (*Icterus galbula*)
1288 5c Scarlet Tanager (*Piranga olivacea*)
1289 13c Indigo Bunting (*Passerina cyanea*)
1290a 3c Painted Bunting (*Passerina ciris*)
1290b 3c American Redstart (*Setophaga*
        ruticilla ruticilla)

1290c 3c Blackburnian Warbler (*Dendroica*
        fusca)
1290d 3c Rose-breasted Grosbeak (*Pneuticus*
        ludovicianus)
1291a 5c Yellow-throated Warbler (*Dendroica*
        dominica dominica)
1291b 5c Blue-winged Warbler (*Vermivora*
        pinus)
1291c 5c Prothonotary Warbler (*Protonotaria*
        citrea)
1291d 5c Hooded Warbler (*Wilsonia citrina*)
1292a 13c Blue-winged Teal (*Anas discors*)
1292b 13c Wood Duck (*Aix sponsa*)
1292c 13c Common Shoveler (*Spatula*
        clypeata)
1292d 13c Black-crowned Night Heron
        (*Nycticorax nycticorax hoactli*)
                                    Set of 15   27.00   22.00

1967

1556 1c Ostrich (*Struthio camelus australis*)
1557 3c Hyacinth Macaw (*Anodorhynchus*
        hyacinthinus)
1558 13c Greater Flamingo (*Phoenicopterus*
        ruber)
1559a 1c Golden Pheasant (*Chysolophus*
        pictus)
1559b 1c White Stork (*Ciconia ciconia ciconia*)
1559c 1c Crowned Crane (*Balearica pavonina*)
1559d 1c Emu (*Dromiceius n. novaehollandiae*)
1560a 3c Grey Parrot (*Psittacus erithacus*)
1560b 3c Chattering Lory (*Domicella garrula*)
1560c 3c Keel-billed Toucan (*Ramphastos*
        sulfuratus)
1560d 3c Sulphur-crested Cockatoo (*Kokatoe*
        galerita galerita)
1561a 13c American White Pelican (*Pelecanus*
        erythrorhynchos)
1561b 13c Egyptian Goose (*Alopochen*
        aegyptiacus)
1561c 13c Mandarin (*Dendronessa*
        galericulata)
1561d 13c Black Swan (*Chenopsis atrata*)
                                    Set of 15   10.00   4.75

1969

1679† 30c Andean Condor 1.75   65

1814d	3c Yellow-headed Warbler (*Teretistris fernandinae*)		
1815a	13c Hook-billed Kite (*Chondrohierax wilsonii*)		
1815b	13c Gundlach's Hawk (*Accipiter gundlachi*)		
1815c	13c Blue-headed Quail Dove (*Starnoenas cyanocephala*)		
1815d	13c Cuban Conure (*Aratinga euops*)		
	Set of 15	10.00	3.75

| 1722† | 13c Cuban Amazon (*Amazona leucocephala*) .. .. | 1.25 | 40 |
| 1723† | 30c Red-winged Blackbird (*Agelaius phoeniceus assimilis*) .. .. | 1.75 | 65 |

1971

1890	1c American Kestrel (*Falco sparverius sparverioides*)		
1891	2c Cuban Pygmy Owl (*Glaucidium siju siju*)		
1892	3c Cuban Trogon (*Priotelus temnurus temnurus*)		
1893	4c Great Lizard Cuckoo (*Saurothera merlini merlini*)		
1894	5c Fernandina's Flicker (*Nesoceleus fernandinae*)		
1895	13c Stripe-headed Tanager (*Spindalis zena pretrei*)		
1896	30c Red-legged Thrush (*Mimocichla plumbea rubripes*)		
1897	50c Cuban Emerald (*Chlorostilbon ricordii ricordii*), Ruby-throated Hummingbird (*Archilochus colubris*)		
	Set of 8	4.00	1.75

1970

1795†	1c Helmet Guineafowl (*Numida meleagris galeata*)	25	10
1796†	2c Black-billed Whistling Duck (*Dendrocygna arborea*)	25	10
1797†	3c Ring-necked Pheasant (*Phasianus colchicus torquatus*)	30	10
1798†	4c Mourning Dove (*Zenaida macroura macroura*)..	40	10
1799†	5c Bobwhite (*Colinus virginianus cubanensis*)	40	15

1972

| 1984† | 30c Adelie Penguin.. .. .. | 1.60 | 65 |

1810	1c Cuban Blackbird (*Dives atroviolaceus*)		
1811	3c Oriente Warbler (*Teretistris fornsi*)		
1812	13c Zapata Sparrow (*Torreornis inexpectata inexpectata*)		
1813a	1c Cuban Pygmy Owl (*Glaucidium siju siju*)		
1813b	1c Cuban Tody (*Todus multicolor*)		
1813c	1c Cuban Green Woodpecker (*Xiphidiopicus percussus percussus*)		
1813d	1c Zapata Wren (*Ferminia cerverai*)		
1814a	3c Cuban Solitaire (*Myadestes elisabeth elisabeth*)		
1814b	3c Blue-grey Gnatcatcher (*Polioptila lambeyei* !)		
1814c	3c Cuban Vireo (*Vireo gundlachii gundlachii*)		

COLLECT RAILWAYS ON STAMPS

A Stanley Gibbons thematic catalogue on this popular subject. Copies available at £7.50 (p. + p. £1.50) from: Stanley Gibbons Publications Ltd, 5 Parkside, Christchurch Road, Ringwood, Hants BH24 3SH.

1974

FAUNA EXTINGUIDA

2146 1c Mauritius Dodo * ('Dodo')
2147 3c Cuban Macaw * ('Ara de Cuba')
2148 8c Passenger Pigeon * ('Paloma
Migratoria')
2149 10c Moa *
2150 13c Great Auk * ('Gran Alca')

Set of 5   2.50   75

1977

2353 1c Cuban Green Woodpecker
(*Xiphidiopicus percussus*)
2354 4c Cuban Grassquit (*Tiaris canora*)
2355 10c Cuban Blackbird (*Dives
atroviolaceus*)
2356 13c Zapata Wren (*Ferminia cerverai*)
2357 30c Bee Hummingbird (*Mellisuga
helenae*)

Set of 5   1.75   75

1975

2214 1c Cuban Vireo (*Vireo g. gundlachi*)
2215 2c Bare-legged Owl (*Gymnoglaux l.
lawrenci*)
2216 3c Cuban Conure (*Aratinga eoups*)
2217 5c Blue-headed Quail Dove (*Starnoenas
cyanocephala*)
2218 13c Hook-billed Kite (*Chondrohierax
wilsoni*)
2219 30c Zapata Rail (*Cyanolimnas cerverai*)

Set of 6   1.75   70

1978

2437 1c Cuban Solitaire (*Myadestes elisabeth*)
2438 4c Cuban Gnatcatcher (*Polioptila
lambeyei*)
2439 10c Oriente Warbler (*Teretistris
fernandinae* !)
2440 13c Zapata Sparrow (*Torreornis
inexpectata*)
2441 30c Cuban Macaw * (*Ara tricolor*),
Mauritius Dodo *, Passenger Pigeon *,
Ivory-billed Woodpecker

Set of 5   1.60   65

1976

2301 1c Oriente Warbler (*Teretistris fornsi*)
2302 2c Cuban Pygmy Owl (*Glaucidium siju*)
2303 3c Fernandina's Flicker (*Nesoceleus
fernandinae*)
2304 5c Cuban Tody (*Todus multicolor*)
2305 13c Gundlach's Hawk (*Accipiter
gundlachi*)
2306 30c Cuban Trogon (*Priotelus temnurus*)

Set of 6   1.60   75

1979

2524 1c Blue-headed Quail Dove (*Starnoenas
cyanocephala*)
2525 3c Key West Quail Dove (*Geotrygon
chysia*)
2526 7c Grey-faced Quail Dove (*Geotrygon
caniceps*)

2527	8c Ruddy Quail Dove (*Geotrygon montana*)		
2528	13c White-crowned Pigeon (*Columba leucocephala*)		
2529	30c Plain Pigeon (*Columba inornata*)		
	Set of 6	1.25	70

1981

2763†	1c Cuban Emerald ('Zun-Zun').	8	8
2764†	2c Cuban Conure ('Catey')..	12	12

1982

2848†	1c Prehistoric Owl sp * (*Ornimegalonyx oteroi*).	5	5
2850†	7c Prehistoric Eagle sp * (*Aquila borrasi*)	20	5

1983

2950†	5c Bee Hummingbird (*Mellisuga helenae*)	12	5
2951†	5c Northern Mockingbird (*Mimus polyglottos*)	12	5
2952†	5c Cuban Tody (*Todus multicolor*)	12	5
2953†	5c Cuban Amazon (*Amazona leucocephala*) .	12	5
2954†	5c Zapata Wren (*Ferminia cerverai*)..	12	5
2955†	5c Brown Pelican (*Pelecanus occidentalis*)	12	5
2956†	5c West Indian Red-bellied Woodpecker (*Melanerpes superciliaris*)	12	5
2957†	5c Red-legged Thrush (*Mimocichla plumbea*)	12	5
2958†	5c Cuban Conure (*Aratinga euops*)	12	5

2959†	5c Eastern Meadowlark (*Sturnella magna*).	12	5
2960†	5c Cuban Grassquit (*Tiaris canora*)	12	5
2961†	5c White-tailed Tropic Bird (*Phaethon lepturus*)	12	5
2962†	5c Cuban Solitaire (*Myadestes elisabeth*)	12	5
2963†	5c Great Lizard Cuckoo (*Saurothera merlini*)	12	5
2964†	5c Cuban Gnatcatcher (*Polioptila lembeyei*).	12	5
MS2965	Two sheets. (b) 1p Cuban Trogon (*Priotelus temnurus*) (other sheet shows flower)		
	Price for 2 sheets	3.50	3.50

1984

MS3032	1p Emu.	2.00	2.00

3046†	5c Bee Hummingbird (*Mellisuga helenae*)	10	5
3048†	30c Cuban Tody (*Todus multicolor*)	65	40
3049†	50c Peach-faced Lovebird ('Cotorra')..	1.10	70

1985

MS3109	1p Andean Condor (*Vulture gryphus*)	2.00	2.00

1986

3152 1c Red-winged Blackbird (*Agelaius assimilis*)
3153 3c Olive-capped Warbler (*Dendroica pityophila*)
3154 7c La Sagra's Flycatcher (*Myiarchus sagrae*)
3155 9c Yellow Warbler (*Dendroica petechia gundlachi*)
3156 30c Grey-faced Quail Dove (*Geotrygon caniceps*)
3157 50c Common Flicker (*Colaptes auratus chrysocaulosus*)

Set of 6   2.25   2.00

SPECIAL DELIVERY STAMPS

1953

E673 10c Roseate Tern 2.25   1.10

1979

524† 50m Black Partridge (*Francolinus francolinus*)   35   20

1986

679† 17c Greater Flamingo ('Flamingos')   50   55
(678/9 Set of 2)   70   80

Turkish Cypriot Posts

100 kurus = 1 lira

1983

140 10li European Bee Eater (*Merops apiaster*)
141 15li Goldfinch (*Carduelis carduelis*)
142 50li European Robin (*Erithacus rubecula*)
143 65li Golden Oriole (*Oriolus oriolus*)

Set of 4   1.10   1.00

CYPRUS
Mediterranean
1969 1000 milliemes = 1 pound
1986 100 cents = 1 pound

1969

334 5m Common Roller ('Roller')
335 15m Audouin's Gull
336 20m Cyprus Warbler
337 30m Jay ('Cyprus Jay')
338 40m Hoopoe
339 90m Eleonora's Falcon

Set of 6   2.50   3.00

1986

MS187 100li Griffon Vulture (*Gyps fulvus fulvus*)
(sheet also contains 200li stamp)   60   65

CZECHOSLOVAKIA
Central Europe
100 haleru = 1 koruna

1938

378 50h Peregrine Falcon
379 1k Peregrine Falcon
Set of 2   1.25   25

1954

848† 30h Black-headed Gull   55   10

1955

857† 80h Barn Swallow 1.50   60

890† 35h Grey Partridge   90   25

1959

1120 20h Great Spotted Woodpecker
     (*Dryobates major pinetorum*)
1121 30h Blue Tit (*Parus caeruleus caeruleus*)

1122 40h European Nuthatch (*Sitta europea caesia*)
1123 60h Golden Oriole (*Oriolus oriolus oriolus*)
1124 80h Goldfinch (*Carduelis carduelis c.*)
1125 1k Bullfinch (*Pyrrhula pyrrhula*)
1126 1k20 Common Kingfisher (*Alcedo atthis*)
                              Set of 7   7.50   2.50

1960

1185 25h Black-crowned Night Heron
     (*Nycticorax nycticorax*)
1186 30h Great Crested Grebe (*Podiceps cristatus*)
1187 40h Lapwing (*Vanellus vanellus*)
1188 60h Grey Heron (*Ardea cinerea*)
1189 1k Greylag Goose (*Anser anser*)
1190 1k60 Mallard (*Anas platyrhyncha*)
                              Set of 6   4.50   1.50

1964

1434 60h Black-headed Gull   40   10

1446 30h Redstart (*Phoenicurus phoenicurus phoenicurus*)
1447 60h Green Woodpecker (*Picus viridus virescens*)
1448 80h Hawfinch (*Coccothraustes coccothraustes coccothraustes*)
1449 1k Black Woodpecker (*Dryocopus martius martius*)

1450 1k20 European Robin (*Erithacus rubecula
rubecula*)
1451 1k60 Common Roller (*Coracias garrulus
garrulus*)

Set of 6   4.50   1.75

1967

1965

1632 30h Black-tailed Godwit (*Limosa limosa*)
1633 40h Common Shoveler (*Spatula clypeata*)
1634 60h Purple Heron (*Ardea purpurea*)
1635 80h Penduline Tit (*Remiz pendulinus*)
1636 1k Avocet (*Recurvirostra avosetta*)
1637 1k40 Black Stork (*Ciconia nigra*)
1638 1k60 Tufted Duck (*Aythya fuligula*)

1495† 60h Ring-necked Pheasant   40   15

Set of 7   8.00   2.50

1519 30h Dotterel (*Charadrius morinellus*)
1520 60h Wallcreeper (*Tichodroma muraria*)
1521 1k20 Redpoll (*Carduelis flammae*)
1522 1k40 Golden Eagle (*Aquila chrysaetos
chrysaetos*)
1523 1k60 Ring Ousel (*Turdus torquatus*)
1524 2k Nutcracker (*Nucifraga caryocatactes*)

Set of 6   5.00   2.50

1971

1967† 20h Ring-necked Pheasant (*Phasianus
colchicus*)   25   10

1966

1621† 1k Snowy Owl 3.50   2.75

1972

STANLEY GIBBONS
STAMP COLLECTING SERIES
Introductory booklets on *How to Start, How to
Identify Stamps* and *Collecting by Theme*. A series
of well illustrated guides at a low price.
Write for details.

2072 60h European Cuckoo
2073 80h European Cuckoo
2074 1k Magpie
2075 1k60 Bullfinch
2076 2k Goldfinch
2077 3k Song Thrush

Set of 6   8.00   1.25

1974

2149† 1k60 Blackbird 55 20

1976

2308† 20h Cattle Egret.. .. .. 25 10

1977

2356† 2k Greater Flamingo 75 25
2357† 3k Barn Swallow 2.50 50

1983

2676† 2k Red Crossbill (Loxia curvirostra) 1.00 55
2677† 3k60 Grey Heron (Ardea cinerea).. .. .. 1.40 65

1985

2815 1k Grey Heron 25 8

1986

2844 50h Eagle Owl (Bubo bubo)
2845 2k Long-eared Owl (Asio otus)
2846 3k Tawny Owl (Strix aluco)
2847 4k Barn Owl (Tyto alba)
2848 5k Short-eared Owl (Asio flammeus)
Set of 5 3.75 1.40

DAHOMEY
West Africa
100 centimes = 1 franc

1966

250 50f African Pygmy Goose (Nettapus
auritus)
251 100f Fiery-breasted Bush Shrike
(Malaconotus cruentus)
252 500f Iris Glossy Starling (Coccyolius iris)
Set of 3 12.00 5.50

1967

271 200f Broad-billed Roller (*Eurystomus glaucurus*)
272 250f African Emerald Cuckoo (*Chrysococcyx cupreus*)
                                    Set of 2 11.00 4.25

1969

No. 250 surcharged **10F**
379 10f on 50f African Pygmy Goose.. .. .. 25 10

612† 50ore Common Kingfisher ('Isfugl'). 60 15
615† 130ore Avocet ('Klyde') 75 60

1986

827 2k80 Raven (*Corvus corax*)
828 2k80 Common Starling (*Sturnus vulgaris*)
829 2k80 Mute Swan (*Cygnus olor*)
830 2k80 Lapwing (*Vanellus vanellus*)
831 2k80 Sky Lark (*Alauda arvensis*)
                                    Set of 5 2.75 75

DENMARK
Northern Europe
100 ore = 1 krone

1935

292† 5ore Mute Swan 5.00 10

1956

407 30ore Whooper Swan
408 60ore Whooper Swan
                                    Set of 2 6.00 50

1975

607† 130ore White Stork 1.00 85

DJIBOUTI REPUBLIC
East Africa
100 centimes = 1 franc

1977

Nos. 653/4 of French Territory of the Afars and the Issas overprinted **REPUBLIQUE DE DJIBOUTI**
699† 100f Namaqua Dove 1.40 1.40
701† 300f African Spoonbill 4.00 4.00

1977

711 90f Ostrich (*Struthio camelus*)
712 100f Vitelline Masked Weaver (*Ploceus vitellinus*)
                                    Set of 2 3.50 1.90

1978

746   90f Jay
747   90f African Spoonbill (on stamp No. 701)
Set of 2   2.25   2.00

1979

763†   55f Namaqua Dove 1.25   75
(763/4 Set of 2)   2.40   1.60

1982

847†   80f Greater Flamingo. 1.75   1.00
(847/8 Set of 2)   2.75   1.75

1984

919†   55f White-eyed Gull   80   60
920†   125f White Spoonbill 1.90   1.40

1985

941   5f White-throated Bee Eater (Merops
albicollis)
942   15f Chestnut-bellied Sandgrouse (Pterocles
exustus)
943   20f Yellow-breasted Barbet (Trachyphonus
margaritatus somalicus)
944   25f Common Roller (Coracias garrulus)
Set of 4   70   50
MS945   200f Osprey (Pandion haliaetus) (air)   ..   2.40   2.40

DOMINICA
West Indies
100 cents = 1 dollar

1963

173†   24c Imperial Amazon ('Sisserou Parrot') ..   70   10

1968
No. 173 overprinted ASSOCIATED STATEHOOD
226†   24c Imperial Amazon.   25   10

1969

253†   12c Red-necked Amazon.   8   10

273†   1c Purple-throated Carib ('Humming Bird')   15   8
275†   3c Red-necked Pigeon ('Ramier')   25   12
276†   4c Imperial Amazon ('Sisserou')   25   12

1970

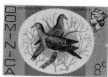

306† 60c Imperial Amazon, Red-necked
Amazon ('Imperial and Red-necked
Parrots'). 1.75   1.50

1979

662†	50c White-tailed Tropic Bird	40	25
663†	60c Brown Pelican	50	30
665†	$2 Brown Booby	1.10	80

1972

366   5c Imperial Amazon
367   $1 Imperial Amazon
Set of 2   60   75

1981

742   20c Forest Thrush
743   30c Wied's Crested Flycatcher ('Stolid
Flycatcher' !)
744   40c Blue-hooded Euphonia
745   $5 Lesser Antillean Pewee
Set of 4   3.25   3.00
MS746 $3 Imperial Amazon ('Imperial Parrot') ..   1.75   1.75

1975

497†   8c Zenaida Dove ('Mountain Dove')   40   10

1982

75th Anniversary of Boy Scouts

COMMONWEALTH OF DOMINICA   75¢

827†   75c Imperial Amazon.   60   55

1976

523   ½c Ringed Kingfisher
524   1c Mourning Dove
525   2c Green Heron
526   15c Broad-winged Hawk
527   30c Blue-headed Hummingbird
528   45c Bananaquit
529   $2 Imperial Amazon ('Imperial Parrot')
Set of 7   11.00   9.50

1978

No. 497 overprinted **INDEPENDENCE 3rd NOVEMBER 1978**
639†   8c Zenaida Dove   30   20

1984

COMMONWEALTH OF
DOMINICA
Plumbeous
Warbler   5c

870   5c Plumbeous Warbler
871   45c Imperial Amazon ('Imperial Parrot')
872   60c Blue-headed Hummingbird
873   90c Red-necked Amazon ('Red-necked
Parrot')
Set of 4   1.25   1.40
MS874 $5 Greater Flamingo ('Roseate
Flamingos') 3.25   3.50

1985

939   45c Clapper Rail ('King Rail')
940    $1 Black & White Warbler
941    $2 Broad-winged Hawk
942    $3 Ring-necked Duck
                             Set of 4   3.25   3.50
MS943 $5 Reddish Egret 2.75   3.00

954†   60c Imperial Amazon.   50   40

1986

1013   25c Black-throated Diver
1014   60c Great Blue Heron
1015   90c Yellow-crowned Night Heron
1016 $4 Common Shoveler ('Shoveler Duck')
                             Set of 4   2.50   2.75
MS1017 $5 Canada Goose ('Goose').. .. .. ..   2.50   2.75

1987

1037   1c Broad-winged Hawk
1038   2c Ruddy Quail Dove
1039   5c Red-necked Pigeon
1040   10c Green Heron
1041   15c Moorhen ('Common Gallinule')
1042   20c Ringed Kingfisher
1043   25c Brown Pelican
1044   35c White-tailed Tropic Bird
1045   45c Red-legged Thrush
1046   60c Purple-throated Carib

1047   90c Magnificent Frigate Bird
1048 $1 Brown Trembler ('Trembler')
1049 $2 Black-capped Petrel
1050 $5 Barn Owl
                             Set of 14   4.25   4.50

DOMINICAN REPUBLIC
West Indies
100 centavos = 1 peso

1964

927   1c Narrow-billed Tody (*Todus
       angustirostris*)
928   2c Hispaniolan Emerald (*Chlorostilbon
       swainsonii*)
929   3c Palm Chat (*Dulus dominicus*)
930   6c Hispaniolan Amazon (*Amazona
       ventralis*)
931   6c Hispaniolan Trogon (*Temnotrogon
       roseigaster*)

932   10c Hispaniolan Woodpecker (*Centurus
       striatus*) (air)
                             Set of 6   1.75   75

1977

1309† 25c Greater Flamingo (*Phoenicopterus
       ruber*)..   75   40

1979

1378 2c Hispaniolan Conure (*Aratinga chloroptera*)
1379 6c Hispaniolan Trogon (*Temnotrogon roseigaster*)
1380 7c Black-crowned Palm Tanager (*Phaenicophilus palmarum*)
1381 10c Chat-Tanager (*Calyptophilus frugivorus tertius*)
1382 45c Black-cowled Oriole (*Icterus dominicensis*)

		Set of 5	1.75	95

1984

1578†	10c Stygian Owl (*Asio stygius*).	10	5
1579†	15c Greater Flamingo (*Phoenicopterus ruber*).	15	5

1967

257†	5d Lanner Falcon		25	10
258†	10d Lanner Falcon		25	10
259†	20d Lanner Falcon		25	10
260†	35d Lanner Falcon		30	15
261†	60d Lanner Falcon		40	20
262†	1r Lanner Falcon..		50	30

1968

310 60d Ring-necked Pheasant ('Pheasant')
311 60d Red Turtle Dove
312 60d Red-footed Falcon
313 60d European Bee Eater ('Bee-Eater')
314 60d Hoopoe
315 60d Great Egret ('Common Egret')
316 60d Little Tern
317 60d Lesser Black-backed Gull

	Set of 8	3.25	1.10

EAST GERMANY
See under Germany

DUBAI
Arabia
1963 100 naye paise = 1 rupee
1966 100 dirhams = 1 riyal

1963

19†	25np Peregrine Falcon	25	10
21†	40np Peregrine Falcon	30	20
23†	60np Peregrine Falcon	40	30
25†	1r Peregrine Falcon	1.50	1.25

ECUADOR
South America
100 centavos = 1 sucre

1937

557 10c Andean Condor
558 20c Andean Condor
558a 40c Andean Condor
559 70c Andean Condor
560 1s Andean Condor
561 2s Andean Condor

	Set of 6	1.75	55

1938

563 2c American Bald Eagle, Andean Condor
564 5c American Bald Eagle, Andean Condor
565 10c American Bald Eagle, Andean Condor
566 20c American Bald Eagle, Andean Condor
567 50c American Bald Eagle, Andean Condor
568 1s American Bald Eagle, Andean Condor
569 2s American Bald Eagle, Andean Condor

570 2c American Bald Eagle (air)
571 5c American Bald Eagle
572 10c American Bald Eagle
573 20c American Bald Eagle
574 50c American Bald Eagle
575 1s American Bald Eagle
576 2s American Bald Eagle

Set of 14   7.50   1.75

1940

No. 567 surcharged CASA DE CORREOS y TELEGRAFOS DE GUAYAQUIL 20 20
625 20c on 50c American Bald Eagle, Andean
     Condor   8   5

No. 567 surcharged CASA DE CORREOS Y TELEGRAFOS DE GUAYAQUIL VEINTE CENTAVOS
655e 20c on 50c American Bald Eagle, Andean
     Condor   12   5

1943

Nos. 567/9 and 574/6 overprinted BIENVENIDO — WALLACE Abril 15 — 1943
668 50c American Bald Eagle, Andean Condor
669 1s American Bald Eagle, Andean Condor
670 2s American Bald Eagle, Andean Condor

671 50c American Bald Eagle (air)
672 1s American Bald Eagle
673 2s American Bald Eagle

Set of 6   5.75   4.00

1945

Nos. 567/9 and 574/6 overprinted LOOR A CHILE OCTUBRE 2 1945 and star
745 50c American Bald Eagle, Andean Condor
746 1s American Bald Eagle, Andean Condor
747 2s American Bald Eagle, Andean Condor

748 50c American Bald Eagle (air)
749 1s American Bald Eagle
750 2s American Bald Eagle

Set of 6   2.75   2.25

1946

Nos. O567/8 overprinted POSTAL
781 10c Andean Condor
782 20c Andean Condor

Set of 2   30   20

1956

1046c† 40c Brown Pelican   60   5
1048† 70c Brown Pelican   25   5

1958

1096 10c Blue and Yellow Macaw ('Guacamayo')
1097 20c Red-breasted Toucan ('Diostede')
1098 30c Andean Condor ('Condor')
1099 40c Sword-billed Hummingbird, Black-tailed Trainbearer ('Quinde')

Set of 4   1.10   50

1120 20c Masked Crimson Tanager ('Cardenal')
1121 30c Andean Cock of the Rock ('Gallo de la Roca')
1122 50c Solitary Cacique ('Mirlo')
1123 60c Red-fronted Conure ('Perico')

Set of 4   1.25   55

1961

1197 2s Great Egret   40   25

STAMP MONTHLY

1966

1320 40c Golden-headed Trogon
(*Pharomachrus auriceps*)
1321 50c Blue-crowned Motmot (*Momotus momota*)
1322 60c Paradise Tanager (*Tangara chilensis*)
1323 80c Wire-tailed Manakin (*Cirrhipipra filicauda*)

1324 1s Yellow-bellied Grosbeak (*Pheucticus chrysopeplus* !) (air)
1325 1s30 Black-headed Caique (*Pionites melanocephala*)
1326 1s50 Scarlet Tanager (*Piranga erythromelas*)
1327 2s Purple Quail Dove (*Osculatia saphirina*)
1328 2s50 Violet-tailed Sylph (*Aglaiocercus kingi coelestis*)
1329 3s Lemon-throated Barbet (*Capito richardsoni*)
1330 4s Yellow-tailed Oriole (*Icterus mesomelas*)
1331 10s Collared Puffbird (*Bucco capensis*)

		Set of 12	4.00	1.75

1967

Nos. 1326, 1328 and 1330 surcharged

1335†	80c on 2s50 Violet-tailed Sylph	25	10
1336†	1s on 4s Yellow-tailed Oriole	25	10
1337†	80c on 1s50 Scarlet Tanager	25	10

1969

No. 1331 surcharged

1357†	80c on 10s Collared Puffbird	25	10
1358†	1s on 10s Collared Puffbird	30	10
1359†	2s on 10s Collared Puffbird	30	15

1973

1524†	30c Blue-footed Booby	25	10
1525†	40c Blue-faced Booby	25	10
1526†	50c Oystercatcher	25	10
1530†	1s30 Blue-footed Booby (air)	30	10
1531†	3s Brown Pelican	40	20

1536 1s Black-chinned Mountain Tanager
(*Anisoghnatus notabilis*)
1537 2s Epaulet Oriole (*Icterus chrysocephalus*)
1538 3s Toucan Barbet (*Semnornis ramphastinus*)
1539 5s Masked Crimson Tanager
(*Ramphocelus nigrogularis*)
1540 10s Blue-necked Tanager (*Tangara cyanicollis*)

		Set of 5	2.75	1.25

1977

1686 1s20 Blue-faced Booby (*Sula dactylatra*)
1687 1s80 Red-footed Booby (*Sula sula*)
1688 2s40 Blue-footed Booby (*Sula nebouxii*)
1689 3s40 Dusky Gull (*Larus fuliginosus*)
1690 4s40 Galapagos Hawk (*Buteo galapagoensis*)
1691 5s40 Woodpecker Finch, Large Insectivorous Tree Finch, Charles Insectivorous Tree Finch

		Set of 6	1.50	90

1983

REPUBLICA DEL ECUADOR

1884†	5s James's Flamingo	60	25
	(1883/4 *Set of 2*)	85	30

BIRDS   BIRDS   BIRDS

1985

1929†	2s Hummingbird sp..	12	5

OFFICIAL STAMPS

1937

Nos. 557/8 and 559/61 overprinted **OFICIAL**

O567†	10c Andean Condor	25	15
O568†	20c Andean Condor	25	15
O569†	70c Andean Condor	25	15
O570†	1s Andean Condor	35	20
O571†	2s Andean Condor	40	25

EGYPT
North Africa
1000 milliemes = 1 pound

1967

913†	35m Red-breasted Goose	70	40

EL SALVADOR
Central America
100 centavos = 1 colon

1963

1183†	5c King Vulture (*Sarcarhamphus papa*) ..	25	10
1186†	5c King Vulture (*Sarcarhamphus papa*) (air).	25	10
1187†	6c Yellow-crowned Amazon (*Amazona ochrocephala auropalliata*)	25	10

1188†	10c Spotted-breasted Oriole (*Icterus pectoralis pectoralis*).	30	15
1189†	20c Turquoise-browed Motmot (*Eumomota superciliosa apiaster*).. ..	40	20
1190†	30c Great-tailed Grackle (*Cassidix mexicanus mexicanus*)	55	25
1191†	40c Great Curassow (*Craxglobicera*).. ..	75	30
1192†	50c White-throated Magpie-Jay (*Calocitta formosa pompata*)	90	40
1193†	80c Golden-fronted Woodpecker (*Melanerpes aurifrons santacruzi*) ..	1.25	60

1980

1643	10c Resplendent Quetzal (*Pharomachrus mocino*)	
1644	20c Highland Guan (*Penelopina nigra*)	
1645	25c Emerald Toucanet (*Aulacorhynchus prasinus*) (air)	
1646	50c Barred Owl (*Strix varia fulvescens*)	
1647	75c Slate-coloured Solitaire (*Myadestes unicolor*)	

	Set of 5	1.50	1.00

1981

1666†	75c Ornate Hawk Eagle (*Spizaetus ornatus*)	65	40

1984

1859	15c Spot-crowned Woodcreeper (*Lepidocolaptes affinis*)
1860	25c Slaty Finch (*Spodiornis rusticus barriliensis*)
1861	55c Purple-breasted Ground Dove (*Claravis mondetoura*) (air)

1862 70c Tody-Motmot (*Hylomanes momotula*)
1863 90c Belted Flycatcher (*Xenotriccus calizonus*)
1864 1col Red-faced Warbler (*Cardellina rubrifrons*)

Set of 6   2.40   1.75

EQUATORIAL GUINEA

West Africa
1968 100 centimos = 1 peseta
1973 100 centimos = 1 ekuele (plural: bikwele)
1985 100 centimes = 1 franc (CFA)

1983

68†   80b Great Egret (?)   45   20

1986

93†   35f Chaffinch, Grey-headed Kingfisher   20   10

Appendix

The following stamps have either been issued in excess of postal needs, or have not been made available to the public in reasonable quantities at face value. Miniature sheets, imperforate stamps etc. are excluded from this section.

1973

Paintings by Picasso. 60e Carrion Crow

1974

Nature Protection (1st series). Australian Animals. 85c Superb Parrot

Nature Protection (3rd series). South American and Australian Birds. Postage 1p25 Broad-billed Motmot, 1p50 Black-necked Aracari, 1p75 Collared Trogon, 2p Cuban Emerald, 2p25 Jandaya Conure, 2p50 Rufous Motmot, 2p75 Blue Crowned Pigeon, 3p Gouldian Finch, 3p50 Raggiana Bird of Paradise, 4p Crimson Finch. Air 20p Crimson-rumped Toucanet, 25p Greater Bird of Paradise, 30p Eastern Broad-billed Roller, 35p Flame-faced Tanager

1976

Bicentenary of American Revolution (5th issue). Fauna. 3e Kea, 25e Rufescent Tiger Heron, 100e Sulphur-crested Cockatoo

Nature Protection (5th series). European Birds. Postage 5c Common Kingfisher, 10c Scops Owl, 15c European Robin, 20c Little Owl, 25c Pied Wagtail. Air 5p Domestic Pigeon, 70p Hawfinch

Nature Protection (7th series). Asian Animals. Postage 55c Wood Pigeon, 60c Luzon Bleeding Heart, 65c Curlew, 70c Rufous-bellied Niltava, 75c Red-whiskered Bulbul. Air 10p Blue-throated Barbet, 50p Indian Roller

Nature Protection (8th series). African Birds and Flowers. Postage 30c Ruppell's Weaver, 35c Goldfinch, 40c Southern Ground Hornbill, 45c Collared Flycatcher, 50c Blue-tailed Pitta. Air 8p Willow Tit, 60p Grey-necked Bald Crow

1977

Nature Protection (10th series). North American Birds. Postage 80c Common Starling, 85c Cardinal Honeyeater, 90c Troupial, 95c Yellow-backed Oriole, 1p Velvet-fronted Nuthatch. Air 15p White-breasted Kingfisher, 40p Magpie

1978

Water Birds. 1e Common Shelduck, 3e Pintail, 5e Surf Scoter, 8e Harlequin Duck, 15e Red-crested Pochard, 30e Long-tailed Duck, 60e Greater Scaup, 100e Green-winged Teal

1979

International Year of the Child. Water birds of 1978 overprinted with I.Y.C. emblem

---

ETHIOPIA

North-east Africa
1919 16 guerche = 1 menelik dollar
1946 100 cents = 1 Ethiopian dollar
1976 100 cents = 1 birr

1919

189†   12g Ostrich   90   60

No. 189 surcharged **1 guerche** *and Amharic characters*
208†   1g on 12g Ostrich. 1.00   80

1962

534   5c Abyssinian Ground Hornbill (*Bucorvus abyssinicus*)
535   15c Abyssinian Roller (*Coracias abyssinica*)

536 30c Bateleur (*Terathopius ecaudatus*)
537 50c Double-toothed Barbet (*Lybius
    bidentatus*)
538 $1 Didric Cuckoo (*Chrysococcyx cupreus* !)

539 10c Dark-headed Oriole (*Oriolus meneliki*)
    (air)
540 15c Broad-tailed Paradise Whydah
    (*Steganura orientalis*)
541 20c Lammergeier (*Gypaetus barbatus*)
542 50c White-cheeked Turaco (*Tauraco
    leucotis*)
543 80c Village Indigobird (*Hypochera
    ultramarina*)
                              Set of 10   10.00   4.50

1972

811† 60c Sacred Ibis 1.25   50

1966

633 10c White-collared Kingfisher (*Halcyon
    chloris abyssinica*)
634 15c Blue-breasted Bee Eater
    (*Melittophagus l. lafresnayii*)
635 25c African Paradise Flycatcher (*Tchitrea
    viridis ferreti*)
636 40c Village Weaver (*Ploceus cucullatus
    abyssinicus*)
637 60c White-collared Pigeon (*Columba
    albitorques*)
                              Set of 5   3.50   1.40

1980

1151 10c Lappet-faced Vulture
1152 15c Long-crested Eagle ('Long-crested
     Hawk Eagle')
1153 25c Secretary Bird
1154 60c Abyssinian Long-eared Owl
1155 70c Lanner Falcon
                              Set of 5   1.50   1.00

1967

673 10c Blue-winged Goose (*Cyanochen
    cyanopterus*)
674 15c African Yellow-bill (*Anas undulata
    rueppelli*)
675 20c Wattled Ibis (*Bostrychia carunculata*)
676 25c Lesser Striped Swallow (*Hirondo
    abyssinica*)
677 40c Black-winged Lovebird (*Agapornis
    taranta*)
                              Set of 5   2.10   90

1985

1305 5c Harwood's Francolin (*Francolinus
     harwoodi*)
1306 15c Rouget's Rail (*Rallus rougetti*)
1307 80c Little Bee Eater (*Merops pusillus*)
1308 85c Red-headed Weaver (*Malimbus
     rubriceps*)
                              Set of 4   1.90   1.40

FALKLAND ISLANDS
South Atlantic
1929 12 pence = 1 shilling,
20 shillings = 1 pound
1971 100 pence = 1 pound

1929

116	½d Gentoo Penguin			
117	1d Gentoo Penguin			
118	2d Gentoo Penguin			
119	2½d Gentoo Penguin			
120	4d Gentoo Penguin			
121	6d Gentoo Penguin			
122	1s Gentoo Penguin			
123	2s6d Gentoo Penguin			
124	5s Gentoo Penguin			
125	10s Gentoo Penguin			
126	£1 Gentoo Penguin			
		Set of 11	£450	£600

1933

136†	5s King Penguin	£500	£650

1938

147a†	1d Black-necked Swan..	3.00	30
150a†	2d Black-necked Swan..	55	35
152†	2½d Magellan Goose ('Upland Goose') ..	1.90	3.50
154†	4d Magellan Goose ('Upland Goose'). ..	1.60	80
159†	1s3d Turkey Vulture.	1.25	1.60
160†	2s6d Gentoo Penguin	40.00	14.00

1952

174†	2d Magellan Goose ('Upland Goose')	2.75	1.50
180†	1s Gentoo Penguin	8.00	1.40
181†	1s3d Kelp Goose..	3.25	10.00

1955

189†	2d Magellan Goose ('Upland Goose')	3.25	4.50
192†	1s Gentoo Penguin	4.00	2.00

1960

227	½d Austral Thrush ('Falkland Islands Thrush')	
194	1d Southern Black-backed Gull ('Dominican Gull')	
195	2d Gentoo Penguin	
196	2½d Long-tailed Meadowlark ('Falkland Islands Marsh Starling')	
197	3d Magellan Goose ('Upland Goose')	
198	4d Falkland Islands Flightless Steamer Duck ('Steamer Ducks')	
199	5½d Rockhopper Penguin	
200	6d Black-browed Albatross	
201	9d Silvery Grebe ('Silver Grebe')	
202	1s Magellanic Oystercatcher ('Pied Oystercatchers')	
203	1s3d Chilean Teal ('Yellow-billed Teal')	
204	2s Kelp Goose	
205	5s King Cormorant	
206	10s Common Caracara ('Carancho')	
207	£1 Black-necked Swan	

Set of 15   £110   55.00

1974

298†	5p Rockhopper Penguin..	5.00	2.50
299†	15p Long-tailed Meadowlark ('Military Starling')	8.00	4.00

1975

317†	5½p Gentoo Penguin	80	90
318†	8p Magellan Goose ('Upland Goose')	1.00	1.50
319†	10p Black-browed Albatross ('Albatross') ..	1.10	1.60

492†	6p Black-browed Albatross, Wilson's Petrel, South American Tern..	15	15

1980

384	3p Forster's Caracara ('Striated Caracara')		
385	11p Red-backed Buzzard		
386	15p Common Caracara ('Crested Caracara')		
387	25p Peregrine Falcon ('Cassins Falcon')		
	Set of 4	2.75	2.40

1985

516†	27p Common Diving Petrel ('Diving Petrel')	55	60

1982

433	5p Blackish Cinclodes ('Tussock Bird')		
434	10p Black-chinned Siskin		
435	13p Short-billed Marsh Wren ('Grass Wren')		
436	17p Black-throated Finch		
437	25p Correndera Pipit ('Falkland-Correndera Pipit')		
438	34p Dark-faced Ground-Tyrant		
	Set of 6	1.90	1.90

1986

532	10p Rockhopper Penguin		
533	24p Rockhopper Penguin		
534	29p Rockhopper Penguin		
535	58p Rockhopper Penguin		
	Set of 4	2.10	2.40

FALKLAND ISLANDS DEPENDENCIES
South Atlantic
1944 12 pence = 1 shilling,
20 shillings = 1 pound
1971 100 pence = 1 pound

1984

489	17p Great Grebe		
490	22p Silvery Grebe ('Silver Grebe')		
491	52p White-tufted Grebe ('Rolland's Grebe')		
	Set of 3	1.75	2.00

1944
Nos. 150a and 154 of Falkland Islands overprinted **GRAHAM LAND DEPENDENCY OF**

A3†	2d Black-necked Swan	30	1.00
A5†	4d Magellan Goose	90	1.40

Nos. 150a and 154 of Falkland Islands overprinted **SOUTH GEORGIA DEPENDENCY OF**

B3†	2d Black-necked Swan	30	1.00
B5†	4d Magellan Goose	90	1.40

Nos. 150a *and* 154 *of Falkland Islands overprinted* **SOUTH ORKNEYS DEPENDENCY OF**

C3†	2d Black-necked Swan	30	1.00
C5†	4d Magellan Goose	90	1.40

Nos. 150a *and* 154 *of Falkland Islands overprinted* **SOUTH SHETLANDS DEPENDENCY OF**

D3†	2d Black-necked Swan	30	1.00
D5†	4d Magellan Goose	90	1.40

1980

84†	20p Chinstrap Penguin	55	60
85†	25p Chinstrap Penguin	65	70

1984

122†	17p Chinstrap Penguin	35	40

1985

125 7p Grey-headed Albatross
126 22p Black-browed Albatross
127 27p Wandering Albatross
128 54p Light-mantled Sooty Albatross

Set of 4	2.00	2.25

135†	22p King Penguin.	45	50
137†	54p Dove Prion	1.10	1.25

FAROE ISLANDS
North Atlantic
100 ore = 1 krone

1977

27 70ore Common Snipe (*Gallinago gallinago faeroeensis*)
28 180ore Oystercatcher (*Haematopus ostralegus malacophaga*)
29 250ore Whimbrel (*Numenius phaeopus phaeopus*)

Set of 3	1.40	1.25

1978

30†	100ore Atlantic Puffin	25	25
33†	150ore Northern Gannet	30	30
34†	180ore Northern Gannet, Atlantic Puffin ..	30	30

35 140ore Northern Gannet (*Morus bassanus bassanus*)
36 180ore Atlantic Puffin (*Fratercula arctica grabae*)
37 400ore Common Guillemot (*Uria aalge spiloptera*)

Set of 3	1.75	1.75

FERNANDO POO
Off West Africa
100 centavos = 1 peso

1964

267 15c Ring-necked Francolin
268 25c Mallard
269 50c Great Blue Turaco
270 70c Ring-necked Francolin
271 1p Mallard
272 1p50 Great Blue Turaco
273 3p Ring-necked Francolin
274 5p Mallard
275 10p Great Blue Turaco

Set of 9 6.50 1.60

FIJI
South Pacific
1959 12 pence = 1 shilling,
20 shillings = 1 pound
1969 100 cents = 1 dollar

1959

308† 4s Red Shining Parrot ('Kandavu Parrot').. 2.00 3.50
323† 5s Orange Dove 9.00 55

1968

374† 3d Eastern Reef Heron ('Reef Heron').. .. 35 5
380† 1s6d Orange-breasted Honeyeater ('Sun
Birds') 3.50 2.75

1969

393† 3c Eastern Reef Heron ('Reef Heron') 25 5
400† 15c Orange-breasted Honeyeater ('Sun
Birds') 4.00 2.00

1971

436† 2c Cardinal Honeyeater 12 12
509† 5c Grey-backed White Eye 20 10
511† 8c Blue-headed Flycatcher ('Blue-crested
Broadbill') 35 5
444† 20c Slaty Flycatcher 90 65
445† 25c Yellow-faced Honeyeater ('Kandavu
Honeyeater') 1.00 40
447† 40c Masked Shining Parrot ('Yellow-
breasted Musk Parrot') 2.25 90
448† 50c White-throated Pigeon 3.00 90
519† $1 Collared Lory 3.50 3.50

1972
No. 400 surcharged **HURRICANE RELIEF** +5c
476† 15c+5c Orange-breasted Honeyeater.. .. 20 25
(476/7 Set of 2) 45 55

1979

566† 25c Long-legged Warbler 50 50
567† 30c Pink-billed Parrot Finch 65 65

BIRDS BIRDS BIRDS
Hundreds of Birds sets from around the World at attractive prices are available from Stanley Gibbons. Write now for our current Birds offers, with no obligation, to: Stanley Gibbons Promotions (Birds Offers), Parkside, Ringwood, Hants BH24 3SH. Tel: (04254) 2363.

1983

651 20c Red-throated Lorikeet ('Red-throated Lory')
652 40c Blue-crowned Lory
653 55c Masked Shining Parrot ('Sulphur-breasted Musk Parrot')
654 70c Red Shining Parrot ('Red-breasted Musk Parrot')

Set of 4   2.50   2.50

1985

710 15c Collared Petrel
711 20c Lesser Frigate Bird
712 50c Brown Booby
713 $1 Crested Tern

Set of 4   2.75   3.00

1952

513 10m + 2m Great Tit (*Parus major*)
514 15m + 3m Spotted Flycatcher (*Muscicapa striata*)
515 25m + 5m Common Swift (*Apus apus*)

Set of 3   4.00   4.00

1956

561 10m + 2m Bohemian Waxwing (*Bombycilla garrulus*)
562 20m + 3m Eagle Owl (*Bubo bubo*)
563 30m + 5m Mute Swan (*Cygnus olor*)

Set of 3   3.00   3.00

565 20m Whooper Swan
566 30m Whooper Swan

Set of 2   14.00   2.40

FINLAND
Northern Europe
100 pennia = 1 markka

1951

500 7m + 2m Capercaillie (*Tetrao urogallus*)
501 12m + 3m Common Crane (*Grus grus*)
502 20m + 5m Caspian Tern (*Sterna caspia*)

Set of 3   4.00   4.00

1960

614 30m European Cuckoo   80   40

1970

762 30p Golden Eagle 3.25   30

1974

854 60p Herring Gull 70 15

1975

883 90p Barn Swallow.. .. .. 70 25

1978

935 1m Golden Eagle 60 10

940 50p Great Tit 50 10

1981

986† 1m80 Razorbill 60 15

1001† 70p Bullfinch, Great Tit 15 10
(1001/2 Set of 2) 40 15

1982

1037† 90p Great Tit 25 10
(1037/8 Set of 2) 50 20

1985

1085 2m10 Barn Swallow 55 8

FRANCE

Western Europe
100 centimes = 1 franc

1947

1013 500f Herring Gull.. .. .. 25.00 27.00

1949

1076 100f Barn Swallow 4.50 3.75

1972

1948 90c King Penguin. 70 40
See also Reunion No. 479.

1960

1504 30c Atlantic Puffin ('Macareux')
1505 50c European Bee Eater ('Guepier')
Set of 2 75 30

1510 20c Lapwing ('Vanneau')
1511 45c Green-winged Teal ('Sarcelle')
Set of 2 90 25

1963† 65c Eagle Owl ('Grand Duc') 90 45
(1962/3 Set of 2) 1.60 70

1973

2003† 60c White Stork ('Cigogne d'Alsace').. .. 50 30
(2002/3 Set of 2) 70 40

1970

1871 45c Greater Flamingo ('Flamant Rose') .. 40 15

1975

2065 70c Little Egret ('Aigrette Garzette') 50 25

COLLECT MAMMALS ON STAMPS
The second Stanley Gibbons thematic catalogue —
copies are available at £7.50 (p. + p. £1.50) from:
Stanley Gibbons Publications Ltd, 5 Parkside,
Christchurch Road, Ringwood, Hants BH24 3SH.

1978

2242†	1f80 Osprey ('Balbuzard')	75	25
	(2241/2 *Set of* 2)	1.25	55

2281	1f White Stork.	35	15

1981

2421	1f60 Grey Heron	40	20

1984

2624	1f Lammergeier (*Gypaetus barbatus aureus*)		
2625	2f Short-toed Eagle (*Circaetus g. gallicus*)		
2626	3f European Sparrow Hawk (*Accipiter n. nisus*)		
2627	5f Peregrine Falcon (*Falco p. peregrinus*)		
	Set of 4	2.40	70

FRENCH EQUATORIAL AFRICA
Central Africa
100 centimes = 1 franc

1953

276†	500f African Darter ('Anhingas').	20.00	2.75

FRENCH GUIANA
South America
100 centimes = 1 franc

1947

236†	10f Cuvier's Toucan	2.50	1.50
237†	15f Cuvier's Toucan	2.50	2.00
238†	20f Cuvier's Toucan	3.00	2.00
239†	25f Blue and Yellow Macaw, Military Macaw, White-eyed Conure	3.75	2.50
240†	40f Blue and Yellow Macaw, Military Macaw, White-eyed Conure	4.00	2.50
241†	50f Yellow-throated Caracara (air)	7.00	6.00
243†	200f Channel-billed Toucan, Cuvier's Toucan, Black-necked Aracari	13.00	11.00

FRENCH INDIAN SETTLEMENTS
East coast of Indian sub-continent
24 caches = 1 fanon,
8 fanon = 1 rupee

1948

283†	5r Short-toed Eagle	9.50	6.00

FRENCH MOROCCO
North-west Africa
100 centimes = 1 franc

1928

157† 3f White Stork 1.50 1.25

1985

457 250f Blue-faced Booby 2.75 2.00

FRENCH POLYNESIA
South Pacific
100 centimes = 1 franc

1980

331 25f White Tern (*Gygis alba*)
332 35f Tahitian Lory (*Vini peruviana*)
333 45f Great Frigate Bird (*Fregata minor*)
Set of 3 2.50 1.60

1981

350 47f Crested Tern (*Sterna bergii*)
351 53f Grey-green Fruit Dove (*Ptilinopus purpuratus*)
352 65f Common Waxbill (*Estrilda astrild*)
Set of 3 3.50 1.75

1982

379 37f Eastern Reef Heron (*Egretta sacra*)
380 39f American Golden Plover (*Pluvialis dominica*)
381 42f Chestnut-breasted Mannikin (*Lonchura castaneothorax*)
Set of 3 2.00 1.50

FRENCH POST OFFICES IN TANGIER
North-west Africa
100 centimes = 1 franc

1928
No. 157 of French Morocco overprinted **Tanger**
38† 3f White Stork 1.75 1.40

FRENCH SOMALI COAST
East Africa
100 centimes = 1 franc

1960

440† 10f Greater Flamingo ('Flamant Rose'). .. 1.00 60
441† 15f Little Bee Eater ('Guepier') 1.50 70
444† 30f Sacred Ibis ('Ibis') 3.75 2.00
446† 75f Pink-backed Pelican ('Pelican') 7.50 4.50

448† 200f Great Bustard ('Outarde') (air). 11.00 7.50

1962

458† 40f Griffon Vulture ('Vautour Fauve') 6.00 3.50

FRENCH SOUTHERN AND ANTARCTIC TERRITORIES

Antarctica and nearby islands
100 centimes = 1 franc

1955

No. 324 of Madagascar overprinted TERRES AUSTRALES ET
ANTARCTIQUES FRANCAISES

1	15f Long-tailed Ground Roller (*Uratelornis*) ..	10.00	25.00

1956

2†	30c Light-mantled Sooty Albatross ('Albatros Fuligineux')	35	1.00
3†	40c Great Skua ('Skuas')	35	1.00
4†	50c Rockhopper Penguin	40	1.00
5†	1f Rockhopper Penguin.	40	1.00
6†	2f Black-faced Sheathbill ('Chionis')	80	1.00
11†	12f Kerguelen Cormorant ('Cormoran')	6.50	6.00
15†	85f King Penguin ('Manchot Royal')	14.00	12.00
16†	50f Emperor Penguin, Snow Petrel (air). ..	25.00	20.00
17†	100f Emperor Penguin, Snow Petrel	25.00	20.00
18†	200f Wandering Albatross.	23.00	23.00

1963

35†	5f King Penguin	20.00	18.00
28†	10f Pintado Petrel ('Damier du Cap')	21.00	16.00
31†	20f Black-browed Albatross ('Albatros a Sourcils Noir')	£250	£175
34†	50f Adelie Penguin ('Manchot Adelie') (air).	32.00	32.00

37†	100f Adelie Penguin	85.00	75.00
	(36/7 *Set of* 2)	£130	£110

1968

46†	50f Emperor Penguin	90.00	80.00
	(45/6 *Set of* 2)	£100	90.00

1974

92	150f Emperor Penguin	5.50	5.50

1975

98†	40c Swallow-tailed Tern ('Sterne Antarctique')	2.50	2.50
99†	50c Antarctic Petrel ('Petrel Antarctique') ..	3.00	3.00
102†	1f20 Kerguelen Cormorant ('Cormoran de Kerguelen')	9.00	8.50
103†	1f40 Gentoo Penguin ('Manchot Papou') ..	12.00	12.00

1977

124†	90c Light-mantled Sooty Albatross ('Albatros Fuligineux a Dos Clair')	75	75

1979

130† 1f40 Kerguelen Cormorant ('Cormoran de
Kerguelen') 80 70

1982

167 8f Rockhopper Penguin, Gentoo Penguin,
King Penguin 3.50 3.50

1980

138 70c Royal Penguin ('Gorfou de Schlegel')
139 1f Soft-plumaged Petrel ('Petrel Soyeux')
Set of 2 1.50 1.25

1983

172 1f50 Pintail ('Canard d'Eaton')
173 1f80 Pintail ('Canard d'Eaton')
Set of 2 75 75

1984

185† 70c Rockhopper Penguin ('Gorfou
Sauteur') 30 30
186† 2f Rockhopper Penguin ('Gorfou Sauteur'). 75 75

149† 50c Adelie Penguin ('Manchot Adelie'). .. 1.50 1.25
150† 60c Adelie Penguin ('Manchot Adelie'). .. 80 60
151† 1f20 Adelie Penguin ('Manchot Adelie') .. 1.00 80

1981

162 1f50 Black-faced Sheathbill ('Chionis') 60 60

1985

196† 1f70 Emperor Penguin ('Manchot
Empereur') 50 50
197† 2f80 Snow Petrel ('Petrel des Neiges') . .. 75 75
199† 3f90 Amsterdam Albatross (*Diomedea
amsterdamensis*) (air) 1.00 1.00
(196/9 *Set of* 4) 2.25 2.25

1986

208 1f Southern Fulmar ('Fulmar Antarctique')
209 1f70 Giant Petrel ('Petrels Geants')

210 4f60 Southern Black-backed Gull ('Goeland
       Dominicain') (air)
                           Set of 3 1.75 1.75

1987

226† 4f80 Macaroni Penguin ('Gorfou
        Macaroni') 1.25 1.25
                   (225/6 *Set of 2*) 1.75 1.75

FRENCH TERRITORY OF THE AFARS AND THE ISSAS

East Africa
100 centimes = 1 franc

1967

504† 10f Grey-headed Kingfisher (*Halcyon
        leucocephala*) 1.25 1.00
505† 15f Oystercatcher (*Haematopus
        ostralegus*) 1.75 1.50
506† 50f Greenshank (*Tringa nebularia*).. .. .. 6.00 3.50
507† 55f Abyssinian Roller (*Coracias
        abyssinicus*) 8.00 4.50

509† 200f Tawny Eagle (*Aquila rapax belisarius*)
        (air) 12.00 6.00

COLLECT RAILWAYS ON STAMPS
A Stanley Gibbons thematic catalogue on this
popular subject. Copies available at £7.50 (p. + p.
£1.50) from: Stanley Gibbons Publications Ltd, 5
Parkside, Christchurch Road, Ringwood, Hants
BH24 3SH.

1972

574 30f Lichtenstein's Sandgrouse (*Pterocles
       lichtensteini*)
575 49f Hoopoe (*Upupa epops*)
576 66f Great Snipe (*Capella media*)
577 500f Pale-bellied Francolin (*Francolinus
       ochropectus*)
                           Set of 4 22.00 11.00

1974

608 5f Greater Flamingo
609 15f Greater Flamingo
610 50f Greater Flamingo
                           Set of 3 2.00 1.10

1975

648 20f Pin-tailed Whydah (*Vidua macroura*)
649 25f Rose-ringed Parakeet (*Psittacula
       krameri*)
650 50f Variable Sunbird (*Cinnyris venustus*)
651 60f Goliath Heron (*Ardea goliath*)
652 100f Hammerkop (*Scopus umbretta*)
653 100f Namaqua Dove (*Oena capensis*)
654 300f African Spoonbill (*Platalea alba*)

655 500f Speckled Pigeon (*Columba guinea*)
       (air)
                           Set of 8 23.00 12.00

FRENCH WEST AFRICA

West Africa
100 centimes = 1 franc

1947

55†	100f Great Egret	4.00	1.90

FUJEIRA

Arabian peninsula
1964 100 naye paise = 1 rupee
1967 100 dirhams = 1 riyal

1964

1†	1np Great Crested Grebe..	25	10
3†	3np Hoopoe.	25	10
5†	5np Great Egret	25	10
9†	30np Lanner Falcon	30	15
10†	40np Great Crested Grebe	40	20
12†	70np Hoopoe	50	30
14†	1r50 Great Egret	75	50
18†	10r Lanner Falcon..	3.75	3.75

1965

39†	15np Great Crested Grebe	25	10
41†	35np Hoopoe	30	15
43†	75np Great Egret	40	30
47†	5r Lanner Falcon	2.25	2.00

1967

Various stamps with new currency names surcharged

85†	1d on 1np Great Crested Grebe (No. 1)	25	10
87†	3d on 3np Hoopoe (No. 3)	25	10
89†	5d on 5np Great Egret (No. 5)	25	10
93†	30d on 30np Lanner Falcon (No. 9)	30	20
94†	40d on 40np Great Crested Grebe (No. 10)	40	25
96†	70d on 70np Hoopoe (No. 12)	50	35
98†	1r50 on 1r50 Great Egret (No. 14)	90	75
102†	10r on 10r Lanner Falcon (No. 18)	5.00	4.50

123†	15d on 15np Great Crested Grebe (No. 39)		
	(air)	25	10
125†	35d on 35np Hoopoe (No. 41)	30	20
127†	75d on 75np Great Egret (No. 43)	45	55
131†	5r on 5r Lanner Falcon (No. 47).	2.25	2.25

OFFICIAL STAMPS

1965

O48†	25np Great Crested Grebe ..	25	10
O50†	50np Hoopoe..	30	20
O52†	1r Great Egret	60	50
O56†	5r Lanner Falcon.	1.75	1.75

1967

Nos. O48/56 with new currency name surcharged

O158†	25d on 25np Great Crested Grebe	25	10
O160†	50d on 50np Hoopoe	35	25
O162†	1r on 1r Great Egret	50	45
O166†	5r on 5r Lanner Falcon.	2.50	2.50

Appendix

The following stamps have either been issued in excess of postal needs, or have not been made available to the public in reasonable quantities at face value. Miniature sheets, imperforate stamps etc. are excluded from this section.

1969

Birds. Postage 25d Peregrine Falcon, 50d European Cuckoo, 1r Yellow-bellied Green Pigeon, 1r50 Yemen Thrush, 2r Lanner Falcon. Air 1r25 Arabian Chukar, 2r50 Western Reef Heron, 3r Houbara Bustard, 5r Lanner Falcon

1972

Tropical Birds. 30d Red-crested Turaco, 70d Red-legged Honeycreeper, 1r Many-coloured Rush Tyrant, 2r King Bird of Paradise, 3r Lance-tailed Manakin

European Birds. 30d Redstart, 70d Little Ringed Plover, 1r Goosander, 2r Dunlin, 3r Skylark

GABON
West Africa
100 centimes = 1 franc

1960

No. 276 of French Equatorial Africa overprinted **XVIIe OLYMPIADE 1960 REPUBLIQUE GABONAISE 250F** and Olympic rings

165   250f on 500f African Darter 6.00   5.50

1961

170   50f Lyre-tailed Honeyguide (*Melichneutes robustus*)
171   100f Madame Verreaux's Sunbird (*Cinnyris johannae*)
172   200f Blue-headed Bee Eater (*Melittophagus mulleri*)
173   250f Crowned Eagle (*Stephanoaetus coronatus*)
174   500f Narina Trogon (*Apaloderma narina*)
             Set of 5   26.00   11.00

1971

432   30f Great Egret ('Grande aigrette')
433   40f Grey Parrot ('Perroquet Jaco')
434   50f Woodland Kingfisher (*Alcyon senegalensis*)
435   75f Grey-necked Bald Crow (*Picathartes orea*)
436   100f Knysna Turaco (*Tauraco persa*)
             Set of 5   7.00   3.50

1974

520   200f American Bald Eagle 1.60   1.00

1978

675   100f White Stork
676   100f Grey Parrot (on stamp No. 433)
             Set of 2   2.25   2.00

1980

740   50f African River Martin (*Pseudochelidon eurystomina*)
741   60f White-fronted Bee Eater (*Merops nubicus* !)
742   80f African Pitta (*Pitta angolensis*)
743   150f Pel's Fishing Owl (*Scotopelia peli*)
             Set of 4   1.90   1.10

1983

850†   125f Pink-backed Pelican ('Pelican')   65   35

1984

909   90f South African Crowned Crane ('Grue Couronnee')
910   125f Snowy-breasted Hummingbird ('Oiseau-Mouche')
911   150f Keel-billed Toucan ('Toucan')
             Set of 3   1.60   1.50

GAMBIA
West Africa
1963 12 pence = 1 shilling,
20 shillings = 1 pound
1971 100 bututs = 1 dalasy

1963

193 ½d Beautiful Sunbird ('Beautiful Long-tailed
     Sunbird')
194 1d Yellow-mantled Whydah
195 1½d Cattle Egret
196 2d Senegal Parrot ('Yellow-bellied Parrot')
197 3d Rose-ringed Parakeet ('Long-tailed
     Parrakeet')
198 4d Violet Starling ('Amethyst Starling')
199 6d Village Weaver
200 1s Rufous-crowned Roller
201 1s3d Red-eyed Dove ('Red-eyed Turtle
     Dove')
202 2s6d Double-spurred Francolin ('Bush
     Fowl')
203 5s Palm-nut Vulture
204 10s Orange-cheeked Waxbill
205 £1 African Emerald Cuckoo ('Emerald
     Cuckoo')
                        Set of 13   40.00   30.00

1963
Nos. 194, 197 and 200/1 overprinted **SELF GOVERNMENT 1963**
206 1d Yellow-mantled Whydah
207 3d Rose-ringed Parakeet
208 1s Rufous-crowned Roller
209 1s3d Red-eyed Dove
                        Set of 4   25   25

1965
Nos. 193/205 overprinted **INDEPENDENCE 1965**
215 ½d Beautiful Sunbird
216 1d Yellow-mantled Whydah
217 1½d Cattle Egret
218 2d Senegal Parrot
219 3d Rose-ringed Parakeet
220 4d Violet Starling
221 6d Village Weaver
222 1s Rufous-crowned Roller
223 1s3d Red-eyed Dove
224 2s6d Double-spurred Francolin
225 5s Palm-nut Vulture
226 10s Orange-cheeked Waxbill
227 £1 African Emerald Cuckoo
                        Set of 13   7.75   11.00

STANLEY GIBBONS
STAMP COLLECTING SERIES
Introductory booklets on *How to Start, How to
Identify Stamps* and *Collecting by Theme*. A series
of well illustrated guides at a low price.
Write for details.

1966

233 ⅓d Red-cheeked Cordon-bleu (*Uraeginthus
     bengalus*)
234 1d White-faced Whistling Duck
     (*Dendrocygna viduata*)
235 1½d Red-throated Bee Eater (*Melittophagus
     bullocki*)
236 2d Lesser Pied Kingfisher (*Ceryle rudis*)
237 3d Golden Bishop (*Euplectes afra*)
238 4d African Fish Eagle (*Cuncuma vocifer
     clamans*)
239 6d Yellow-bellied Green Pigeon (*Vinago
     waalia*)
240 1s Blue-bellied Roller (*Coracias
     cyanogaster*)
241 1s6d African Pygmy Kingfisher (*Ispidina
     picta picta*)
242 2s6d Spur-winged Goose (*Plectropterus
     gambensis*)
243 5s Cardinal Woodpecker (*Dendropicos
     fuscescens zechi*)
244 10s Violet Turaco (*Musophuga violacea*)
245 £1 Pin-tailed Whydah (*Vidua macroura*)
                        Set of 13   8.25   10.00

1977

384† 10b Crowned Crane   15   5

1978

400 20b Verreaux's Eagle Owl
401 25b Lizard Buzzard
402 50b African Harrier Hawk ('West African
     Harrier Hawk')
403 1d25 Long-crested Eagle ('Long-crested
     Hawk Eagle')
                        Set of 4   3.75   3.25

1983

510   10b Osprey
511   60b Osprey
512   85b Osprey
513   1d10 Osprey

Set of 4	2.00	1.75

1985

581   60b Turkey Vulture
582   85b American Anhinga
583   1d50 Green Heron
584   5d Wood Duck

Set of 4	3.25	3.00

MS585   10d Great Northern Diver ('Common
       Loon'). 3.50   3.75

GERMANY

Central Europe, divided after the Second World War into West
Germany, West Berlin and East Germany
100 pfennige = 1 reichsmark

1934

526†	5p Golden Eagle ..	..	..	..	..	..	..	50	20
527†	10p Golden Eagle.	..	..	..	..	..	..	50	30
528†	15p Golden Eagle.	..	..	..	..	..	..	50	30
529†	20p Golden Eagle.	..	..	..	..	..	..	75	45
530†	25p Golden Eagle.	..	..	..	..	..	..	75	50
531†	40p Golden Eagle.	..	..	..	..	..	..	75	35
532†	50p Golden Eagle.	..	..	..	..	..	..	2.00	30
533†	80p Golden Eagle.	..	..	..	..	..	..	1.75	1.75
534†	100p Golden Eagle	..	..	..	..	..	..	2.00	1.25

West Germany

100 pfennige = 1 deutschmark

1957

1194†	20p European Robin	.. ..	50	15
	(1193/4 *Set of* 2)		80	25

1963

1315   10p + 5p Hoopoe
1316   15p + 5p Golden Oriole
1317   20p + 10p Bullfinch
1318   40p + 20p Common Kingfisher

Set of 4	2.25	3.00

1965

1384   10p + 5p Woodcock ('Waldschneppe')
1385   15p + 5p Ring-necked Pheasant ('Fasan')
1386   20p + 10p Black Grouse ('Birkhahn')
1387   40p + 20p Capercaillie ('Auerhahn')

Set of 4	90	1.10

1972

1616	60p + 30p Mute Swan.	.. ..	1.90	1.90

1973

1648 25p+10p Osprey ('Fischadler')
1649 30p+15p Common Buzzard
       ('Mausebussard')
1650 40p+20p Red Kite ('Rotmilan')
1651 70p+35p Montagu's Harrier
       ('Wiesenweihe')
                     Set of 4   16.00   14.50

1976

1793 50p Golden Plover ('Goldregenpfeifer') .. 60   12

1981

1966 60p Common Coot (chick)   40   10

West Berlin

100 pfennige = 1 deutschmark

1965

B261 10p+5p Woodcock ('Waldschneppe')
B262 15p+5p Ring-necked Pheasant ('Fasan')
B263 20p+10p Black Grouse ('Birkhahn')
B264 40p+20p Capercaillie ('Auerhahn')
                     Set of 4   1.00   90

1969

MSB332 20p Dalmatian Pelican ('Pelikan') 2.10   1.60

1973

B430 20p+10p Northern Goshawk ('Habicht')
B431 30p+15p Peregrine Falcon
       ('Wanderfalke')
B432 40p+20p European Sparrow Hawk
       ('Sperber')
B433 70p+35p Golden Eagle ('Steinadler')
                     Set of 4   5.50   5.50

1984

B684 80p White Stork   50   50

East Germany

100 pfennige = 1 mark

1956

E288† 10p Greater Flamingo   25   5

1959

E422† 5p Grey Heron ('Fischreiher')   25   5
E423† 10p Eurasian Bittern ('Rohrdommel') . ..   25   5

E432 5p Common Cormorant ('Kormoran')
E433 10p Black Stork ('Schwarzstorch')
E434 15p Eagle Owl ('Uhu')
E435 20p Black Grouse ('Birkhahn')
E436 25p Hoopoe ('Wiedehopf')
E437 40p Peregrine Falcon ('Wanderfalke')

Set of 6   2.50   1.75

E1077† 10p Ring-necked Pheasant (*Phasianus colchicus*)   25   10
E1078† 15p Grey Partridge (*Perdix perdix*)   25   10
E1079† 20p Mallard (*Anas platyrhynchos*)   25   10
E1080† 25p Greylag Goose (*Anser anser*)   25   10
E1081† 30p Wood Pigeon (*Columba palumbus*) .   30   15
(E1077/82 *Set of 6*)   2.50   1.40

1965

E865 5p Red Kite ('Rotmilan')
E866 10p Lammergeier ('Bartgeier')
E867 20p Common Buzzard ('Mausebussard')
E868 25p Common Kestrel ('Turmfalk')
E869 40p Northern Goshawk ('Habicht')
E870 70p Golden Eagle ('Steinadler')

Set of 6   2.50   1.50

1970

E1339† 15p Whale-headed Stork ('Schuhschnabel')   25   5

1967

E991 5p Barn Owl (*Tyto alba*)
E992 10p Common Crane (*Grus grus*)
E993 20p Peregrine Falcon (*Falco peregrinus*)
E994 25p Bullfinch (*Pyrrhula pyrrhula*)
E995 30p Common Kingfisher (*Alcedo atthis*)
E996 40p Common Roller (*Coracias garrulus*)

Set of 6   1.75   1.40

1973

E1533† 5p Eastern White Pelican (29x24 mm) ..   25   5
E1547† 5p Eastern White Pelican (22x18 mm) ..   25   5

1968

E1560† 35p Archaeopteryx * (*Archaeopteryx lithographica*)   15   5

E1072† 25p Fulmar..   30   20
(E1071/2 *Set of 2*)   35   25

COLLECT MAMMALS ON STAMPS

The second Stanley Gibbons thematic catalogue —
copies are available at £7.50 (p.+p. £1.50) from:
Stanley Gibbons Publications Ltd, 5 Parkside,
Christchurch Road, Ringwood, Hants BH24 3SH.

E1568   5p Firecrest ('Sommergoldhahnchen')
E1569   10p White-winged Crossbill
          ('Bindenkreuzschnabel')
E1570   15p Bohemian Waxwing
          ('Seidenschwanz')
E1571   20p Bluethroat ('Weiss- und Rotstern-
          Blaukehlchen')
E1572   25p Goldfinch ('Stieglitz')
E1573   35p Golden Oriole ('Pirol')
E1574   40p Grey Wagtail ('Gebirgsstelze')
E1575   50p Wallcreeper ('Mauerlaufer')
                              Set of 8   3.50   2.50

1975

E1745†   5p Blue and Yellow Macaw ('Ararauna')   25   10

1977

E1987†   20p Ring-necked Pheasant   25   10

1979

E2098   5p Chaffinch ('Buchfink')
E2099   10p European Nuthatch ('Kleiber')
E2100   20p European Robin ('Rotkehlchen')
E2101   25p Common Rosefinch
          ('Karmingimpel')
E2102   35p Blue Tit ('Blaumeise')
E2103   50p Linnet ('Bluthanfling')
                              Set of 6   3.50   2.40

1980

E2216†   20p Lesser Kestrel (*Falco naumanni*) ..   25   5

E2245†   25p White Eared-Pheasant ('Weisser
          Ohrfasan')   25   15

1982

E2410   10p Osprey ('Nisthilfen Fur Fischadler')
E2411   20p White-tailed Sea Eagle
          ('Winterfutterung Fur Seeadler')
E2412   25p Little Owl ('Nistrohren Fur
          Steinkauze')
E2413   35p Eagle Owl ('Kunstliche Nistnischen
          Fur Uhus')
                              Set of 4   1.40   1.25

1985

E2662†   5p Harpy Eagle ('Harpyie')   30   10
E2663†   10p Red-breasted Goose ('Rothalsgans')   55   30

GHANA
West Africa
1957 12 pence = 1 shilling,
20 shillings = 1 pound
1965 100 pesewas = 1 cedi
1967 100 new pesewas = 1 new cedi
1972 100 pesewas = 1 cedi

1957

166	2d Palm-nut Vulture		
167	2½d Palm-nut Vulture		
168	4d Palm-nut Vulture		
169	1s3d Palm-nut Vulture		
	Set of 4	40	12

193†	2½d Palm-nut Vulture..	8	5
195†	2s Yellow-nosed Albatross	15	20
196†	2s6d Palm-nut Vulture	25	30
	(193/6 Set of 4)	55	65

Nos. 166/9 overprinted **PRIME MINISTER'S VISIT, U.S.A. AND
CANADA**

197	2d Palm-nut Vulture		
198	2½d Palm-nut Vulture		
199	4d Palm-nut Vulture		
200	1s3d Palm-nut Vulture		
	Set of 4	20	20

1959

220†	6d Red-crowned Bishop ('Fire-crowned Bishop')	25	5
223†	2s6d Great Blue Turaco ('Giant Plantain Eater')	1.00	15
226†	1s3d Pennant-winged Nightjar (air)	70	5
227†	2s Crowned Crane	80	5

1964

358†	1½d Secretary Bird	25	50
360†	3d Grey Parrot	30	30
361†	4d Blue-naped Mousebird ('Mousebird')	40	40
363†	1s3d Violet Starling ('Amethyst Starling')	90	1.25

1965
Nos. 220, 223 and 226/7 surcharged **Ghana New Currency 19th
July, 1965** and value

385†	6p on 6d Red-crowned Bishop	15	5
388†	30p on 2s6d Great Blue Turaco	1.50	90
392†	15p on 1s3d Pennant-winged Nightjar (air)	90	15
393†	24p on 2s Crowned Crane	1.00	25

1967
Nos. 220, 223, 226 and 393 surcharged

447†	5np on 6d Red-crowned Bishop	20	5
450†	25np on 2s6d Great Blue Turaco	2.25	1.75
453†	12½np on 1s3d Pennant-winged Nightjar (air)	1.25	70
454†	20np on 24p on 2s Crowned Crane	2.00	1.50

461†	1½np Forest Kingfisher	25	5
465†	4np Rufous-crowned Roller	25	5
471†	50np Black-winged Stilt	1.50	20

494†	20np Carmine Bee Eater.	1.75	1.90

1969

Nos. 461, 465 and 471 overprinted **NEW CONSTITUTION 1969**

542†	1½np Forest Kingfisher	15	20
546†	4np Rufous-crowned Roller..	30	15
552†	50np Black-winged Stilt	3.00	3.00

1981

GHANA 20ᴾ

939	20p Narina Trogon		
940	65p White-crowned Robin Chat		
941	2c Swallow-tailed Bee Eater		
942	4c Rose-ringed Parakeet ('Long-tailed Parakeet')		
	Set of 4	4.50	4.75
MS943	25p Narina Trogon; 50p White-crowned Robin Chat; 1c Swallow-tailed Bee Eater; 3c Rose-ringed Parakeet ('Long-tailed Parakeet').	3.50	4.00

1983

c3   GHANA

1022†	3c African Fish Eagle	1.50	1.50

GHANA

1047	10c Grey-backed Camaroptera (Camaroptera brevicaudata)	15	20

1984

No. 1022 surcharged

1086†	50c on 3c African Fish Eagle	2.10	2.25

1985

1159	5c Fork-tailed Flycatcher ('York-tailed Fly Catcher')		
1160	8c Barred Owl		
1161	12c Black-throated Mango		
1162	100c White-crowned Pigeon		
	Set of 4	2.00	2.25
MS1163	110c Downy Woodpecker	2.00	2.50

GIBRALTAR

South-west Europe

1960 12 pence = 1 shilling,
20 shillings = 1 pound
1971 100 pence = 1 pound

1960

170†	2s Barbary Partridge	6.50	2.00
171†	5s Blue Rock Thrush	8.00	6.50

1977

377†	2½p Sardinian Warbler (Sylvia melanocephala)	40	15
381†	6p Black Kite (Milvus migrans)..	45	20
385†	20p Audouin's Gull (Larus audouinii)	1.25	50
389†	£2 Hoopoe (Upupa epops)	7.50	5.50

STAMP MONTHLY

— finest and most informative magazine for all collectors. Obtainable from your newsagent or by postal subscription — details on request.

1982

482† 15½p Common Swift ('Swift')   40   45

1986

533† 29p Herring Gull   60   65
         (532/3 *Set of* 2)   1.00   1.10

GILBERT AND ELLICE ISLANDS
Central Pacific
12 pence = 1 shilling,
20 shillings = 1 pound

1939

43† ¾d Great Frigate Bird   20   35

1956

64† ½d Great Frigate Bird   20   20

1960

76† 2d Great Frigate Bird   35   20

1964

83† 1s Eastern Reef Heron   40   20

GILBERT ISLANDS
Central Pacific
100 cents = 1 dollar

1976

27† 6c Eastern Reef Heron ('Reef Egret')   35   25

1978

70† 45c Great Frigate Bird.   55   75

GREAT BRITAIN
North-west Europe
1963 12 pence = 1 shilling,
20 shillings = 1 pound
1971 100 pence = 1 pound

1963

638† 4½d Long-tailed Tit, Wood Lark, Great
       Spotted Woodpecker   25   25
         (637/8 *Set of* 2)   30   30

1966

696 4d Black-headed Gull
697 4d Blue Tit
698 4d European Robin ('Robin')
699 4d Blackbird

Set of 4   50   35

1977

1044†	7p Turtle Dove	15	15
1045†	7p Blackbird..	15	15
1046†	7p Mute Swan	15	15
1049†	9p Grey Partridge	15	15

1980

1109 10p Common Kingfisher ('Kingfisher')
1110 11½p Dipper
1111 13p Moorhen
1112 15p Yellow Wagtail

Set of 4   1.25   1.40

1982

1177† 26p Cactus Ground Finch, Large Ground
Finch   65   65

1983

1231†	12½p Magpie..	35	30
1233†	20½p Blackbird	55	55
1234†	28p Blackbird	75	75
1235†	31p Goldfinch, Firecrest, European Nuthatch, European Robin, Pied Wagtail, Great Tit	85	90

(1231/5 Set of 5)   2.75   2.75

1985

1284† 31p European Cuckoo   80   85

1986

1320† 17p Barn Owl   40   45

GREECE

South-east Europe
100 lepta = 1 drachma

1970

1153† 6d Rock Partridge (*Alectoris graeca*).. ..   3.50   50

1979

ΕΛΛΑΣ ΗΕLLAS **6**

1475 6d Purple Heron (*Ardea purpurea*)
1476 8d Audouin's Gull (*Larus audouini*)
1477 10d Eleonora's Falcon (*Falco eleonorae*)
1478 14d Common Kingfisher (*Alcedo athis*)
1479 20d Eastern White Pelican (*Pelecanus onocrotalus*)
1480 25d White-tailed Sea Eagle (*Haliaetus albicila*)

Set of 6	2.25	1.25

1986

ΕΛΛΗΝΙΚΗ ΔΗΜΟΚΡΑΤΙΑ **110**

1734†	110d Dalmatian Pelican.	80	50
	(1733/4 *Set of 2*)	1.25	75

1969

68	80ore White-tailed Sea Eagle	2.00	1.60

1975

93	90ore Gyrfalcon..	50	35

1981

130	1k60+20ore King Eider	75	75

GREENLAND
North Atlantic
100 ore = 1 krone

1945

16†	5k Eider	30.00	22.00

No. 16 *overprinted* **DANMARK BEFRIET 5 MAJ 1945**

25†	5k Eider	85.00	45.00

1967

65	90ore Great Northern Diver, Raven	3.00	3.00

1982

135	2k+40ore Greater Shearwater	70	70

1987

MS164	2k80 Fulmar; 6k50 Fulmar (sheet also contains 3k80 stamp)	3.75	3.75

GRENADA
West Indies
100 cents = 1 dollar

1968

318†	$1 Bananaquit (*Coereba flaveola*)	25	1.50
319†	$2 Brown Pelican (*Pelecanus occidentalis*)	2.50	4.25
320†	$3 Magnificent Frigate Bird (*Fregata magnificens*)	2.75	4.50
321†	$5 Bare-eyed Thrush (*Turdus nudigenis*) ..	3.75	8.00

1970

414†	½c Goldfinch	5	5
418†	3c Goldfinch	5	5

1972
Nos. 318/21 *overprinted* **AIR MAIL**

513†	$1 Bananaquit.	95	60
515†	$2 Brown Pelican.	2.00	1.50
516†	$3 Magnificent Frigate Bird	2.75	2.25
517†	$5 Bare-eyed Thrush.	3.75	4.50

1973

548†	25c Greater Flamingo (*Phoenicopterus ruber ruber*)	70	50
550†	60c Blue and Yellow Macaw (*Ara ararauna*), Scarlet Macaw (*Ara macao*)..	1.40	1.25

1974
Nos. 318/21 *overprinted* **INDEPENDENCE 7TH FEB. 1974**

604†	$1 Bananaquit.	3.75	1.50
605†	$2 Brown Pelican.	6.00	3.50
606†	$3 Magnificent Frigate Bird	10.00	5.00
607†	$5 Bare-eyed Thrush.	15.00	9.50

1976

761†	¼c Bananaquit	5	5
MS768	$1 Belted Kingfisher	2.00	1.75

1978

922	¼c Black-headed Gull		
923	1c Wilson's Petrel		
924	2c Killdeer		
925	50c White-necked Jacobin ('Jacobin Hummingbird')		
926	75c Blue-faced Booby		
927	$1 Broad-winged Hawk		
928	$2 Red-necked Pigeon ('Ramier Pigeon')		
	Set of 7	5.50	3.00
MS929	$3 Scarlet Ibis	3.50	3.50

1979

1014†	90c Brown Booby.	50	40
1015†	$1 Magnificent Frigate Bird	55	45
MS1016	$2.50 Sooty Tern	1.25	1.25

1980

1060 20c Tropical Kingbird
1061 40c Rufous-breasted Hermit
1062 $1 Troupial
1063 $2 Ruddy Quail Dove
                              Set of 4   2.50   2.25
MS1064 $3 Prairie Warbler 1.75   2.00

1985

1378 50c Clapper Rail
1379 70c Hooded Warbler
1380 90c Common Flicker ('Flicker')
1381 $4 Bohemian Waxwing
                              Set of 4   4.00   4.00
MS1382 $5 Merlin ('Pigeon Hawk') 3.50   3.75

1986

1480 50c Snowy Egret
1481 90c Greater Flamingo ('Flamingo')
1482 $1.10 Canada Goose ('Barnacle Goose')
1483 $3 Smew
                              Set of 4   3.00   3.25
MS1484 $5 Brent Goose ('Brant Goose'). 3.00   3.50

STAMP MONTHLY
— finest and most informative magazine for all
collectors. Obtainable from your newsagent or by
postal subscription — details on request.

GRENADINES OF GRENADA
West Indies
100 cents = 1 dollar

1974

Nos. 318/21 of Grenada overprinted **GRENADINES**
12† $1 Bananaquit (*Coereba flaveola*) 1.25   60
13† $2 Brown Pelican (*Pelecanus occidentalis*) .   2.00   1.25
14† $3 Magnificent Frigate Bird (*Fregata
      magnificus*) 2.25   1.50
15† $5 Bare-eyed Thrush (*Turdus nidigenis*) ..   3.25   2.25

1976

148† 1c Cocoa Thrush   5   5
150† 35c Hooded Tanager   65   45
152† 75c Grenada Dove 1.50   1.25
MS154 $2 Blue-hooded Euphonia. 3.50   3.50

1978

294 5c Audubon's Shearwater
295 10c Semipalmated Plover ('Northern Ring-
     necked Plover')
296 18c Purple-throated Carib ('Garnet-
     throated Hummingbird')
297 22c Red-billed Whistling Duck ('Black-
     bellied Tree Duck')
298 40c Caribbean Martin
299 $1 White-tailed Tropic Bird ('Yellow-billed
     Tropicbird')
300 $2 Long-billed Curlew
                              Set of 7   5.25   3.50
MS301 $5 Snowy Egret. 4.50   4.50

1979

350† 75c Great Blue Heron..   40   40
352† $1 Red-footed Booby   55   55
MS353 $2.50 Collared Plover 1.25   1.25

1980

382 25c Yellow-bellied Seedeater
383 40c Blue-hooded Euphonia
384 90c Yellow Warbler
385 $2 Tropical Mockingbird

	Set of 4	3.00	2.00
MS386 $3 Barn Owl		2.25	2.25

1984

598 40c Bobolink
599 50c Eastern Kingbird
600 60c Barn Swallow
601 70c Yellow Warbler
602 $1 Rose-breasted Grosbeak
603 $1.10 Yellowthroat
604 $2 Catbird

	Set of 7	4.50	4.50
MS605 $5 Fork-tailed Flycatcher		3.50	3.75

1985

645 50c Blue-winged Teal
646 90c White Ibis
647 $1.10 Swallow-tailed Kite
648 $3 Moorhen ('Common Gallinule')

	Set of 4	3.00	3.00
MS649 $5 Mangrove Cuckoo		3.00	3.25

STANLEY GIBBONS
STAMP COLLECTING SERIES
Introductory booklets on *How to Start, How to Identify Stamps* and *Collecting by Theme*. A series of well illustrated guides at a low price.
Write for details.

1986

736 50c Louisiana Heron
737 70c Black-crowned Night Heron
738 90c American Bittern ('Bittern')
739 $4 Glossy Ibis

	Set of 4	3.25	3.25
MS740 $5 King Eider		3.00	3.25

GRENADINES OF ST. VINCENT
West Indies
100 cents = 1 dollar

1974

Nos. 286a/9, 364 and *291/300 of St. Vincent overprinted*
GRENADINES OF

3 1c Green Heron
4 2c Lesser Antillean Bullfinch ('Bullfinch')
25 3c St. Vincent Amazon ('St. Vincent Parrot')
6 4c Rufous-throated Solitaire ('Soufriere Bird')
7 5c Red-necked Pigeon ('Ramier')
8 6c Bananaquit
9 8c Purple-throated Carib ('Humming Bird')
10 10c Mangrove Cuckoo
11 12c Common Black Hawk ('Black Hawk')
12 20c Bare-eyed Thrush
13 25c Hooded Tanager ('Prince')
14 50c Blue-hooded Euphonia
15 $1 Barn Owl
16 $2.50 Yellow-bellied Elaenia ('Crested Elaenia')
17 $5 Ruddy Quail Dove

	Set of 15	14.00	8.75

1978

110 1c Tropical Mockingbird
111 2c Mangrove Cuckoo
112 3c Osprey
113 4c Smooth-billed Ani
114 5c House Wren
115 6c Bananaquit
116 8c Carib Grackle
117 10c Yellow-bellied Elaenia
118 12c Collared Plover
119 15c Cattle Egret
120 20c Red-footed Booby
121 25c Red-billed Tropic Bird
122 40c Royal Tern

123	50c Grenada Flycatcher ('Rusty Tailed Flycatcher')
124	80c Purple Gallinule
125	$1 Broad-winged Hawk
126	$2 Scaly-breasted Ground Dove ('Common Ground Dove')
127	$3 Laughing Dove
128	$5 Common Noddy ('Brown Noddy')
129	$10 Grey Kingbird

Set of 20   12.50   8.00

1983

No. 123 surcharged **45c**

241	45c on 50c Grenada Flycatcher	25	25

1986

495	10c American Kestrel ('Sparrow Hawk')
496	45c Common Black Hawk ('Black Hawk')
497	60c Peregrine Falcon ('Duck Hawk')
498	$4 Osprey ('Fish Hawk')

Set of 4   2.75   2.75

Union Island

Appendix

The following stamps have either been issued in excess of postal needs, or have not been made available to the public in reasonable quantities at face value. Miniature sheets, imperforate stamps etc. are excluded from this section.

1985

Leaders of the World. Birth Bicentenary of John J. Audubon. Birds. 15c Hooded Warbler, 15c Carolina Wren, 50c Song Sparrow, 50c Black-headed Grosbeak, $1 Scarlet Tanager, $1 Lazuli Bunting, $1.50 Sharp-shinned Hawk, $1.50 Merlin

GUATEMALA

Central America

1879 100 centavos = 8 reales = 1 peso
1927 100 centavos de quetzal = 1 quetzal

1879

15	½r Resplendent Quetzal
16	1r Resplendent Quetzal

Set of 2   17.00   22.00

1881

Nos. 15/16 surcharged

17†	1c on ½r Resplendent Quetzal	11.00	16.00
19†	10c on 1r Resplendent Quetzal	15.00	22.00

As No. 16 (various frames) but inscribed 'UNION POSTAL UNIVERSAL – GUATEMALA'

21	1c Resplendent Quetzal (green and black)
22	2c Resplendent Quetzal (green and brown)
23	5c Resplendent Quetzal (green and red)
24	10c Resplendent Quetzal
25	20c Resplendent Quetzal

Set of 5   15.00   9.75

1918

157	1p50 Resplendent Quetzal	90	25

1923

198†	1p Resplendent Quetzal..	90	30

1935

295†	3c Resplendent Quetzal (green and orange)..	1.10	25
296†	3c Resplendent Quetzal (green and red) ..	1.10	25

1937

Nos. 295/6 surcharged **EXPOSICION FILATELICA 1937 + 1**

326	3c + 1c Resplendent Quetzal (green and orange)	90	70
327	3c + 1c Resplendent Quetzal (green and red)	90	70

COLLECT MAMMALS ON STAMPS

The second Stanley Gibbons thematic catalogue — copies are available at £7.50 (p. + p. £1.50) from: Stanley Gibbons Publications Ltd, 5 Parkside, Christchurch Road, Ringwood, Hants BH24 3SH.

1954

333†	½c Resplendent Quetzal	80 50

1939

402†	3c Resplendent Quetzal (green and brown)	1.50 75
403†	3c Resplendent Quetzal (green and red) ..	1.50 75

1945

447	½c Resplendent Quetzal
448	3c Resplendent Quetzal (blue)
449	3c Resplendent Quetzal (green)
450	10c Resplendent Quetzal (air)

Set of 4   1.10   70

1951

MS518	1c Resplendent Quetzal (red) (as No. 21) (sheet also contains 10c stamp)	65 65

1953

546†	1q Resplendent Quetzal ('El Quetzal')	14.00 11.00

554	1c Resplendent Quetzal (blue)
555	2c Resplendent Quetzal (violet)
556	2c Resplendent Quetzal (brown)
557	3c Resplendent Quetzal (red)
558	3c Resplendent Quetzal (blue)
1224	3c Resplendent Quetzal (brown)
1225	3c Resplendent Quetzal (green)
1226	3c Resplendent Quetzal (orange)
559	4c Resplendent Quetzal (orange)
560	4c Resplendent Quetzal (violet)
561	5c Resplendent Quetzal (brown)
562	5c Resplendent Quetzal (red)
563	5c Resplendent Quetzal (green)
564	5c Resplendent Quetzal (grey)
565	6c Resplendent Quetzal (green)
1227	6c Resplendent Quetzal (blue)

Set of 16   4.00   1.75

1958

606†	1c Resplendent Quetzal	50 25

1960

No. 606 overprinted or surcharged **ANO MUNDIAL DE REFUGIADOS**

637†	1c Resplendent Quetzal	1.75 1.00
641†	6c on 1c Resplendent Quetzal	3.50 2.10

1961

No. 606 overprinted **MAYO DE 1960**

653†	1c Resplendent Quetzal	75 40

1964

No. 606 overprinted **OLIMPIADAS TOKIO – 1964** and Olympic rings

708†	1c Resplendent Quetzal	1.25 1.00

No. 606 overprinted **FERIA MUNDIAL DE NEW YORK**

712†	1c Resplendent Quetzal	1.25 90

No. 606 surcharged **HABILITADA 7c.—1964**

716†	7c on 1c Resplendent Quetzal	40 25

No. 606 overprinted **VIII VUELTA CICLISTICA**

720†	1c Resplendent Quetzal	1.75 1.40

No. 559 overprinted **HOMENAJE A LA 'I. S. G. C.' 1948—1963**

736	4c Resplendent Quetzal	50 25

1968

No. 606 overprinted **III REUNION DE PRESIDENTES Nov. 15–18, 1967**

817†	1c Resplendent Quetzal	1.25	90

1970

889†	9c Atitlan Grebe (Podilymbus gigas)	60	30
890†	20c Atitlan Grebe (Podilymbus gigas)	1.00	50

1971

909	2c Resplendent Quetzal	
910a	10c Resplendent Quetzal	
911	50c Resplendent Quetzal	
912	1q Resplendent Quetzal	
	Set of 4	5.25 3.75

1972

No. **MS**518 cut smaller and overprinted **JUEGOS OLYMPICOS MUNICH 1972**

MS926	1c Resplendent Quetzal (sheet also contains 10c stamp)	45	45

1974

No. 800 surcharged **VALE 10c. Proteccion del Ave Nacional el Quetzal** and bird

1002	10c on 11c Resplendent Quetzal	50	25

COLLECT RAILWAYS ON STAMPS

A Stanley Gibbons thematic catalogue on this popular subject. Copies available at £7.50 (p. + p. £1.50) from: Stanley Gibbons Publications Ltd, 5 Parkside, Christchurch Road, Ringwood, Hants BH24 3SH.

1975

1007	8c Resplendent Quetzal	
1008	20c Resplendent Quetzal	
	Set of 2	90 40

1976

1029†	1c Resplendent Quetzal	25	10
1032†	4c Resplendent Quetzal	25	10
1036†	20c Resplendent Quetzal	40	20
1039†	35c Resplendent Quetzal	75	30

1979

1124†	1c Ocellated Turkey ('Pavo del Peten') ..	20	10
1126†	5c King Vulture ('Rey Zope')	50	10
1127†	7c Great Horned Owl ('Tecolote Atigrado')	50	10
MS1129	30c Resplendent Quetzal ('Quetzal') ..	2.00	1.50

1980

1165†	6c Resplendent Quetzal	25	10
1166†	10c Resplendent Quetzal	40	4C
	(1164/6 Set of 3)	65	50

GUERNSEY
100 pence = 1 pound

1978

169 5p Northern Gannet ('Gannet')
170 7p Firecrest
171 11p Dartford Warbler
172 13p Spotted Redshank

	Set of 4	85	90

1982

257†	26p Common Snipe	..	..	..	..	..	..	75	85

1984

316†	5p Grey Partridge ('partridge') ..	..	15	15
317†	5p Turtle Dove ..	..	15	15
319†	5p Blackbird ('colly birds') ..	..	15	15
322†	5p Mute Swan ('swans')..	..	15	15

1986

366†	10p Northern Gannet ('Gannet').	25	25

STAMP MONTHLY
— finest and most informative magazine for all
collectors. Obtainable from your newsagent or by
postal subscription — details on request.

Alderney

1983

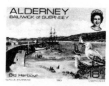

A12†	18p Herring Gull..	30	35

1984

A13 9p Oystercatcher
A14 13p Turnstone
A15 26p Ringed Plover
A16 28p Dunlin
A17 31p Curlew

	Set of 5	3.75	3.75

GUINEA
West Africa
1961 100 centimes = 1 franc
1973 100 caury = 1 syli

1961

277 5f Helmet Guineafowl
278 10f Helmet Guineafowl
279 25f Helmet Guineafowl
280 40f Helmet Guineafowl
281 50f Helmet Guineafowl
282 75f Helmet Guineafowl

	Set of 6	4.50	2.40

1962
Nos. 277/82 surcharged **POUR LA PROTECTION DE NOS
OISEAUX +5 FRS.**

305 5f+5f Helmet Guineafowl
306 10f+5f Helmet Guineafowl
307 25f+5f Helmet Guineafowl

308 40f+5f Helmet Guineafowl
309 50f+5f Helmet Guineafowl
310 75f+5f Helmet Guineafowl

Set of 6   8.00   4.25

349 30c Crowned Crane (*Balearica pavonina*)
350 50c Grey Parrot (*Psittacus erythacus*)
351 1f Abyssinian Ground Hornbill (*Bucorvus*)
352 1f50 White Spoonbill (*Platalea leucorodia*)
353 2f Bateleur (*Terathopius ecaudatus*)
354 3f Crowned Crane (*Balearica pavonina*)
355 10f Grey Parrot (*Psittacus erythacus*)
356 20f Abyssinian Ground Hornbill (*Bucorvus*)
357 25f White Spoonbill (*Platalea leucorodia*)
358 40f Bateleur (*Terathopius ecaudatus*)
359 50f Crowned Crane (*Balearica pavonina*)
360 75f Grey Parrot (*Psittacus erythacus*)

361 100f Abyssinian Ground Hornbill
     (*Bucorvus*) (air)
362 200f White Spoonbill (*Platalea leucorodia*)
363 500f Bateleur (*Terathopius ecaudatus*)

Set of 15   21.00   9.00

1971

741 5f Violet-crested Turaco (*Gallirex
     porphyreolophus*)
742 20f Golden Oriole (*Oriolus oriolus*)
743 30f Blue-headed Coucal (*Centropus
     monachus*)
744 40f Great Grey Shrike (*Lanius excubitor*)
745 75f Vulturine Guineafowl (*Acryllium
     vulturinum*)
746 100f Southern Ground Hornbill (*Burcorvus
     leadbeateri*)

747 50f Violet-crested Turaco (*Gallirex
     porphyreolophus*) (air)
748 100f Golden Oriole (*Oriolus oriolus*)
749 200f Vulturine Guineafowl (*Acryllium
     vulturinum*)

Set of 9   9.75   5.25

1985

1178 7s Black-billed Cuckoo (*Coccizus
      erythrophtalmus*)
1179 10s Carolina Parakeet * (*Conuropsis
      carolinensis*)
1180 15s American Anhinga (*Anhinga anhinga*)
1181 20s Red-shouldered Hawk (*Buteo
      lineatus*)

1182 30s Screech Owl (*Otus asio*) (air)
1183 35s Brown Thrasher (*Toxostoma rufum*)
                      Set of 6   6.25   5.25
MS1184 50s Mourning Dove (*Zenaidura
           macroura*) 3.00   3.00

GUINEA-BISSAU
West Africa
100 centavos = 1 peso

1978

555† 5p Spotted Eagle Owl   25   15
556† 6p Secretary Bird ('O Serpentario').   35   15

1985

920 5p Brown Pelican
921 10p American White Pelican
922 20p Great Blue Heron
923 40p Greater Flamingo ('American
     Flamingo')
                      Set of 4   75   25

GUYANA
South America
100 cents = 1 dollar

1966
Nos. 333 and 343 of British Guiana overprinted **GUYANA**
INDEPENDENCE 1966
395†	3c Wattled Jacana	5	5
405†	$1 Channel-billed Toucan ('Toucan')	35	35

1967

441	5c Blue and Yellow Macaw (background green)		
443	5c Blue and Yellow Macaw (background red)		
442	25c Blue and Yellow Macaw (background violet)		
444	25c Blue and Yellow Macaw (background green)		
	Set of 4	35	20

1968

490†	10c Spix's Guan ('Marudi')	15	8
491†	15c Harpy Eagle	20	12
492†	20c Hoatzin ('Canje Pheasant')..	20	15
493†	25c Guianan Cock of the Rock ('Cock of the Rock')	20	10
457†	40c Great Kiskadee ('Kiskadee')	45	20

1977

672†	15c Harpy Eagle	12	12
673†	35c Hoatzin	30	30

1978

687†	35c Harpy Eagle	60	50

1981
Nos. 491 and 457 overprinted **1981**
791†	15c Harpy Eagle	1.50	5
792†	40c Great Kiskadee	1.50	30
	(791/3 Set of 3)	4.00	1.10

1982

886†	15c Rusty-margined Flycatcher..	15	8

No. 333 of British Guiana and No. 395 surcharged **GUYANA**
H.R.H. Prince William 21st June 1982 $1.10
983†	$1.10 on 3c Wattled Jacana (No. 333)	1.00	80
985†	$1.10 on 3c Wattled Jacana (No. 395)	7.00	3.00

No. 687 overprinted **1982**
992†	35c Harpy Eagle	1.75	40

1983
No. 672 overprinted **1983**
1037†	15c Harpy Eagle	50	8

No. O17 overprinted **POSTAGE**
1044	15c Harpy Eagle	1.75	8

1984
Various stamps overprinted or surcharged **Protecting Our Heritage**
1238†	20c on 15c Harpy Eagle (No. 491)	1.00	10
1239†	20c on 15c Harpy Eagle (No. 791)	1.00	10
1240a†	20c on 15c Harpy Eagle (No. 1044)	3.50	1.00
1243†	40c Great Kiskadee (No. 457)	1.00	20
1250†	225c on 10c Spix's Guan (No. 490)	3.00	90

No. 983 further surcharged **60**
1288†	60c on $1.10 on 3c Wattled Jacana	75	30

1425 60c Swallow-tailed Kite (Elanoides
      forficatus) (pair)
1426 60c Swallow-tailed Kite (Elanoides
      forficatus) (landing on branch)
1427 60c Swallow-tailed Kite (Elanoides
      forficatus) (in flight, wings raised)
1428 60c Swallow-tailed Kite (Elanoides
      forficatus) (in flight, wings lowered)
1429 60c Swallow-tailed Kite (Elanoides
      forficatus) (in flight, gliding)
                           Set of 5   1.25   1.10

1985

1448† 320c Scarlet Macaw. 2.00   1.25

No. 992 surcharged J. J. Audubon 1785–1985 240
1546   240c on 35c Harpy Eagle 2.75   1.60

OFFICIAL STAMP

1981
No. 491 overprinted OPS
O17† 15c Harpy Eagle 1.75   10

HAITI
West Indies
100 centimes = 1 gourde

1956

539† 10c Greater Flamingo   65   25
540† 25c Mallard 1.50   40
545† 2g50 Greater Flamingo 5.00   1.75
546† 5g Mallard. 7.50   3.00

1958

580† 20c King Penguin 1.10   50
584† 1g50 King Penguin 2.50   90

1969

1127 5c Blue-hooded Euphonia (Euphonia
      musica)
1128 10c Hispaniolan Trogon (Temnotrogon
      roseigaster)
1129 20c Palm Chat (Dulus dominicus)
1130 25c Stripe-headed Tanager (Spindalis
      dominicensis)
1131 50c Blue-hooded Euphonia (Euphonia
      musica)
1132 50c Hispaniolan Trogon (Temnotrogon
      roseigaster) (air)
1133 1g Black-cowled Oriole (Icterus
      dominicensis)
1134 1g50 Stripe-headed Tanager (Spindalis
      dominicensis)
1135 2g Hispaniolan Woodpecker (Centurus
      striatus)
                           Set of 9   4.50   2.50

Appendix
The following stamps have either been issued in excess of
postal needs, or have not been made available to the public in
reasonable quantities at face value. Miniature sheets,
imperforate stamps etc. are excluded from this section.

1969
Moon landing of 'Apollo 11'. Overprint on Nos. 1132/5

HONDURAS
Central America
100 centavos = 1 lempira

1935

374† 50c Great Horned Owl 2.75 1.40

1937

376 6c Andean Condor
377 21c Andean Condor
378 46c Andean Condor
379 55c Andean Condor

Set of 4 3.50 2.25

HONG KONG
South-east coast of China
100 cents = 1 dollar

1975

335 50c Hwamei
336 $1.30 Chinese Bulbul
337 $2 Black-capped Kingfisher

Set of 3 7.00 7.00

1980

391† 20c Greater Flamingo 10 10

1984

465† $5 Humboldt Penguin 1.60 1.75

HUNGARY
Central Europe
1943 100 filler = 1 pengo
1946 100 filler = 1 forint

1943

767† 20fi + 20fi White-tailed Sea Eagle 75 50

1952

1224 20fi Avocet ('Gulipan')
1225 30fi White Stork ('Golya')
1226 40fi Golden Oriole ('Sargarigo')
1227 50fi Kentish Plover ('Szeki Lile')
1228 60fi Black-winged Stilt ('Golyatocs')
1229 70fi Lesser Grey Shrike ('Kis Orgebics')

1230 80fi Great Bustard ('Tuzok')
1231 1fo Red-footed Falcon ('Kek Vercse')
1232 1fo40 European Bee Eater ('Gyurgyalag')
1233 1fo60 Glossy Ibis ('Batla')
1234 2fo50 Great Egret ('Nemes Kocsag')
               Set of 11   8.50   2.75

1956

1452† 1fo Mallard   50   25

1959

1574 10fi Common Cormorant ('Karokatona')
1575 20fi Little Egret ('Kis Kocsag')
1576 30fi Purple Heron ('Voros Gem')
1577 40fi Great Egret ('Nagy Kocsag')
1578 60fi White Spoonbill ('Kanalas Gem')
1579 1fo Grey Heron ('Szurke Gem')
1580 2fo Squacco Heron (Ustokos Gem')
1581 3fo Glossy Ibis ('Batla')
               Set of 8   5.50   2.50

1590† 30fi Black-headed Gull   12   5

**STANLEY GIBBONS
STAMP COLLECTING SERIES**
Introductory booklets on *How to Start, How to
Identify Stamps* and *Collecting by Theme.* A series
of well illustrated guides at a low price.
Write for details.

1961

1746† 3fo Goldfinch (*Carduelis carduelis*) (silver
     background) 1.50   1.00
1750† 3fo Goldfinch (*Carduelis carduelis*) (gold
     background) 1.50   95

1781 30fi Nightingale (*Luscinia megarhynchos*)
1782 40fi Great Tit (*Parus major*)
1783 60fi Chaffinch (*Fringilla coelebs*)
1784 1fo Jay (*Garrulus glandarius*)
1785 1fo20 Golden Oriole (*Oriolus oriolus*)
1786 1fo50 Blackbird (*Turdus merula*)
1787 2fo Yellowhammer (*Emberiza citrinella*)
1788 3fo Lapwing (*Vanellus vanellus*)
               Set of 8   4.00   95

1962

1851 30fi Eagle Owl (*Bubu bubu*)
1852 40fi Osprey (*Pandion haliaetus*)
1853 60fi Marsh Harrier (*Circus aeruginosus*)
1854 80fi Booted Eagle (*Hieraaetus pennatus*)
1855 1fo African Fish Eagle (*Haliaetus
     leucocephalus* !)
1856 2fo Lammergeier (*Gypaetus barbatus*)
1857 3fo Golden Eagle (*Aquila chrysaetus*)
1858 4fo Common Kestrel (*Falco tinnunculus*)
               Set of 8   4.75   1.60

1964

2018† 2fo + 1fo Mallard.   75   50

2034† 20fi Ring-necked Pheasant (*Phasianus*
        colchicus torquatus) 25 10
2036† 40fi Grey Partridge (*Perdix perdix*) 30 10
2041† 2fo Great Bustard (*Otis t. tarda*) 90 25

1968

2346 20fi White Stork ('Fehergolya')
2347 50fi Golden Oriole ('Sargarigo')
2348 60fi Imperial Eagle ('Parlagisas')
2349 1fo Red-footed Falcon ('Kekvercse')
2350 1fo20 Scops Owl ('Fules Kuvik')
2351 1fo50 Great Bustard ('Tuzok')
2352 2fo European Bee Eater ('Gyurgyoka')
2353 2fo50 Greylag Goose ('Nyarilud')
                              Set of 8   4.50   1.25

1965

2062† 2fo Adelie Penguin 50 25

1971

2586† 1fo Gyrfalcon. 40 10
2588† 2fo Great Bustard 70 25

1966

2596† 60fi Green Peafowl 25 5

2184 20fi Barn Swallow (*Hirundo rustica*)
2185 30fi Long-tailed Tit (*Aegithalos caudatus*)
2186 60fi Red Crossbill (*Loxia curvirostra*)
2187 1fo40 Middle Spotted Woodpecker
        (*Dendrocopos medius*)
2188 1fo50 Hoopoe (*Upupa epops*)
2189 3fo Lapwing
                    Set of 6   3.75   1.60

COLLECT MAMMALS ON STAMPS
The second Stanley Gibbons thematic catalogue —
copies are available at £7.50 (p. + p. £1.50) from:
Stanley Gibbons Publications Ltd, 5 Parkside,
Christchurch Road, Ringwood, Hants BH24 3SH.

1973

2791 40fi Winter Wren (Okorszem')
2792 60fi Rock Thrush ('Kovirigo')
2793 80fi European Robin ('Vorosbegy')
2794 1fo Firecrest ('Kiralyka')
2795 1fo20 Linnet ('Kenderike')
2796 2fo Blue Tit ('Kekcinke')
2797 4fo Bluethroat ('Kekbegy')
2798 5fo Grey Wagtail ('Hegyi Billegeto')
                                    Set of 8   4.50   1.25

2803† 1fo Goldfinch (on stamp No. 1746).   30   5

2838† 1fo Goldfinch, Siskin   12   5

1977

3083 40fi White Spoonbill (*Platalea leucorodia*)
3084 60fi White Stork (*Ciconia ciconia*)

3085 1fo Purple Heron (*Ardea purpurea*)
3086 2fo Great Bustard (*Otis tarda*)
3087 3fo Common Crane (*Grus grus*)
3088 4fo Pied Wagtail (*Motacilla alba*)
3089 5fo Garganey (*Anas querquedula*)
                                    Set of 7   4.50   1.40

3097 40fi Common Peafowl (*Pavo cristatus*)
3098 60fi Green Peafowl (*Pavo muticus*)
3099 1fo Congo Peafowl (*Afropavo congensis*)
3100 3fo Great Argus Pheasant (*Argusianus argus*)
3101 4fo Himalayan Monal Pheasant (*Lophophorus impeyanus*)
3102 6fo Burmese Peacock-Pheasant (*Polyplectron bicalcaratum*)
                                    Set of 6   3.00   90

1980

3340 40fi Greylag Goose (*Anser anser*)
3341 60fi Black-crowned Night Heron (*Nycticorax nycticorax*)
3342 1fo Common Shoveler (*Anas clypeata*)
3343 2fo White-winged Black Tern (*Chlidonias leucopterus*)
3344 4fo Great Crested Grebe (*Podiceps cristatus*)
3345 6fo Black-winged Stilt (*Himantopus himantopus*)
                                    Set of 6   2.75   1.40
MS3346 20fo Great Egret (*Egretta alba*).. .. ..   4.50   4.50

1983

1.*Ft*

MAGYAR POSTA

3507 1fo Lesser Spotted Eagle (*Aquila pomarina*)
3508 1fo Imperial Eagle (*Aquila heliaca*)

3509 2fo White-tailed Sea Eagle (*Haliaetus albicilla*)
3510 2fo Red-footed Falcon (*Falco vespertinus*)
3511 4fo Saker Falcon (*Falco cherrug*)
3512 6fo Rough-legged Buzzard (*Buteo lagopus*)
3513 8fo Common Buzzard (*Buteo buteo*)

Set of 7   3.75   2.40

1984

3600 1fo Barn Owl (*Tyto alba*)
3601 1fo Little Owl (*Athene noctua*)
3602 2fo Tawny Owl (*Strix aluco*)
3603 2fo Long-eared Owl (*Asio otus*)
3604 4fo Snowy Owl (*Nyctea scandiaca*)
3605 6fo Ural Owl (*Strix uralensis*)
3606 8fo Eagle Owl (*Bubo bubo*)

Set of 7   3.00   1.50

1985

3635 2fo Common Flicker (*Colaptes cafer*)
3636 2fo Bohemian Waxwing (*Bombycilla garrulus*)
3637 2fo Pileated Woodpecker (*Dryocopus pileatus*)
3638 4fo Northern Oriole (*Icterus galbula*)
3639 4fo Common Flicker (*Colaptes auratus*) (air)
3640 6fo Common Cardinal (*Richmondena cardinalis*)

Set of 6   3.00   1.50

BIRDS   BIRDS   BIRDS

ICELAND
North Atlantic
100 aurar = 1 krona

1930

166† 35a Gyrfalcon.. .. ..   4.50   6.00

173† 10a Gyrfalcon (air) 14.00   30.00

1956

344 1k50 Whooper Swan
345 1k75 Whooper Swan

Set of 2   11.50   10.50

1959

369† 90a Eider   35   5
370† 2k Eider   45   5
372† 25k Gyrfalcon.. .. ..   10.00   10.00

1965

419 3k50 + 50a Rock Ptarmigan
420 4k50 + 50a Rock Ptarmigan

Set of 2   1.50   2.00

1966

430 20k Great Northern Diver (*Gavia immer*)
431 50k White-tailed Sea Eagle
Set of 2   10.00   10.00

1967

444 4k + 50a Ringed Plover (*Charadrius hiaticula*)
445 5k + 50a Rock Ptarmigan (*Lagopus mutus*)
Set of 2   90   1.50

1972

500 7k + 1k Arctic Tern
501 9k + 1k Arctic Tern
Set of 2   85   1.10

1977

555 40k Harlequin Duck (*Histrionicus histrionicus*)   40   10

1980

584† 170k Atlantic Puffin (*Fratercula arctica*)   ..   65   35

1981

598 50a Winter Wren (*Troglodytes troglodytes*)
599 100a Golden Plover (*Pluvialis apricaria*)
600 200a Raven (*Corvus corax*)
Set of 3   1.40   1.40

1983

630† 11k Kittiwake   70   90

1986

673 6k Pied Wagtail (*Motacilla alba*)
674 10k Pintail (*Anas acuta*)
675 12k Merlin (*Falco columbarius*)
676 15k Razorbill (*Alca torda*)
Set of 4   1.50   1.40

682† 250k Gyrfalcon 8.75   8.50
(681/2 Set of 2)   9.25   9.00

OFFICIAL STAMPS

1930

Nos. 166 and 173 overprinted **Pjonustumerki**

O182† 35a Gyrfalcon 6.75   21.00

O189† 10a Gyrfalcon (air) 12.50   70.00

IFNI

North-west Africa
100 centimos = 1 peseta

1952

81 5c + 5c Shag
82 10c + 5c Shag
83 60c + 15c Shag

Set of 3   70   25

1954

101† 5c Mediterranean Gull   25   10
104† 35c Mediterranean Gull   25   10
107† 1p Mediterranean Gull 9.00   50

1957

133 5c + 5c Rock Dove (Columba livia)
134 15c + 5c Stock Dove (Columba aenas
     (zurita))
135 70c Rock Dove (Columba livia)

Set of 3   70   30

1958

140 10c + 5c Barn Swallow
141 15c + 10c Barn Swallow
142 50c + 10c Barn Swallow

Set of 3   45   35

1960

159† 35c Red-legged Partridge   25   10

161 25c White Stork
162 50c Goldfinch
163 75c Sky Lark
164 1p White Stork
165 1p50 Goldfinch
166 2p Sky Lark
167 3p White Stork
168 5p Goldfinch
169 10p Sky Lark

Set of 9   7.50   1.75

1965

213† 50c Golden Eagle.   25   10
215† 1p50 Golden Eagle   40   10

INDIA

Southern Asia
100 paise = 1 rupee

1968

578 20p Red-billed Blue Magpie ('Blue
     Magpie')
579 50p Brown-fronted Pied Woodpecker
     ('Wood Pecker')

580 1r Slaty-headed Scimitar Babbler
     ('Babbler')
581 2r Yellow-backed Sunbird ('Sunbird')
                              Set of 4   4.00   2.25

1973

703† 2r Common Peafowl 1.50   2.00

1974

733† 50p Demoiselle Crane   30   5

1975

763 25p Blue-winged Pitta ('Indian Pitta')
764 50p Asian Black-headed Oriole
     ('Blackheaded Oriole')
765 1r Western Tragopan
766 2r Himalayan Monal Pheasant ('Monal
     Pheasant')
                              Set of 4   4.50   5.00

1976

800 25p Painted Stork   30   15

1980

986 2r30 Great Indian Bustard   30   35

1983

1076 2r85 Great White Crane ('Siberian Crane')   35   50

1094 1r Great Indian Hornbill   15   15

1985

1154 2r White-winged Wood Duck   30   30

INDONESIA
South-east Asia
100 sen = 1 rupiah

1963

964† 6r Greater Bird of Paradise.. .. .. 10 10

1965

1022 4r + 1r Pied Fantail (*Rhipidura javanica*)
1023 6r + 1r50 Zebra Dove (*Geopelia striata*)
1024 12r + 3r Black Drongo (*Dicrurus macrocercus*)
1025 20r + 5r Black-naped Oriole (*Oriolus chinensis*)
1026 30r + 7r50 Java Sparrow (*Padda oryzivora*)
Set of 5 65 55

1980

1599 75r Pesquet's Parrot (*Psittrichas fulgidus*)
1600 100r Chattering Lory (*Lorius garula*)
1601 200r Rainbow Lory (*Trichoglossus haematodus rubritorquis*)
Set of 3 1.25 70
MS1602 250r Rainbow Lory (*Trichoglossus haematodus rubritorquis*); 350r Pesquet's Parrot (*Psittrichas fulgidus*); 400r Chattering Lory (*Lorius garula*).. .. .. 3.75 3.75

1981

1637 75r Salmon-crested Cockatoo (*Cacatua moluccensis*)
1638 100r Sulphur-crested Cockatoo (*Cacatua galerita galerita*)
1639 200r Palm Cockatoo (*Probosciger aterrimus stenolophus*)
Set of 3 1.25 70
MS1640 150r Sulphur-crested Cockatoo (*Cacatua galerita galerita*); 350r Palm Cockatoo (*Probosciger aterrimus stenolophus*) 1.90 1.90

1982

1682 100r Rothschild's Mynah (*Leucopsar rothschildi*)
1683 250r King Bird of Paradise (*Cincinnurus regius*)
Set of 2 1.25 90
MS1684 500r Rothschild's Mynah (*Leucopsar rothschildi*). 75 60

1686 100r Arfak Parotia (*Parotia sefilata*)
1687 150r Twelve-wired Bird of Paradise (*Seleucides melanoleuca*)
1688 250r Red Bird of Paradise (*Paradisea rubra*)
Set of 3 1.60 1.10
MS1689 200r Arfak Parotia (*Parotia sefilata*); 300r Red Bird of Paradise (*Paradisea rubra*) 1.90 1.90

1983

1721 110r Wilson's Bird of Paradise
(*Diphyllodes respublica*)
1722 175r Black Sicklebill (*Epimachus fastuosus*)
1723 275r Black-billed Sicklebill (*Drepanornis albertisi*)
1724 500r Black-billed Sicklebill (*Drepanornis albertisi*)

Set of 4   3.25   2.25

1984

1765 75r Lauterbach's Bowerbird (*Chlamydera lauterbachi*)
1766 110r Flamed Bowerbird (*Sericulus aureus*)
1767 275r Arfak Bird of Paradise (*Astrapia nigra*)
1768 325r Superb Bird of Paradise (*Lophorhina superba*)

Set of 4   2.50   1.25

IRAN
Western Asia
100 dinars = 1 rial

1967

1493† 8r Barn Swallow.   45   25

1969

1570†	1r Goldfinch	5	5
1571†	2r Ring-necked Pheasant	20	5
	(1570/2 *Set of 3*)	60	25

1971

1651 1r Common Shelduck
1652 2r Ruddy Shelduck
1653 8r Greater Flamingo

Set of 3   75   25

1655 1r Red Junglefowl
1656 2r Barn Swallow
1657 6r Hoopoe

Set of 3   1.40   25

1972

1705 1r Chukar Partridge
1706 1r Pin-tailed Sandgrouse
1707 2r Yellow-bellied Waxbill, Red-cheeked Cordon-bleu

Set of 3   55   15

1974

1854†	2r Great Bustard	5	5
1856†	8r Georgian Black Grouse	35	12

IRAQ
Western Asia
1000 fils = 1 dinar

1968

794 5f White-cheeked Bulbul (*Pycnonotus leucotis*)
795 10f Hoopoe (*Upupa epops*)
796 15f Jay (*Garrulus glandarius*)
797 25f Peregrine Falcon (*Falco peregrinus*)
798 30f White Stork (*Ciconia alba*)
799 40f Black Partridge (*Francolinus francolinus*)
800 50f Marbled Teal (*Anas angustirostris*)
Set of 7   3.75   1.40

1976

1253 5f Common Kingfisher (*Alcedo atthis*)
1254 10f Turtle Dove (*Streptopelia turtur*)
1255 15f Pin-tailed Sandgrouse (*Pterocles alchata*)
1256 25f Blue Rock Thrush (*Monticola solitarius*)
1257 50f Purple Heron (*Ardea purpurea*), Grey Heron (*Ardea cinerea*)
Set of 5   2.25   1.00

1982

1520†	25f White Stork	35	8
1522†	45f White Stork	60	25

OFFICIAL STAMPS

1975
No. 798 overprinted **Official** in English and Arabic
O1178† 30f White Stork.   1.75   1.25

1976
Nos. 1253/7 additionally inscribed 'OFFICIAL' in English and Arabic
O1258 5f Common Kingfisher
O1259 10f Turtle Dove
O1260 15f Pin-tailed Sandgrouse
O1261 25f Blue Rock Thrush
O1262 50f Purple Heron, Grey Heron
Set of 5   2.50   1.60

IRELAND
North-west Europe
100 pence = 1 pound

1978

429†	8p Woodcock	20	15

1979

442 8p Winter Wren (*Troglodytes troglodytes*)
443 10p Great Crested Grebe (*Podiceps cristatus*)
444 11p White-fronted Goose (*Anser albifrons flavirostris*)
445 17p Peregrine Falcon (*Falco peregrinus*)
Set of 4   1.25   1.40

1983

560† 26p Mallard 50 25

ISLE OF MAN
North-west Europe
100 pence = 1 pound

1973

32† 50p Manx Shearwater 90 1.00

1978

126† 50p Chough 1.10 1.10

141† 11p American Bald Eagle 35 35

1979

145† 7p Peregrine Falcon 20 20
146† 11p Fulmar 30 35

1980

181 6p Winter Wren
182 8p European Robin

Set of 2   40   50

188† 1p Peregrine Falcon 5 5
(188/9 Set of 2) 12 15

1982

226 11p European Robin 40 40
(225/6 Set of 2) 70 70

1983

232†	1p Atlantic Puffin ('Puffins')	5	5
233†	2p Northern Gannet ('Gannets').	5	5
234†	5p Lesser Black-backed Gull	8	10
235†	8p Common Cormorant ('Cormorants'). ..	15	20
236†	10p Kittiwake	20	25
237†	11p Shag	20	25
238†	12p Grey Heron ('Herons')	20	25
239†	13p Herring Gull	25	30
240†	14p Razorbill	25	30
241†	15p Great Black-backed Gull	25	30
242†	16p Common Shelduck ('Shelducks')	30	35
243†	18p Oystercatcher	30	35
244†	20c Arctic Tern	35	40
245†	25p Common Guillemot ('Guillemots')	45	50
246†	50p Redshank	90	95
247†	£1 Mute Swan	1.75	1.90
	(232/48 Set of 17)	13.00	14.00

1986

318† 12p Hen Harrier 30 30

331† 11p European Robin 20 25

1975

614 I£1.10 Pratincole (*Glareola pratincola*)
615 I£1.70 Spur-winged Plover (*Hoplopterus spinosus*)
616 I£2 Black-winged Stilt (*Himantopus himantopus*)

Set of 3 (without tabs)	1.10	1.10
Set of 3 (with tabs)	1.50	1.25

1985

944 100s Lappet-faced Vulture (*Torgos tracheliotus negevensis*)
945 200s Bonelli's Eagle (*Hieraetus fasciatus*)
946 300s Sooty Falcon (*Falco concolor*)
947 500s Griffon Vulture (*Gyps fulvus*)

Set of 4 (without tabs)	1.75	1.75
Set of 4 (with tabs)	3.00	3.00

ISRAEL
Western Asia
1963 100 agorot = 1 pound
1980 100 agorot = 1 shekel

1963

244 5a Sinai Rosefinch (*Erythrina sinoica*)
245 20a White-breasted Kingfisher (*Halcyon smyrnensis*)
246 28a Mourning Wheatear (*Oenanthe lugens*)
247 30a European Bee Eater (*Merops superciliosus* !)
248 40a Graceful Prinia (*Prinia gracilis*)
249 45a Palestine Sunbird (*Cinnyris osea*)
250 55a Houbara Bustard (*Chlamydotis undulata*)
251 70a Scops Owl (*Otus scops*)
252 I£1 Purple Heron (*Ardea purpurea*)
253 I£3 White-tailed Sea Eagle (*Haliaetus albicilla*)

Set of 10 (without tabs)	4.50	4.50
Set of 10 (with tabs)	8.50	6.50

1987

1015 30a Eagle Owl (*Bubo bubo*)
1016 40a Striated Scops Owl (*Otus brucei*)
1017 50a Barn Owl (*Tyto alba*)
1018 80a Hume's Tawny Owl (*Strix butleri*)

Set of 4 (without tabs)	1.50	1.50
Set of 4 (With tabs)	2.75	2.75

ITALIAN EAST AFRICA

East Africa
100 centesimi = 1 lira

1938

25†	1li Bateleur.	25	10
29†	5li Bateleur.	90	35

ITALY

Southern Europe
100 centesimi = 1 lira

1945

671†	2li Barn Swallow	25	10
952†	5li Barn Swallow	25	15
675†	25li Barn Swallow (blue).	9.00	2.25
676†	25li Barn Swallow (brown)	15	5

1954

867	25li Golden Eagle	1.25	15

1978

1549†	170li Audouin's Gull (*Larus audouinii*) ..	50	10

1984

1835†	450li European Bee Eater	60	30
1836†	450li Hoopoe.	60	30

1985

1884†	500li Black-winged Stilt ('Cavaliere d'Italia')	75	35

1910†	500li Mute Swan (on Western Australia stamp No. 1)	75	35

IVORY COAST

West Africa
100 centimes = 1 franc

1965

261	1f Yellow-bellied Green Pigeon (*Vinago waalia*)
262	2f Spur-winged Goose (*Plectropterus gambensis*)
263	5f Stone Partridge (*Ptilopachus petrosus*)
264	10f Hammerkop (*Scopus umbretta*)
265	15f White-breasted Guineafowl (*Agelastes meleagrides*)
266	30f Namaqua Dove (*Oena capensis*)
267	50f Lizard Buzzard (*Kaupifalco monogrammicus*)

268   75f Yellow-billed Stork (*Ibis ibis*)
269   90f Latham's Francolin (*Francolinus lathami*)

Set of 9   8.00   4.00

1978

559   100f Ring-necked Pheasant
560   100f Latham's Francolin (on stamp No. 269)

Set of 2   2.25   1.40

1980

665a   60f Superb Starling (*Spreo superbus*)
665b   65f Red-billed Dwarf Hornbill (*Tockus camurus*)
665c   65f South African Crowned Crane (*Balearica pavonina* !)
665d   100f Saddle-bill Stork (*Ephippiorhynchus senegalensis*)

Set of 4   4.75   4.75

1983

771   100f African Fish Eagle (*Haliaetus vocifer*)
772   125f Grey Parrot (*Psittacus erithacus*)
773   150f Violet Turaco (*Musophaga violacea*)

Set of 3   2.50   1.50

1985

839   100f Red-breasted Merganser (*Mergus serrator*)
840   150f American White Pelican (*Pelecanus erythrorhynchos*)
841   200f American Wood Stork (*Mycteria americana*)
842   350f Velvet Scoter (*Melanitta deglandi*)

Set of 4   3.25   2.75

JAIPUR
Indian sub-continent
16 annas = 1 rupee

1931

44†   2½a Common Peafowl 13.00   18.00

JAMAICA
West Indies
1956 12 pence = 1 shilling,
20 shillings = 1 pound
1969 100 cents = 1 dollar

1956

166†   6d Streamertail ('Doctor Bird') 1.25   10

1962
No. 166 overprinted **INDEPENDENCE 1962**

186†   6d Streamertail   75   10

1964

224† 8d Streamertail ('Doctor Bird') 1.00 60

1977

434 10c Streamertail
435 20c Streamertail
436 25c Streamertail
437 50c Streamertail

Set of 4 1.60 1.75

1980

467† 8c Jamaican Tody 5 5
468† 10c Jamaican Mango. 5 5
469† 12c Yellow-billed Amazon ('Yellow Billed
Parrot') 5 5
470† 15c Streamertail 5 5
471† 35c White-chinned Thrush 5 8
472† 50c Jamaican Woodpecker 10 12

497† 75c Jamaican Owl 40 55

1982

565 $1 Jamaican Lizard Cuckoo (prey
captured)
566 $1 Jamaican Lizard Cuckoo (searching for
prey)
567 $1 Jamaican Lizard Cuckoo (calling prior
to prey search)
568 $1 Jamaican Lizard Cuckoo (adult landing)
569 $1 Jamaican Lizard Cuckoo (adult flying in)
Set of 5 3.50 3.50

1984
No. 469 surcharged
606† 10c on 12c Yellow-billed Amazon 5 5

1985

620 20c Brown Pelican
621 55c Brown Pelican
622 $2 Brown Pelican
623 $5 Brown Pelican
Set of 4 2.25 2.25

1986

642 25c Chestnut-bellied Cuckoo
643 55c Jamaican Becard
644 $1.50 White-eyed Thrush
645 $5 Rufous-tailed Flycatcher
Set of 4 2.00 2.00

1987

No. 472 surcharged **5c**

662† 5c on 50c Jamaican Woodpecker 5 5

(662/3 *Set of* 2) 10 12

JAPAN

Eastern Asia

100 sen = 1 yen

1875

61 12s Bean Goose?
62 15s Pied Wagtail?
63 45s Northern Goshawk?

Set of 3 £850 £400

1946

429† 1y30 Snow Goose, White-fronted Goose .. 3.75 1.10
446† 4y Snow Goose, White-fronted Goose 5.00 25

439† 1y Barn Swallow? 3.25 3.25

1948

486† 5y + 2y50 Varied Tit 12.50 10.50
MS487 5y + 5y Varied Tit (sheet also contains
one other stamp) 24.00 25.00

1949

556 8y Brent Goose 85.00 42.00

1950

575 16y Japanese Pheasant
576 34y Japanese Pheasant
577 59y Japanese Pheasant
578 103y Japanese Pheasant
579 144y Japanese Pheasant

Set of 5 £225 70.00

1952

655† 3y Little Cuckoo 25 10
657† 5y Mandarin 25 5
669† 100y Japanese Cormorant 32.00 5

1953

715† 10y Manchurian Crane 6.00 2.25
(714/15 *Set of* 2) 8.75 3.75

1957

766   10y Emperor Penguin.. .. ..   1.10   55

1959

808†   10y Japanese Cormorant 2.25   30
                    (807/8 Set of 2)   4.25   60

811   10y Manchurian Crane   70   30

1960

827   10y Japanese Crested Ibis 1.25   25

1961

864†   80y Copper Pheasant 1.10   10
866†   100y Manchurian Crane.. .. ..   13.00   10

STANLEY GIBBONS
STAMP COLLECTING SERIES
Introductory booklets on *How to Start, How to Identify Stamps* and *Collecting by Theme.* A series of well illustrated guides at a low price.
Write for details.

1963

929   10y Purple Jay
930   10y Rock Ptarmigan
931   10y Eastern Turtle Dove
932   10y White Stork
933   10y Japanese Bush Warbler
934   10y Siberian Meadow Bunting
                    Set of 6   3.25   1.25

1965

1006   10y Japanese Gull   30   10

1966

1034†   15y Manchurian Crane..   50   10

1066a†   100y Manchurian Crane 1.00   5

1969

1155   15y Japanese Gull   35   10

1971

1226†	3y Little Cuckoo..	25	10
1227†	5y Mute Swan	25	10
1235†	80y Copper Pheasant	65	10
1237†	90y Golden Eagle	1.00	10

1366†	50y Mandarin	45	10
	(1365/6 Set of 2)	55	15

1259	15y Great Tit	30	10

1367	50y Hawk sp	40	15

1975

1260	15y Adelie Penguin?..	30	10

1377	20y Short-tailed Albatross (*Diomedea albatrus*)	30	10

1973

1330†	20y Scops Owl	30	10
	(1329/30 Set of 2)	40	15

1381	20y Manchurian Crane (*Grus japonensis*)..	30	10

1974

1343†	20y Manchurian Crane (crane 'weaving').	20	10
1344†	20y Manchurian Crane (flying flock)	20	10
	(1342/4 Set of 3)	55	25

1405	20y Bonin Island Honeyeater (*Apalopteron familiare hahasima*)	30	5

1411   50y Green Peafowl   50   15

1976

1419   50y Riukiu Robin (*Erithacus komadori
       komadori*)   50   25

1435   100y Rook..   60   25

1977

1478   100y Mandarin   55   25

1978

1493   50y Manchurian Crane   40   20

1509   100y Copper Pheasant   75   25

1979

1546   100y Ural Owl   55   25

1980

1608   100y Manchurian Crane, Japanese White-
       necked Crane   60   35

1981

1634   60y Japanese Crested Ibis   50   30

1642   130y Eastern Turtle Dove 1.00   75

1982

1660†   60y Greater Flamingo   70   55
1661†   60y King Penguin   70   55

1667   60y Blue and White Flycatcher   35   25

1983

1713   60y Okinawa Rail (*Rallus okinawae*)
1714   60y Blakiston's Fish Owl (*Ketupa blakistoni*)
                              Set of 2   95   75

1721   60y Adelie Penguin   45   25

1724   60y Pryer's Woodpecker (*Sapheopipo noguchii*)
1725   60y Canada Goose (*Branta canadensis leucopareia*)
                              Set of 2   95   75

1984

1729   60y Japanese Marsh Warbler (*Megalurus pryeri pryeri*)
1730   60y Crested Serpent Eagle (*Spilornis cheela perplexus*)
                              Set of 2   90   60

1735   60y Black Wood Pigeon (*Columba janthina nitens*)
1736   60y Spotted Greenshank (*Tringa guttifer*)
                              Set of 2   90   60

1742   60y White-backed Woodpecker (*Dendrocopos leucotos owstoni*)
1743   60y Peregrine Falcon (*Falco peregrinus fruitii*)
                              Set of 2   90   60

As Nos. 1714, 1730 and 1743, *but colours changed*
MS1768   60y Blakiston's Fish Owl; 60y Crested
           Serpent Eagle; 60y Peregrine Falcon   1.40   1.40

1986

1840   60y Bull-headed Shrike   70   30

JAPANESE OCCUPATION OF NORTH BORNEO

1942

Nos. 304 and 319 of North Borneo overprinted with seven Japanese letters in one line

J2†   2c Palm Cockatoo (No. 304) 45.00   65.00
J17†   2c Palm Cockatoo (No. 319).. .. ..   70.00   42.00

1944

No. 304 of North Borneo overprinted with twelve Japanese letters in three lines

J21†   2c Palm Cockatoo 1.00   1.50

JERSEY

North-west Europe
1970 12 pence = 1 shilling,
20 shillings = 1 pound
1971 100 pence = 1 pound

1970

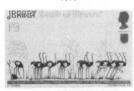

41†   1s9d Ostrich 14.00   3.50

1971

57†   2p White Eared-Pheasant ('White-eared Pheasant')   60   25
58†   2½p Thick-billed Parrot.   60   25

1972

74†   3p Rothschild's Mynah   30   25

1975

129   4p Common Tern
130   5p British Storm Petrel ('Storm-Petrel')
131   8p Brent Goose
132   25p Shag
                                    Set of 4   1.00   1.10

1979

217†   6p Pink Pigeon   15   15
219†   11½p Waldrapp ('Waldrapp Ibis').   30   35

1984

328†   28p Coscoroba Swan.   80   80
329†   31p St. Lucia Amazon ('St. Lucia Parrot') ..   90   90

1986

403† 14p European Robin 30 35

1970

929 120f White-crowned Black Wheatear ('Black Chat')
930 180f Masked Shrike
931 200f Palestine Sunbird

Set of 3   4.25   3.00

JORDAN
Middle East
1000 fils = 1 dinar

1964

627 150f Four-coloured Bush Shrike
628 500f Ornate Hawk Eagle
629 1000f Grey-headed Kingfisher

Set of 3   16.00   7.00

1968

821† 5f Goldfinch 25 10
822† 10f Chukar Partridge ('Rock Partridge') .. 30 15
823† 15f Ostrich 35 20
824† 20f Sand Partridge 40 25
827† 50f Houbara Bustard ('Bustard') 75 45

829† 100f Mallard ('Duck') (air) 1.10 85

KAMPUCHEA
South-east Asia
100 cents = 1 riel

1983

461 20c Rainbow Lory ('Loriquet')
462 50c Barn Swallow ('L'Hirondelle')
463 80c Golden Eagle ('Aigle')
454 1r Griffon Vulture ('Vautour')
465 1r50 Javanese Collared Dove ('Tourterelle')
466 2r Magpie ('Pie')
467 3r Great Indian Hornbill ('Calao')

Set of 7   4.50   1.60

1984

508 10c Cattle Egret (*Bubulcus ibis coromandus*)
509 40c Black-headed Shrike (*Lanius schach nigriceps*)

510 80c Slaty-headed Parakeet (*Psittacula himalayana sinschii*)
511 1r Golden-fronted Leafbird (*Chloropsis aurifrons inornata*)
512 1r20 Red-winged Crested Cuckoo (*Clamator coromandus*)
513 2r Grey Wagtail (*Motacilla cinerea*)
514 2r50 Forest Wagtail (*Dendronanthus indicus*)

Set of 7   4.50   1.60

1985

648 20c Saffron-cowled Blackbird (*Xanthospar flavus*)
649 50c Saffron Finch (*Sicalis flaveola pelzelni*)
650 80c Blue & Yellow Tanager (*Thraupis bonariensis*)
651 1r Scarlet-headed Blackbird (*Amblyramphus holosericeus*)
652 1r50 Amazon Kingfisher (*Chiloceryle amazona*)
653 2r Toco Toucan (*Ramphastos toco*)
654 3r Rufous-bellied Thrush (*Turdus rufiventris*)

Set of 7   4.00   1.25

KENYA
East Africa
100 cents = 1 shilling

1964

18† 1s30 Hartlaub's Turaco ('Kenya Touraco') ..   1.75   50

1966

28† 70c Ostrich 1.75   90

1984

303 70c White-backed Night Heron
304 2s50 Quail Plover
305 3s50 Taita Olive Thrush ('Heller's Ground Thrush')
306 5s Mufumbiri Shrike ('Yellow Gonolek')
307 10s White-winged Apalis

Set of 5   3.25   3.25

KENYA, UGANDA AND TANGANYIKA
East Africa
100 cents = 1 shilling

1935

110† 1c South African Crowned Crane   12   30
114† 20c South African Crowned Crane   65   5
122† 10s South African Crowned Crane 48.00   48.00

1938

131a† 1c South African Crowned Crane   10   30
139b† 20c South African Crowned Crane   40   5
143 † 40c South African Crowned Crane   80   55
149b† 10s South African Crowned Crane 8.00   2.75

1960

187† 25c Ostrich 50 40

1966

225† 1s30 Lesser Flamingo 40 10

KIRIBATI
South Pacific
100 cents = 1 dollar

1979

127† 15c Eastern Reef Heron ('Reef Egret').. .. 35 20

1982

163 1c Pomarine Skua ('Pomarine Jaeger')
164 2c Mallard
165 4c White-winged Petrel ('Collared Petrel')
166 5c Blue-faced Booby
167 7c Friendly Quail Dove
168 8c Common Shoveler
169 12c Polynesian Reed Warbler ('Christmas Island Warbler')
170 15c American Golden Plover ('Pacific Plover')
171 20c Eastern Reef Heron ('Reef Heron')
171a 25c Common Noddy ('Brown Noddy')
172 30c Brown Booby
173 35c Audubon's Shearwater
174 40c White-throated Storm Petrel
175 50c Bristle-thighed Curlew
175a 55c White Tern ('Fairy Tern')
176 $1 Kuhl's Lory ('Scarlet-breasted Lorikeet')
177 $2 Long-tailed Koel ('Long-tailed Cuckoo')
178 $5 Great Frigate Bird

Set of 18 7.75 8.50

KHMER REPUBLIC
South-east Asia
100 cents = 1 riel

1972

No. 164 of Cambodia overprinted XXe JEUX OLYMPIQUES MUNICH 1972, Olympic rings and emblem
347† 12r Grey Heron 65 50

No. 164 of Cambodia surcharged SECOURS AUX VICTIMES DE GUERRE, red cross and value
355† 12r + 7r Grey Heron 55 55

1985

237† 12c Great Frigate Bird ('Frigate Bird').. .. 12 15

KHOR FAKKAN
Arabian peninsula
100 naye paise = 1 rupee

Appendix

The following stamps have either been issued in excess of postal needs, or have not been made available to the public in reasonable quantities at face value. Miniature sheets, imperforate stamps etc. are excluded from this section.

1965

Birds. Nos 101/6 of Sharjah overprinted 'Khor Fakkan'. 30np, 150np Rock Dove, 40np, 2r Red Junglefowl, 75np, 3r Hoopoe

COLLECT MAMMALS ON STAMPS
The second Stanley Gibbons thematic catalogue — copies are available at £7.50 (p. + p. £1.50) from: Stanley Gibbons Publications Ltd, 5 Parkside, Christchurch Road, Ringwood, Hants BH24 3SH.

1986

258†	35c Red-footed Booby	30	35

OFFICIAL STAMPS

1983

Nos. 169, 172/3, 175 *and* 177 *overprinted* **O.K.G.S.**

O25	12c Polynesian Reed Warbler		
O26	30c Brown Booby		
O27	35c Audubon's Shearwater		
O28	50c Bristle-thighed Curlew		
O29	$2 Long-tailed Koel		
	Set of 5	3.50	3.75

KOREA

Eastern Asia

South Korea

1949 100 weun = 1 hwan
1962 100 chon = 1 won

1949

116†	10w Manchurian Crane	40	15
121†	65w Magpie	50	20

1951

140a†	5w Manchurian Crane	75	50

Nos. 116 *and* 121 *surcharged*

148†	300w on 10w Manchurian Crane	60	50
154†	300w on 65w Magpie	60	60

1960

371	40h Barn Swallow..	50	30

1961

414†	40h White-bellied Black Woodpecker	1.40	20

1966

621	3w Mandarin		
622	5w Manchurian Crane		
623	7w Ring-necked Pheasant		
	Set of 3	1.60	70

1973

1063a†	3w Magpie	25	10
1065 †	10w Manchurian Crane (blue)	30	10

1976

1223	20w Japanese White-necked Crane		
1224	20w Great Bustard		
	Set of 2	60	20

1243   20w Blue-winged Pitta
1244   20w White-bellied Black Woodpecker

                   Set of 2   60   20

1251   20w Black Wood Pigeon
1252   20w Oystercatcher

                   Set of 2   50   20

1257   20w Black-faced Spoonbill
1258   20w Black Stork

                   Set of 2   50   20

1266   20w European Black Vulture
1267   20w Whistling Swan

                   Set of 2   80   25

1269†   20w Manchurian Crane   20   5
              (1268/9 *Set of 2*)   40   10

1979

1365†   20w Mandarin   25   10
             (1365/6 *Set of 2*)   40   15

1367†   10w Manchurian Crane (black and green)   30   10

1980

1423   30w Duck sp
1424   60w Magpie

                   Set of 2   90   45

1453†   30w Manchurian Crane   20   5

1982

1546†   60w Magpie   20   5

1983

1599† 70w Manchurian Crane   30   5

1986

1762 80w Eastern Broad-billed Roller ('Roller')
1763 80w Japanese Waxwing ('Waxwing')
1764 80w Black-naped Oriole ('Oriole')
1765 80w Black-capped Kingfisher
       ('Kingfisher')
1766 80w Hoopoe
             Set of 5   65   20

NORTH KOREAN OCCUPATION

1950

No. 116 *overprinted with Korean characters in a double circle*
1† 10w Manchurian Crane 3.50

North Korea

100 chon = 1 won

1959

N206† 10ch Ring-necked Pheasant   90   50

1960

N268   2ch White-backed Woodpecker
N268a   5ch Mandarin
N269   5ch Scops Owl
N270   10ch Black-naped Oriole
             Set of 4   1.75   65

1962

N396   5ch Black-faced Spoonbill
N397   5ch Brown Hawk Owl
N398   10ch Eastern Broad-billed Roller
N399   10ch Black Paradise Flycatcher
N400   20ch Whistling Swan
             Set of 5   2.50   85

1963

N495† 10ch Barn Swallow..   30   8

1964

N531† 40ch Helmet Guineafowl 1.25   60

1965

N640   4ch Black-capped Kingfisher
N641   10ch Great Tit
N642   10ch Pied Wagtail
N643   10ch Azure-winged Magpie
N644   40ch Black-tailed Hawfinch
             Set of 5   2.50   90

1973

N648 2ch Hooded Crane
N649 10ch Japanese White-necked Crane
N650 10ch Manchurian Crane
N651 40ch Grey Heron
Set of 4   2.40   85

N1208 5ch Oriental Great Reed Warbler
N1209 10ch Grey Starling
N1210 10ch Daurian Starling
Set of 3   90   45

1974

N654 2ch Spotbill Duck
N655 4ch Ruddy Shelduck
N656 10ch Mallard
N657 20ch Baikal Teal
Set of 4   2.25   95

1966

N1307† 40ch Bean Goose   50   20

1975

N740 2ch Common Rosefinch
N741 5ch Hoopoe
N742 10ch Black-breasted Thrush
N743 10ch Crested Lark
N744 40ch White-bellied Black Woodpecker
Set of 5   2.25   90

1967

N1383† 15ch Golden Pheasant   40   15
N1384† 25ch Water Cock   70   30
N1385† 30ch Red Junglefowl   80   30

N822 2ch European Black Vulture
N823 10ch Booted Eagle
N824 40ch White-bellied Sea Eagle
Set of 3   2.25   80

N1416 10ch Blue and Yellow Macaw
N1417 15ch Sulphur-crested Cockatoo
N1418 20ch Blyth's Parakeet
N1419 25ch Rainbow Lory
N1420 30ch Budgerigar

Set of 5   2.10   90

1976

N1522 2ch Golden Pheasant
N1523 5ch Lady Amherst's Pheasant
N1524 10ch Silver Pheasant
N1525 15ch Reeves's Pheasant
N1526 25ch Temminck's Tragopan
N1527 40ch Ring-necked Pheasant (albino)

Set of 6   3.00   85

MSN1528 50ch Ring-necked Pheasant 2.75   1.40

N1558† 2ch Azure-winged Magpie   25   10
N1561† 15ch Black-naped Oriole   35   15

STAMP MONTHLY
— finest and most informative magazine for all
collectors. Obtainable from your newsagent or by
postal subscription — details on request.

1978

N1777 5ch White-bellied Black Woodpecker
       (*Dryocopus richardsi*)
N1778 10ch White-bellied Black Woodpecker
       (*Dryocopus richardsi*)
N1779 15ch White-bellied Black Woodpecker
       (*Dryocopus richardsi*)
N1780 25ch White-bellied Black Woodpecker
       (*Dryocopus richardsi*)
N1781 50ch White-bellied Black Woodpecker
       (*Dryocopus richardsi*)

Set of 5   2.40   1.25

1979

N1901 5ch Moscovy Duck
N1902 10ch Ostrich
N1903 15ch Common Turkey
N1904 20ch Dalmatian Pelican
N1905 30ch Vulturine Guineafowl

1906 50ch Mandarin (air)

Set of 6   2.25   85

1980

N1969† 20ch Rainbow Lory (on stamp No.
N1419)   70   20

N1997† 10ch Japanese Quail 30 20

KUWAIT

Arabian Peninsula
1000 fils = 1 dinar

1965

286 8f Saker Falcon
287 15f Saker Falcon
288 20f Saker Falcon
289 25f Saker Falcon
290 30f Saker Falcon
291 45f Saker Falcon
292 50f Saker Falcon
293 90f Saker Falcon

Set of 8 5.25 2.25

1973

581†	5f Mourning Dove (Zenaidura macroura) ..	10	5
582†	5f Hoopoe (Upupa epops)	10	5
583†	5f Rock Dove (Columba livia)	10	5
584†	5f Stone-Curlew (Burhinus oedicnemus) ..	10	5
585†	8f Great Grey Shrike (Lanius excubitor) ..	15	5
586†	8f Red-backed Shrike (Lanius collurio). ..	15	5
587†	8f Black-headed Shrike (Lanius schach) ..	15	5
588†	8f Golden Oriole (Oriolus chinensis !)	15	5
589†	10f Willow Warbler (Phylloscopus trochilus)	15	5
590†	10f Great Reed Warbler (Acrocephalus arundinaceus)	15	5
591†	10f Blackcap (Sylvia atricapilla).	15	5
592†	10f Barn Swallow (Hirundo rustica).	15	5
593†	15f Rock Thrush (Monticola solitarius !) ..	20	5
594†	15f Redstart (Phoenicurus phoenicurus) ..	20	5
595†	15f Common Wheatear (Oenanthe oenanthe)	20	5

596†	15f Bluethroat (Luscinia svecica)	20	5
597†	20f Houbara Bustard (Chlamydotis undulata)	30	10
598†	20f Pin-tailed Sandgrouse (Pterocles alchata)..	30	10
599†	20f Giant Wood Rail (Aramides ypecaha) ..	30	10
600†	20f Spotted Crake (Porzana porzana)	30	10
601†	25f American Kestrel (Falco sparverius) ..	40	20
602†	25f Great Black-backed Gull (Larus marinus)	40	20
603†	25f Purple Heron (Ardea purpurea).	40	20
604†	25f Wryneck (Jynx torquilla).	40	20
605†	30f European Bee Eater (Merops apiaster)	45	25
606†	30f Saker Falcon (Accipiter !)	45	25
607†	30f Grey Wagtail (Motacilla cinerea)	45	25
608†	30f Pied Wagtail (Motacilla alba)	45	25
610†	45f Great Grey Shrike (driving birds into net)	70	50
611†	45f Rock Dove.	70	50
612†	45f Great Grey Shrike (disguised lure) . ..	70	50
	(581/612 Set of 32)	8.75	4.25

LABUAN

Off north coast of Borneo
100 cents = 1 dollar

1894

As No. 72 of North Borneo (in different colours) overprinted
LABUAN

65a† 5c Great Argus Pheasant 2.75 1.60

1896

No. 65a overprinted **1846 JUBILEE 1896**

86† 5c Great Argus Pheasant.. .. .. 7.50 6.50

1897

As No. 100 of North Borneo (in different colours) overprinted
LABUAN

92† 5c Great Argus Pheasant (black and green) 4.75 5.50

1899

No. 92 surcharged **4 CENTS**

102† 4c on 5c Great Argus Pheasant 6.50 9.50
See also No. 127.

1900

As No. 100 of North Borneo (in different colours) overprinted
LABUAN

114† 5c Great Argus Pheasant (black and blue) 5.00 6.00

1904

No. 92 surcharged **4 cents**

127† 4c on 5c Great Argus Pheasant 5.50 9.50
See also No. 102.

POSTAGE DUE STAMPS

1901

No. 114 overprinted **POSTAGE DUE**

D4† 5c Great Argus Pheasant 6.50 50

LAOS
South-east Asia
100 cents = 1 kip

1966

178 5k Slaty-headed Parakeet (*Psittacula himalayana*)
179 15k White-crested Laughing Thrush (*Garrulay leucolophus*)
180 20k Osprey (*Pandion haliaetus*)
181 45k Indian Roller (*Coracias benghalensis*)
Set of 4   3.25   2.75

1982

539 50c Barn Swallow (*Hirundo rustica*)
540 1k Hoopoe (*Upupa epops*)
541 2k Common Kingfisher (*Alcedo atthis*)
542 3k Black-naped Blue Monarch (*Hypothymis azurea*)
543 4k Grey Wagtail (*Motacilla cinerea*)
544 10k Long-tailed Tailor Bird (*Orthotomus sutorius*)
Set of 6   4.25   3.00

1986

903† 5k Greater Flamingo (*Phoenicopterus ruber*)   20   8

908 50c Great Argus Pheasant (*Argusianus argus*)
909 1k Silver Pheasant (*Gennaeus nycthemerus*)
910 2k Ring-necked Pheasant (*Phasianus colchicus*)
911 3k Lady Amherst's Pheasant (*Chrysolophus amherstiae*)
912 4k Reeves's Pheasant (*Symaticus reevesii*)
913 5k Golden Pheasant (*Chrysolophus pictus*)
914 6k Copper Pheasant (*Syrmaticus soemmerringii*)
Set of 7   1.00   45

MS937 10k Grey Partridge   40   40

LEBANON
Middle East
100 centiemes = 1 piastre

1946

320 12p50 Grey Heron

321 10p Grey Heron (air)
322 25p Grey Heron
323 50p Grey Heron
324 100p Grey Heron
Set of 5   24.00   5.25

1950

418† 5p House Martin   80   25
419† 15p House Martin 1.40   45

1965

867	5p Bullfinch
868	10p Goldfinch
869	15p Hoopoe
870	17p50 Red-legged Partridge
871	20p Golden Oriole
872	32p50 European Bee Eater

Set of 6   1.60   55

1972

No. 872 surcharged **25P.**

1119† 25p on 32p50 European Bee Eater   25   10

LESOTHO
Southern Africa
1971 100 cents = 1 rand
1979 100 lisente = 1 maloti

1971

204	2½c Lammergeier
205	5c Bald Ibis
206	10c Rufous Rockjumper ('Orange Breasted Rock Jumper')
207	12½c Blue Bustard ('Blue Korhaan')
208	15c Painted Snipe
209	20c Golden-breasted Bunting
210	25c Ground Woodpecker

Set of 7   13.00   13.00

1981

500	1s Greater Kestrel
501	2s Speckled Pigeon ('Rock Pigeon')

502	3s South African Crowned Crane ('Crowned Crane')
503	5s Bokmakierie Shrike ('Bokmakierie')
504	6s Cape Robin Chat ('Cape Robin')
505	7s Yellow Canary
506	10s Red-billed Pintail ('Red-billed Teal')
507	25s Malachite Kingfisher
508	40s Yellow-tufted Malachite Sunbird ('Malachite Sunbird')
509	60s Cape Longclaw ('Orange-throated Longclaw')
510	75s Hoopoe ('African Hoopoe')
511	1m Red Bishop
512	2m Egyptian Goose
513	5m Lilac-breasted Roller

Set of 14   9.50   11.00

1984

MS604   1m75 Mute Swan (on Western Australia stamp No. 3).. .. ..   1.60   1.75

1985

646	5s American Cliff Swallow ('Cliff Swallow')
647	6s Great Crested Grebe
648	10s Vesper Sparrow
649	30s Greenshank
650	60s Stilt Sandpiper
651	2m Glossy Ibis

Set of 6   3.25   3.50

1986

677†	7s Lammergeier	8	10
680†	15s Lammergeier	15	20
682†	50s Lammergeier	55	60
683†	1m Lammergeier	1.10	1.25
MS685	2m Verreaux's Eagle ('Black Eagle'). ..	2.10	2.25

LIBERIA
West Africa
100 cents = 1 dollar

1906

227†	10c Great Blue Turaco	4.50	90
229†	20c Great Egret	4.75	1.60

1909
No. 227 surcharged **Inland 3 Cents**

261	3c on 10c Great Blue Turaco	3.00	4.50

1918

356†	30c Palm-nut Vulture	7.00	60

No. 356 surcharged **TWO CENTS.** *and red cross*

382†	30c + 2c Palm-nut Vulture	7.50	4.00

1921

412†	$2 Great Indian Hornbill..	15.00	1.25

No. 412 overprinted **1921**

426†	$2 Great Indian Hornbill..	17.00	2.00

1936
No. 356 surcharged **1936 12**

541†	12c on 30c Palm-nut Vulture.	1.50	2.00

No. O369 surcharged with star and **1936 12**

552†	12c on 30c Palm-nut Vulture.	1.25	1.75

BIRDS BIRDS BIRDS

1937

559†	1c Black and White Casqued Hornbill	70	35
563†	5c Western Reef Heron	1.10	50

1938

565†	1c Tawny Eagle	25	10
567†	3c Lesser Black-backed Gull	12	10
568†	4c Little Egret	15	10
569†	5c Little Egret	25	10
572†	30c Lesser Black-backed Gull	45	12
573†	50c Tawny Eagle..	65	12

1941
Nos. 565, 567/9 and 572/3 overprinted or surcharged **First Flight**
LIBERIA – U.S. 1941

594†	50c on 1c Tawny Eagle	£2000	£250
596†	50c on 3c Lesser Black-backed Gull	£150	75.00
597†	50c on 4c Little Egret.	45.00	30.00
598†	50c on 5c Little Egret.	45.00	30.00
601†	50c on 30c Lesser Black-backed Gull	50.00	25.00
602†	50c Tawny Eagle..	50.00	30.00

1942
Nos. 594, 596/8 and 601/2 with date obliterated by two bars

604†	50c on 1c Tawny Eagle	6.00	6.50
606†	50c on 3c Lesser Black-backed Gull	5.50	6.00
607†	50c on 4c Little Egret.	4.50	5.00
608†	50c on 5c Little Egret.	4.50	4.50
611†	50c on 30c Lesser Black-backed Gull	5.00	5.50
612†	50c Tawny Eagle..	5.00	6.00

1944
Nos. 559 and 563 surcharged

636†	4c on 5c Western Reef Heron	15.00	16.00
637†	5c on 1c Black and White Casqued Hornbill	60.00	38.00

Nos. 567/9 and 573 surcharged

644†	10c on 5c Little Egret.	12.00	12.00
645†	30c on 3c Lesser Black-backed Gull	90.00	80.00
646†	30c on 4c Little Egret.	11.00	11.00
647†	$1 on 3c Lesser Black-backed Gull	40.00	40.00
648†	$1 on 50c Tawny Eagle	25.00	20.00

1953

735 1c Common Bulbul ('Pepper Bird')
736 3c Blue-throated Roller ('Roller')
737 4c Yellow-casqued Hornbill ('Hornbill')
738 5c Giant Kingfisher ('Kingfisher')
739 10c African Jacana ('Jacana')
740 12c Broad-tailed Paradise Whydah
    ('Weaver')

Set of 6   1.75   70

1956

784† 4c Emu.   10   15

1971

1091† 3c Black Woodpecker (Dryocopus
    martius)   25   10
1093† 10c Common Guillemot (Uria aalge
    inornata)   40   15
1095† 25c Manchurian Crane (Grus japonensis)   80   35

1975

1242† 5c Cattle Egret   20   5

1977

1307 5c Latham's Francolin
1308 10c Narina Trogon
1309 15c Rufous-crowned Roller
1310 20c Brown-cheeked Hornbill
1311 25c Common Bulbul ('Pepper Bird')
1312 50c African Fish Eagle ('Fish Eagle')

Set of 6   2.40   1.25
MS1313 80c Knysna Turaco ('Gold Coast
    Touraco') 1.75   1.75

1979

1378† 50c Common Bulbul.   70   70

1984

1587† 6c White-backed Duck, White-faced
    Whistling Duck, Spur-winged Plover,
    Egyptian Goose, African Jacana   15   10

1985

1599 1c Bohemian Waxwing
1600 3c Bay-breasted Warbler
1601 6c White-winged Crossbill
1602 31c Grey Phalarope ('Red Phalarope')
1603 41c Eastern Bluebird
1604 62c Common Cardinal ('Northern
    Cardinal')

Set of 6   2.75   2.25

OFFICIAL STAMPS

1906
Nos. 227 and 229 (in different colours) overprinted **OS**
O240† 10c Great Blue Turaco 3.50 60
O242† 20c Great Egret.. .. .. 3.50 75

1918
No. 356 (in different colours) overprinted **OS**
O369 30c Palm-nut Vulture 4.00 50

1921
No. 412 (in different colours) overprinted **O S**
O440† $2 Great Indian Hornbill 10.00 1.25

No. O440 overprinted **1921**
O454† $2 Great Indian Hornbill 9.50 2.00

699† 70dh Bonelli's Eagle.. .. .. 80 25

1978

857† 30dh Blue-eyed Cormorant 50 15
858† 50dh Albatross sp 60 20
MS860 100dh White-tailed Sea Eagle. 2.25 2.00

LIBYA
North Africa
1965 1000 milliemes = 1 pound
1972 1000 dirhams = 1 dinar

1965

335 5m Long-legged Buzzard
336 10m European Bee Eater
337 15m Black-bellied Sandgrouse
338 20m Houbara Bustard
339 30m Spotted Sandgrouse
340 40m Barbary Partridge
                              Set of 6 3.50 1.25

1976

690 5dh Little Bittern
691 10dh Great Grey Shrike
692 15dh Fulvous Babbler
693 20dh European Bee Eater
694 25dh Hoopoe
                              Set of 5 2.25 1.25

1982

1190 15dh Lanner Falcon
1191 15dh Common Swift
1192 15dh Peregrine Falcon
1193 15dh Greater Flamingo
1194 25dh Whitethroat
1195 25dh Turtle Dove
1196 25dh Black-bellied Sandgrouse
1197 25dh Egyptian Vulture
1198 45dh Golden Oriole
1199 45dh European Bee Eater
1200 45dh Common Kingfisher
1201 45dh Common Roller
1202 95dh Barbary Partridge
1203 95dh Barn Owl
1204 95dh Cream-coloured Courser
1205 95dh Hoopoe
                              Set of 16 5.50 5.00

LIECHTENSTEIN
Central Europe
100 rappen = 1 franc

1934

145 10r Golden Eagle
146 15r Golden Eagle
147 20r Golden Eagle
148 30r Osprey
149 50r Golden Eagle

Set of 5 55.00 75.00

1939

176 10r Barn Swallow
177 15r Black-headed Gull
178 20r Herring Gull
179 30r Common Buzzard
180 50r Northern Goshawk
181 1f Lammergeier
182 2f Lammergeier

Set of 7 11.00 20.00

1946

284† 30r Black Grouse 16.00 3.00
254† 1f50 Capercaillie 6.50 8.50
257† 1f50 Golden Eagle 6.50 8.50

1973

583† 40r Curlew (Numenius arquata) 50 20

1974

599† 1f10 Three-toed Woodpecker (Picoides
tridactylus) 1.25 65

1976

633† 80r Lapwing (Vanellus vanellus) 1.25 75

1986

889 50c Barn Swallow
890 90c European Robin

Set of 2 95 95

LUXEMBOURG
Western Europe
100 centimes = 1 franc

1961

691† 1f Great Spotted Woodpecker 30 12

1970

854 1f50 Firecrest   25   10

1985

1161† 4f Little Owl (*Athene noctua*)   20   10

1987

1199† 12f Dipper (*Cinclus cinclus*)   45   30

MACAO
South-east Asia
100 avos = 1 pataca

1984

592 30a White-breasted Kingfisher (*Halcyon*
     smyrnensis), Common Kingfisher
     (*Alcedo atthis*)
593 40a Jay (*Garrulus glandarius*)
594 50a Japanese White Eye (*Zosterops*
     japonica)
595 70a Hoopoe (*Upupa epops*)
596 2p50 Pekin Robin (*Leiothrix lutea*)
597 6p Mallard (*Anas platyrhynchos*)
                          Set of 6   3.25   2.75

MADAGASCAR AND DEPENDENCIES
Indian Ocean off East Africa
100 centimes = 1 franc

1954

323† 8f Long-tailed Ground Roller (*Uratelornis*).   60   15
324† 15f Long-tailed Ground Roller (*Uratelornis*)   1.50   10
326† 100f Grey-headed Gull 3.75   1.00

MADEIRA
Atlantic Ocean
100 centavos = 1 escudo

1986

224 68e50 Cory's Shearwater..   80   45

1987

230 25e Firecrest (*Regulus ignicapillus*
     madeirensis)
231 57e Trocaz Pigeon (*Columba trocaz*)
232 74e50 Barn Owl (*Tyto alba schmitzi*)
233 125e Soft-plumaged Petrel (*Pterodroma*
     madeira)
                          Set of 4   2.50   1.40

MALAGASY REPUBLIC
Indian Ocean off East Africa
100 centimes = 1 franc

1963

57†	1f Madagascar Blue Pigeon (*Alectroenas madagascariensis*)	40	25
58†	2f Blue Madagascar Coucal (*Coua caerulea*)	40	25
59†	3f Madagascar Red Fody (*Foudia madagascariensis*)	40	25
60†	6f Madagascar Pygmy Kingfisher (*Ispidina madagascariensis*)	40	25

64†	40f Helmet Bird (*Euryceros prevostii*) (air)	85	35
65†	100f Pitta-like Ground Roller (*Atelornis pittoides*)..	2.25	80
66†	200f Crested Wood Ibis (*Lophotibis cristata*)	4.00	1.50

1975

320†	25f Pryer's Woodpecker (*Saphopipo noguchi*)	45	10
MS325	30f Purple Jay (*Garrulus lidthi*)	4.00	1.50

1982

450	25f Hook-billed Vanga (*Vanga curvirostris*)
451	30f Courol (*Leptostomus discolor*)
452	200f Madagascar Fish Eagle (*Haliaeetus vociferoides*)

Set of 3   1.40   90

1986

602	60f Giant Madagascar Coucal (*Coua gigas*)		
603	60f Crested Madagascar Coucal (*Coua cristata*)		
604	60f Rufous Vanga (*Cianolanius madagascariensis* !)		
605	60f Red-tailed Vanga (*Xenopirostris daimi* !)		
606	60f Sicklebill (*Falculea palliata*)		
	Set of 5	80	35
MS607	450f Cattle Egret (*Bubulcus ibis ibis*) ..	1.40	1.40

MALAWI
Central Africa
1968 12 pence = 1 shilling,
20 shillings = 1 pound
1970 100 tambalas = 1 kwacha

1968

310	1d Scarlet-chested Sunbird
311	2d Violet Starling ('Violet-backed Starling')
312	3d White-browed Robin Chat ('White-browed Robin')
313	4d Red-billed Fire Finch
314	6d Nyasa Lovebird ('Lilian's Lovebird')
315	9d Yellow-rumped Bishop ('Yellow Bishop')
316	1s Carmine Bee Eater
317	1s6d Grey-headed Bush Shrike
318	2s Paradise Whydah
319	3s African Paradise Flycatcher ('Paradise Flycatcher')
320	5s Bateleur
321	10s Saddle-bill Stork ('Saddlebill')
322	£1 Purple Heron
323	£2 Knysna Turaco ('Livingstone's Loerie')
	Set of 14 65.00 80.00

1970
No. 317 overprinted **Rand Easter Show 1970**

350	1s6d Grey-headed Bush Shrike	15	40

Nos. 316 and 318 surcharged

356	10t on 1s Carmine Bee Eater		
357	20t on 2s Paradise Whydah		
	Set of 2	1.00	95

1971

No. 319 surcharged 30t Special United Kingdom Delivery Service
369 30t on 3s African Paradise Flycatcher 25 2.00

370 3t Broad-tailed Paradise Whydah, Grey Heron
371 8t Broad-tailed Paradise Whydah, Grey Heron
372 15t Broad-tailed Paradise Whydah, Grey Heron
373 3ot Broad-tailed Paradise Whydah, Grey Heron
    Set of 4   70   60

1975

473 1t African Snipe
474 2t Double-banded Sandgrouse
475 3t Blue Quail
476 5t Bare-throated Francolin ('Rednecked Francolin')
477 8t Harlequin Quail
478 10t Spur-winged Goose ('Spurwing Goose')
479 15t Barrow's Bustard ('Stanley Bustard')
480 20t Comb Duck ('Knob-billed Duck')
481 30t Helmet Guineafowl ('Crowned Guinea Fowl')
482 50t African Pygmy Goose ('Pygmy Goose')
483 1k Garganey
484 2k White-faced Whistling Duck ('White Face Tree Duck')
485 4k African Green Pigeon ('Green Pigeon')
    Set of 13   32.00   30.00

No. 482 overprinted 10th ACP Ministerial Conference 1975
514 50t African Pygmy Goose   75   1.10

COLLECT RAILWAYS ON STAMPS
A Stanley Gibbons thematic catalogue on this popular subject. Copies available at £7.50 (p. + p. £1.50) from: Stanley Gibbons Publications Ltd, 5 Parkside, Christchurch Road, Ringwood, Hants BH24 3SH.

1976

Nos. 479 *and* 481 *overprinted* Blantyre Mission Centenary 1876–1976
535 15t Barrow's Bustard
536 30t Helmet Guineafowl
    Set of 2   1.00   1.25

1980

615† 5t African Fish Eagle   10   5

632† 1k Malachite Kingfisher   70   1.10

1982

653† 1k Greater Flamingo..   .. ..   1.75   1.75

1983

671† 20t Common Crane   25   20

674 30t African Fish Eagle ('Fish Eagle –
     Lakeside sentinel')
675 30t African Fish Eagle ('Fish Eagle – Gull
     like far carrying call')
676 30t African Fish Eagle ('Fish Eagle – Diving
     on its fish prey')
677 30t African Fish Eagle ('Fish Eagle – Prey
     captured')
678 30t African Fish Eagle ('Fish Eagle –
     Feeding on its catch')
                            Set of 5   2.25   2.75

1985

733 7t Stierling's Woodpecker
734 15t Lesser Seedcracker
735 20t East Coast Akelat ('Gunning's Akalat')
736 1k Boehm's Bee Eater
                            Set of 4   2.25   2.25

1987

759 8t Wattled Crane (Bugeranus carunculatus)
760 15t Wattled Crane (Bugeranus
     carunculatus)
761 20t Wattled Crane (Bugeranus
     carunculatus)
762 75t Wattled Crane (Bugeranus
     carunculatus)
                            Set of 4   1.00   1.10

MALAYSIA
South-east Asia
100 cents (sen) = 1 dollar

1965

20 25c Crested Wood Partridge ('Burong Siul')
21 30c Blue-backed Fairy Bluebird ('Murai
    Gajah')
22 50c Black-naped Oriole ('Burong Kunyit
    Basar')
23 75c Rhinoceros Hornbill ('Enggang')
24 $1 Zebra Dove ('Merbok')
25 $2 Great Argus Pheasant ('Kuang')
26 $5 Asiatic Paradise Flycatcher ('Murai Ekor
    Gading')
27 $10 Blue-tailed Pitta ('Burong Pachat')
                            Set of 8   40.00   5.50

1967

48 25c Crested Wood Partridge (on stamp No.
    20)
49 30c Blue-backed Fairy Bluebird (on stamp
    No. 21)
50 50c Black-naped Oriole (on stamp No. 22)
                            Set of 3   2.75   1.90

1983

272 15c Helmeted Hornbill (Rhinoplax vigil)
273 20c Wrinkled Hornbill (Rhyticeros
     corrugatus)
274 50c Long-crested Hornbill (Berenicornis
     comatus)
275 $1 Rhinoceros Hornbill (Buceros
     rhinoceros)
                            Set of 4   1.50   1.40

1986

MALAYSIA

323 20c Crested Fireback Pheasant (*Lophura
     ignita*)
324 20c Malay Peacock-Pheasant (*Pavo
     malacense*)
325 40c Bulwer's Pheasant (*Lophura bulweri*)
326 40c Great Argus Pheasant (*Argusianus
     argus*)
                                    Set of 4   1.00   95

1973

458† 1la Golden-fronted Leafbird (*Chloropsis
      aurifrons*)   5   5
463† 2r Golden-fronted Leafbird (*Chloropsis
      aurifrons*) 2.25 2.75

1977

702 1la Lesser Frigate Bird (*Fregata ariel
     iredalei*)
703 2la Crab Plover (*Dronas ardeola*)
704 3la White-tailed Tropic Bird (*Phaeton
     lepturus*)
705 4la Wedge-tailed Shearwater (*Procellaria
     pacifica*)
706 5la Grey Heron (*Ardea cinerea*)
707 20la White Tern (*Gygis alba*)
708 95la Cattle Egret (*Ardeola ibis*)
709 1r25 Black-naped Tern (*Sterna sumatrana*)
710 5r Pheasant Coucal (*Centropus
     phasianinus*)
                                    Set of 9   7.50   7.50
MS711 10r Green Heron (*Butorides striatus
       didii*).. .. ..   9.50 11.00

MALDIVE ISLANDS
Indian Ocean
100 larees = 1 rupee

1966

179† 15la Crab Plover, Gull sp   20   5
182† 50la Crab Plover, Gull sp   55   15
187† 5r Crab Plover, Gull sp 3.50 2.25

1968

288† 2la Redshank, Curlew   5   5
291† 50la Redshank, Curlew   70   15

1980

873 75la White-tailed Tropic Bird
874 95la Sooty Tern
875 1r Common Noddy ('Brown Noddy')
876 1r55 Curlew ('Eurasian Curlew')
877 2r Wilson's Petrel
878 4r Caspian Tern ('Caspian')
                                    Set of 6   2.75   2.10
MS879 5r Red-footed Booby, Brown Booby.. .. 1.40   1.50

STANLEY GIBBONS
STAMP COLLECTING SERIES
Introductory booklets on *How to Start*, *How to
Identify Stamps* and *Collecting by Theme*. A series
of well illustrated guides at a low price.
Write for details.

1985

1083   3r Pale-footed Shearwater ('Flesh-footed
       Shearwater')
1084   3r50 Little Grebe
1085   4r Common Cormorant ('Great
       Cormorant')
1086   4r50 White-faced Storm Petrel

		Set of 4	2.50	2.75
MS1087	15r Red-necked Phalarope		2.75	3.00

1986

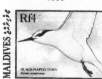

1188†	4r Black-naped Tern	75	80

1192   3la Little Blue Heron
1193   4la White-tailed Kite
1194   5la Greater Shearwater
1195   10la Magnificent Frigate Bird
1196   15la Black-necked Grebe ('Eared Grebe')
1197   20la Goosander ('Common Merganser')
1198   13r Peregrine Falcon ('Great Footed
       Hawk')
1199   14r Prairie Chicken ('Greater Prairie
       Chicken')

		Set of 8	5.00	5.25
MS1200	Two sheets. (a) 15r Fulmar ('Northern Fulmar'); (b) 15r White-fronted Goose			
		Price for 2 sheets	5.50	5.75

BIRDS   BIRDS   BIRDS

Hundreds of Birds sets from around the World at
attractive prices are available from Stanley
Gibbons. Write now for our current Birds offers,
with no obligation, to: Stanley Gibbons Promotions
(Birds Offers), Parkside, Ringwood, Hants
BH24 3SH. Tel: (04254) 2363.

MALI
West Africa
100 centimes = 1 franc

1960

10   100f Violet Starling ('Merle Amethyste')
11   200f Bateleur ('Aigle Bateleur')
12   500f Common Gonolek ('Gonolek')

	Set of 3	22.00	11.00

Nos. 10/12 overprinted or surcharged **REPUBLIQUE DU MALI**

17†	100f Violet Starling.	3.00	1.50
18†	200f Bateleur	4.75	3.00
19†	300f on 500f Common Gonolek	7.50	4.50
20†	500f Common Gonolek	16.00	9.00

1963

75   25f South African Crowned Crane
76   200f South African Crowned Crane

	Set of 2	4.00	2.40

1965

93   100f Knysna Turaco ('Touraco')
94   200f Abyssinian Ground Hornbill ('Bucorve')
95   300f Egyptian Vulture ('Percnoptere')
96   500f Goliath Heron ('Heron Goliath')

	Set of 4	28.00	9.50

1973

1978

620† 420f Mute Swan 1.75   70
(619/20 *Set of* 2)   2.50   1.25

381 70f South African Crowned Crane (on stamp
No. 76)   60   30

1976

534 100f American Bald Eagle
535 400f American Bald Eagle
536 440f American Bald Eagle
                 Set of 3   3.75   1.90

1977

579 15f Village Indigobird (*Hypochera
      chalybeata*)
580 25f Yellow-breasted Barbet (*Trachyphonus
      margaritaceus*)
581 30f Vitelline Masked Weaver (*Sitagra
      vitellina*)
582 40f Carmine Bee Eater (*Merops*)
583 50f Senegal Parrot (*Poicephalus*)
                 Set of 5   1.25   65

632 20f Red-cheeked Cordon-bleu (*Granatina
      bengala*)
633 30f Black-faced Fire Finch (*Lagonosticta
      vinacea*)
634 50f Red-billed Fire Finch (*Lagonosticta*)
635 70f African Collared Dove (*Streptopelia
      rosea grisea*)
636 80f White-billed Buffalo Weaver
      (*Bubalornis albirostris*)
                 Set of 5   1.25   60

654† 100f Ostrich   50   20
(654/5 *Set of* 2)   1.00   50

677 200f Ruff
678 200f Abyssinian Ground Hornbill (on stamp
No. 94)
                 Set of 2   2.40   1.75

1983

960† 800f American Bald Eagle 1.25 1.10
(959/60 Set of 2) 2.50 2.25

1984

1054† 30f Archaeopteryx * 20 10
1057† 350f Archaeopteryx * 1.40 1.10

1985

1073 180f Common Kingfisher ('Martin-
Pecheur')
1074 300f Great Bustard ('Outarde')
1075 470f Ostrich ('Autruche')
1076 540f Ruppell's Griffon ('Vautour')
Set of 4 6.50 5.50

COLLECT MAMMALS ON STAMPS
The second Stanley Gibbons thematic catalogue —
copies are available at £7.50 (p.+p. £1.50) from:
Stanley Gibbons Publications Ltd, 5 Parkside,
Christchurch Road, Ringwood, Hants BH24 3SH.

MALTA
Mediterranean
1971 12 pence = 1 shilling,
20 shillings = 1 pound
1972 100 cents = 1 pound

1971

457† 5d Blue Rock Thrush (Monticola solitarius) 10 5
458† 10d Blue Rock Thrush (Monticola
solitarius) 25 10

1981

655 3c Barn Owl (Tyto alba)
656 8c Sardinian Warbler (Sylvia
melanocephala)
657 12c Woodchat Shrike (Lanius senator)
658 23c British Storm Petrel (Hydrobates
pelagicus)
Set of 4 2.00 1.75

1987

796 3c European Robin (Erithacus rubecula)
797 8c Peregrine Falcon (Falco peregrinus)
798 13c Hoopoe (Upupa epops)
799 23c Cory's Shearwater (Calonectris
diomedea)
Set of 4 1.75 2.00

MANAMA
Arabian peninsula
100 dirhams = 1 riyal

1966
No. 18 of Ajman surcharged **Manama** and new value
4† 10r on 10r Lanner Falcon 6.00 6.00

Appendix

The following stamps have either been issued in excess of postal needs, or have not been made available to the public in reasonable quantities at face value. Miniature sheets, imperforate stamps etc. are excluded from this section.

1969

Birds. 1r x 11 Secretary Bird, South African Crowned Crane, Whale-headed Stork, Sacred Ibis, Grey Parrot, Sclater's Parrotlet, Muller's Parrot, Moluccan Hanging Parrot, Yellow-crowned Amazon, Wilson's Bird of Paradise, Twelve-wired Bird of Paradise

1971

Birds. Postage 5d Goldfinch, 20d Parula Warbler, 25d Maroon-breasted Crowned Pigeon, 30d Ring-necked Pheasant, 50d American Kestrel. Air 60d Derbyan Parakeet, 1r Cuban Amazon, 2r Red-tailed Hawk

World Wildlife Conservation. 5d Griffon Vulture, 10d Ostrich, 20d Baglafecht Weaver

MARSHALL ISLANDS

Western Pacific
100 cents = 1 dollar

1985

37	22c Leach's Storm Petrel ('Forked-tailed Petrel')		
38	22c Pectoral Sandpiper		
39	44c Brown Booby ('Booby Gannet') (air)		
40	44c Whimbrel ('Great Esquimaux Curlew')		
		Set of 4	1.25	85

1987

103	44c Wedge-tailed Shearwater		
104	44c Red-footed Booby		
105	44c Red-tailed Tropic Bird		
106	44c Lesser Frigate Bird ('Great Frigatebird')		
		Set of 4	2.10	1.00

MANCHURIA

See under China

MARTINIQUE

West Indies
100 centimes = 1 franc

1947

250†	200f Wandering Albatross	.. ..	19.00	11.00

MAURITANIA

West Africa
1960 100 centimes = 1 franc
1973 100 cents = 1 ouguiya (um)

1960

146	100f Greater Flamingo ('Flamant Rose')		
147	200f African Spoonbill ('Spatule')		
148	500f Slender-billed Gull ('Goeland Railleur')		
		Set of 3	22.00	11.00

1964

185	100f Lichtenstein's Sandgrouse ('Ganga de Lichtenstein')		
186	200f Reed Cormorant ('Cormoran Africain')		
187	500f Dark Chanting Goshawk ('Autour Chanteur')		
		Set of 3	18.00	7.50

1967

265 100f South African Crowned Crane (Balearica pavonina !)
266 200f Great Egret (Egretta alba)
267 500f Ostrich (Struthio camelus)

Set of 3 13.00 5.50

1973

No. 267 surcharged **Apollo XVII Decembre 1972 250F**
417 250f on 500f Ostrich 3.00 1.40

1976

520† 20u White Stork 1.25 50

525 50u Sacred Ibis ('Ibis Sacre'), Yellow-billed Stork ('Ibis Tantale')
526 100u Marabou Stork ('Marabout')
527 200u Long-crested Eagle ('Lophaete Huppe'), Martial Eagle ('Aigle Belliqueux')

Set of 3 13.00 7.00

1978

578† 100u Ostrich 4.00 1.60

591 20u Water Rail
592 20u South African Crowned Crane (on stamp No. 265)

Set of 2 2.25 1.40

1981

713 2u Eastern White Pelican ('Pelican Blanc')
714 18u Greater Flamingo ('Flamant Rose')

Set of 2 75 65

1985

820† 14u Ostrich 25 15

Appendix
The following stamps have either been issued in excess of postal needs, or have not been made available to the public in reasonable quantities at face value. Miniature sheets, imperforate stamps etc. are excluded from this section.

1962
European Coal and Steel Communication. No. 148 overprinted **EUROPA CECA MIFERMA**

Malaria Eradication. Nos. 146/7 overprinted **LE MONDE UNI CONTRE LE PALUDISME**

825	14u Western Tanager, Scarlet Tanager (Passeriformes Thraupidae)			
826	18u Bonaparte's Gull (Larus philadelphia)			
827	19u Blue Jay (Cyanocitta cristata)			
828	44u Black Skimmer (Rhyncops nigra)			
	Set of 4	2.00	1.60
MS826	100u American Anhinga (Anhinga anhinga)	2.25	2.25

1986

875†	22u White Spoonbill ('Spatule Blanche') ..	50	30
876†	32u Bridled Tern ('Sterne Bridee')	70	45

POSTAGE DUE STAMPS

1963

D177	50c Ruppell's Griffon ('Gyps de Ruppel')		
D178	50c Common Crane ('Grue Cendree')		
D179	1f Eastern White Pelican ('Pelican Rose')		
D180	1f Garganey ('Sarcelle d'Ete')		
D181	2f Golden Oriole ('Coriot')		
D182	2f Variable Sunbird ('Souimanga de Falkenstein')		
D183	5f Great Snipe ('Becassine Double')		
D184	5f Common Shoveler ('Canard Souchet')		
D185	10f Vulturine Guineafowl ('Pintade')		
D186	10f Black Stork ('Cigogne Noire')		
D187	15f Grey Heron ('Heron Cendre')		
D188	15f White Stork ('Cigogne Blanche')		
D189	20f Paradise Whydah ('Veuve Paradisier')		
D190	20f Red-legged Partridge ('Perdrix Rouge')		
D191	25f Little Stint ('Becasseau Minute')		
D192	25f Arabian Bustard ('Outarde')		
	Set of 16	7.50	6.00

MAURITIUS
Indian Ocean
100 cents = 1 rupee

1950

282†	12c Mauritius Dodo * ('The Dodo')	1.25	30

1953

302a†	60c Mauritius Dodo * ('The Dodo')	1.75	5

1965

317	2c Bourbon White Eye ('Grey White-Eye') (lemon background)	
318	3c Rodriguez Fody ('Rodrigues Fody') (brown background)	
319	4c Mauritius Olive White Eye ('Olive White-Eye')	
320	5c Mascarene Paradise Flycatcher ('Paradise Flycatcher')	
321	10c Mauritius Fody	
322	15c Mauritius Parakeet ('Parakeet') (grey background)	
323	20c Mauritius Greybird ('Cuckoo-Shrike') (yellow background)	
324	25c Mauritius Kestrel ('Kestrel')	
325	35c Pink Pigeon	
326	50c Reunion Bulbul ('Mascarene Bul-Bul')	

327 60c Mauritius Blue Pigeon * ('Dutch
Pigeon')
328 1r Mauritius Dodo * (green background)
329 2r50 Rodriguez Solitaire * ('Rodrigues
Solitaire')
330 5r Mauritius Red Rail * ('Red Rail')
331 10r Broad-billed Parrot *

Set of 15   27.00   11.00

1978

551† 3r Mauritius Dodo * ('Dodo').   55   65

1967

345 2c Red-tailed Tropic Bird
346 10c Rodriguez Brush Warbler
347 60c Rose-ringed Parakeet ('Rodrigues
Parakeet') (this subspecies *)
348 1r Grey-rumped Swiftlet ('Mauritius
Swiftlet')

Set of 4   70   30

560† 5r Mauritius Kestrel 1.75   2.40

Nos. 317/331 *overprinted* SELF GOVERNMENT 1967
349 2c Bourbon White Eye
350 3c Rodriguez Fody
351 4c Mauritius Olive White Eye
352 5c Mascarene Paradise Flycatcher
353 10c Mauritius Fody
354 15c Mauritius Parakeet
355 20c Mauritius Greybird
356 25c Mauritius Kestrel
357 35c Pink Pigeon
358 50c Reunion Bulbul
359 60c Mauritius Blue Pigeon *
360 1r Mauritius Dodo *
361 2r50 Rodriguez Solitaire *
362 5r Mauritius Red Rail *
363 10r Broad-billed Parrot *

Set of 15   7.50   11.50

1979

578† 2r Mauritius Dodo * (on stamp No. 302a) ..   35   40

1968

1984

365† 3c Mauritius Dodo *   10   20
367† 20c Mauritius Dodo *   10   5
369† 1r Mauritius Dodo *   20   10

As Nos. 317/18, 322/3 *and* 327/8 *but background colours changed*
370 2c Bourbon White Eye (yellow background)
371 3c Rodriguez Fody (blue background)
372 15c Mauritius Parakeet (brown
background)
373 20c Mauritius Greybird (brown
background)
374 60c Mauritius Blue Pigeon * (pink
background)
375 1r Mauritius Dodo * (purple background)

Set of 6   4.25   2.75

678 25c Mauritius Kestrel (*Falco punctatus*)
679 2r Mauritius Kestrel (*Falco punctatus*)
680 2r50 Mauritius Kestrel (*Falco punctatus*)
681 10r Mauritius Kestrel (*Falco punctatus*)

Set of 4   2.25   2.50

1985

Mauritius 25c

708   25c Pink Pigeon (*Columba mayeri*)
709   2r Pink Pigeon (*Columba mayeri*)
710   2r50 Pink Pigeon (*Columba mayeri*)
711   5r Pink Pigeon (*Columba mayeri*)

Set of 4   1.75   1.90

714†   5r Cory's Shearwater   60   70

MEXICO
North America
100 centavos = 1 peso

1922

454   25c Golden Eagle (red frame)
455   25c Golden Eagle (green frame)
456   50c Golden Eagle

Set of 3   1.40   70

1932

Nos. 454/5 surcharged **40 HABILITADO CUARENTA c**
519†   40c on 25c Golden Eagle (red frame)   90   65
520†   40c on 25c Golden Eagle (green frame)   ..   27.00   27.00

STANLEY GIBBONS
STAMP COLLECTING SERIES
Introductory booklets on *How to Start, How to Identify Stamps* and *Collecting by Theme*. A series of well illustrated guides at a low price.
Write for details.

1980

1548   80p Common Turkey (*Meleagris gallopavo*)
1549   1p60 Greater Flamingo (*Phoenicopterus ruber*)

Set of 2   50   25

1981

1591   80c Northern Mockingbird (*Mimus polyglottos*)
1592   1p60 Mountain Trogon (*Trogon mexicanus*)

Set of 2   75   40

1984

1703   12p Muscovy Duck (*Cairina moschata*)
1704   20p Red-billed Whistling Duck (*Dendrocygna autumnalis*)

Set of 2   40   25

OFFICIAL STAMPS

1929

Nos. 454/5 overprinted **OFICIAL.**
O492†   25c Golden Eagle (red frame) 2.75   2.75
O490†   25c Golden Eagle (green frame) 1.25   1.25

1932

No. 456 overprinted **SERVICIO OFICIAL** *in one line*
O531†   50c Golden Eagle   70   70

1933

No. 456 overprinted **SERVICIO OFICIAL** in two lines

O553† 50c Golden Eagle 70   70

510   500f Wandering Albatross ('Albatros')
511a   1000f Common Cormorant ('Cormorans')
Set of 4   £110   70.00

MICRONESIA
Western Pacific
100 cents = 1 dollar

1985

39   22c Common Noddy ('Noddy Tern')
40   22c Turnstone
41   22c American Golden Plover ('Golden Plover')
42   22c Grey Plover ('Black-bellied Plover')

43   44c Sooty Tern (air)
Set of 5   1.75   1.25

1962

730   5c Yellow Wagtail ('Bergeronnette')
731   10c European Robin ('Rouge-Gorge')
732   15c Goldfinch ('Chardonneret')
733   20c Blackcap ('Fauvette a Tete Noire')
734   25c Great Spotted Woodpecker ('Pic Epeiche')
735   30c Nightingale ('Rossignol')
736   45c Barn Owl ('Effraie')
737   50c Common Starling ('Etourneau')
738   85c Red Crossbill ('Bec-croise')
739   1f White Stork ('Cigogne Blanche')
Set of 10   4.50   3.50

MONACO
Southern Europe
100 centimes = 1 franc

1942

275†   50f Common Gull? 1.75   1.50

1945

As No. 275 but in different colour surcharged

305†   1f + 4f on 50f Common Gull?.   15   15

1955

508a   100f Roseate Tern ('Sternes')
509   200f Herring Gull? ('Mouettes')

1970

972†   30c Manchurian Crane 25   20
974†   70c Manchurian Crane 50   50

981†   1f White-tailed Sea Eagle ('Pygargue') . .. 90   35

1971

1008 50c Razorbill 65 35

1982

1559 60c Nutcracker (*Nucifraga caryocatactes*)
1560 70c Black Grouse (*Lyrurus tetrix*)
1561 80c Rock Partridge (*Alectoris graeca saxatilis*)
1562 90c Wallcreeper (*Tichodroma muraria*)
1563 1f40 Rock Ptarmigan (*Lagopus mutus*)
1564 1f60 Golden Eagle (*Aquila chrysaetos*)
　　　　　　　　　　　　　　 Set of 6　 2.75　 1.10

MONGOLIA
Central Asia
100 mung = 1 tugrik

1956

120† 30m Golden Eagle 16.00 9.00

BIRDS BIRDS BIRDS
Hundreds of Birds sets from around the World at attractive prices are available from Stanley Gibbons. Write now for our current Birds offers, with no obligation, to: Stanley Gibbons Promotions (Birds Offers), Parkside, Ringwood, Hants BH24 3SH. Tel: (04254) 2363.

1958

128† 30m Dalmatian Pelican (pale blue) 3.00 1.25
129† 30m Dalmatian Pelican (turquoise) 2.75 1.10

1959

172† 10m Ring-necked Pheasant 60 10

1961

203 5m Rose-coloured Starling (*Pastor roseus*)
204 10m Hoopoe (*Upupa epops*)
205 15m Golden Oriole (*Oriolus oriolus*)
206 20m Siberian Capercaillie (*Tetrao urogalloides*)
207 50m Eastern Broad-billed Roller (*Eurystomus orientalis*)
208 70m Tibetan Sandgrouse (*Syrrhaptes tibetanus*)
209 1t Mandarin (*Aix galericulata*)
　　　　　　　　　　　　　　 Set of 7　 5.50　 1.90

245† 20m Golden Eagle 85 25

1965

365† 10m Golden Eagle 70 10

1970

575 10m Common Buzzard (*Buteo buteo*)
576 20m Tawny Owl (*Strix aluco*)
577 30m Northern Goshawk (*Accipiter gentilis*)
578 50m White-tailed Sea Eagle (*Haliaetus albicilla*)
579 60m Peregrine Falcon (*Falco peregrinus*)
580 1t Common Kestrel (*Falco tinnunculus*)
581 1t30 Black Kite (*Milvus migrans*)
                                    Set of 7   5.00   1.50

1973

764 5m Common Shelduck (*Tadorna tadorna*)
765 10m Black-throated Diver (*Gavia arctica*)
766 15m Bar-headed Goose (*Anser indicus*)
767 30m Great Crested Grebe (*Podiceps cristatus*)
768 50m Mallard (*Anas platyrhynchos*)
769 60m Mute Swan (*Cygnus olor*)
770 1t Greater Scaup (*Aythya marila*)
                                    Set of 7   5.75   1.60

COLLECT MAMMALS ON STAMPS
The second Stanley Gibbons thematic catalogue —
copies are available at £7.50 (p. + p. £1.50) from:
Stanley Gibbons Publications Ltd, 5 Parkside,
Christchurch Road, Ringwood, Hants BH24 3SH.

1974

855† 40m Herring Gull.. .. .. 55 25

875† 10m Lapwing 35 10
878† 40m Dalmatian Pelican .. .. 75 20 ·

1975

926† 10m Golden Eagle 35 10

1976

990 10m Osprey (*Pandion haliaetus*)
991 20m Griffon Vulture (*Gyps fulvus*)
992 30m Lammergeier (*Gypaetus barbatus*)
993 40m Marsh Harrier (*Circus aeruginosus*)

994 60m European Black Vulture (*Aegypius monachus*)
995 80m Golden Eagle (*Aquila chrysaetus*)
996 1t Tawny Eagle (*Aquila rapax*)
Set of 7   4.50   1.40

1978

1139† 30m Tibetan Sandgrouse, Grey Jay (on Canada stamp No. 620)   40   25
1140† 40m Black-throated Diver, White-billed Diver (on Canada stamp No. 495)   50   30
1144† 1t20 Herring Gull, Northern Gannet (on Canada stamp No. 474) 1.50   60

1979

1235 10m Demoiselle Crane (*Anthropoides virgo*)
1236 30m Barred Warbler (*Sylvia nisoria*)
1237 50m Ruddy Shelduck (*Tadorna ferruginea*)
1238 60m Azure-winged Magpie (*Cyanopica cyanus*)
1239 70m Goldfinch (*Carduelis carduelis*)
1240 80m Great Tit (*Parus major*)
1241 1t Golden Oriole (*Oriolus oriolus*)
Set of 7   3.75   1.75

1980

1315† 20m Adelie Penguin (*Pygoscelis adelie*) ..   45   10
1317† 40m Wandering Albatross (*Diomeda exulans*)   65   25

1319† 60m Emperor Penguin (*Aptenodytes forsteri*)   95   35
1320† 70m Great Skua (*Stercorarius skua*) 1.00   35
1322† 1t20 Adelie Penguin. 1.75   50

1981

1391† 20m White-tailed Sea Eagle   35   10
1395† 60m Snowy Owl..   75   30
1396† 80m Atlantic Puffin   85   40

1982

1483† 80m Golden Eagle   85   40

1983

1527† 60m Imperial Eagle?   70   25

COLLECT RAILWAYS ON STAMPS
A Stanley Gibbons thematic catalogue on this popular subject. Copies available at £7.50 (p.+p. £1.50) from: Stanley Gibbons Publications Ltd, 5 Parkside, Christchurch Road, Ringwood, Hants BH24 3SH.

MONTSERRAT
West Indies
100 cents = 1 dollar

1970

242	1c Red-footed Booby
243	2c American Kestrel ('Killy Hawk')
244	3c Magnificent Frigate Bird ('The Frigate Bird')
245	4c Great Egret ('White Egret')
246	5c Brown Pelican
247	10c Bananaquit
248	15c Smooth-billed Ani ('Ani')
249	20c Red-billed Tropic Bird ('Tropic Bird')
250	25c Montserrat Oriole
251	50c Green-throated Carib
252	$1 Antillean Crested Hummingbird
253	$2.50 Little Blue Heron
254	$5 Purple-throated Carib
254a	$10 Forest Thrush

Set of 14   28.00   29.00

1974
No. 252 surcharged

335†	2c on $1 Antillean Crested Hummingbird ..	65	65
338†	20c on $1 Antillean Crested Hummingbird.	90	90

1976
Nos. 244 and 246/7 surcharged

368	2c on 5c Brown Pelican
369	30c on 10c Bananaquit
370	45c on 3c Magnificent Frigate Bird

Set of 3   50   65

1981

507†	65c Cattle Egret	45	35

1983

571	35c Blue-headed Hummingbird (female)
572	75c Green-throated Carib
573	$2 Antillean Crested Hummingbird
574	$3 Purple-throated Carib

Set of 4   3.50   3.50

1984

600	5c Cattle Egret
601	10c Carib Grackle
602	15c Moorhen ('Common Gallinule')
603	20c Brown Booby
604	25c Black-whiskered Vireo
605	40c Scaly-breasted Thrasher
606	55c Laughing Gull
607	70c Glossy Ibis
608	90c Green Heron
609	$1 Belted Kingfisher
610	$1.15 Bananaquit
611	$3 American Kestrel ('Sparrow Hawk')
612	$5 Forest Thrush
613	$7.50 Black-crowned Night Heron
614	$10 Bridled Quail Dove

Set of 15   12.00   13.00

1985

630†	$3 Montserrat Oriole..	1.75	1.90

657 15c Black-throated Blue Warbler
658 15c Palm Warbler
659 30c Bobolink
660 30c Lark Sparrow
661 55c Chipping Sparrow
662 55c Northern Oriole
663 $2.50 American Goldfinch
664 $2.50 Blue Grosbeak

Set of 8   3.50   3.75

MOROCCO
North-west Africa
100 francs = 1 dirham

1970

292 25f Ruddy Shelduck
293 40f Houbara Bustard

Set of 2   1.00   50

1987
Nos. 601, 603, 607/8 and 611 surcharged
724 5c on 70c Glossy Ibis
725 $1 on 20c Brown Booby
726 $1.15 on 10c Carib Grackle
727 $1.50 on 90c Green Heron
728 $2.30 on $3 American Kestrel

Set of 5   2.40   2.50

1973

378† 50f Eleonora's Falcon ('Faucon
d'Eleonore')   65   25
(377/8 Set of 2)   80   40

OFFICIAL STAMPS

1976
Nos. 246/7, 254/a and 369/70 overprinted O.H.M.S.
O1 5c Brown Pelican
O2 10c Bananaquit
O3 30c on 10c Bananaquit
O4 45c on 3c Magnificent Frigate Bird
O5 $5 Purple-throated Carib
O6 $10 Forest Thrush

Set of 6   †   £700
These stamps were issued for use on mail from the Montserrat
Philatelic Bureau. They were not sold to the public, either unused
or used.

1974

404† 25f Double-spurred Francolin ('Francolin').   40   15
(404/5 Set of 2)   90   55

1985
Nos. 600/12 and 614 overprinted OHMS
O62 5c Cattle Egret
O63 10c Carib Grackle
O64 15c Moorhen
O65 20c Brown Booby
O66 25c Black-whiskered Vireo
O67 40c Scaly-breasted Thrasher
O68 55c Laughing Gull
O69 70c Glossy Ibis
O70 90c Green Heron
O71 $1 Belted Kingfisher
O72 $1.15 Bananaquit
O73 $3 American Kestrel
O74 $5 Forest Thrush
O75 $10 Bridled Quail Dove

Set of 14   9.00   10.00

1975

426† . 40f Waldrapp ('Ibis Chauve') 50 25
(426/7 Set of 2) 90 65

1976

470 40f Dark Chanting Goshawk (*Melierax metabates*)
471 1d Purple Swamphen (*Porphyrio porphyrio*)

Set of 2 70 40

1979

533† 1d Moussier's Redstart (*Phoenicurus moussieri*).. .. .. 60 30
(532/3 Set of 2) 85 45

1980

544 40f Peregrine Falcon ('Chasse au Faucon'). 45 15

MOZAMBIQUE
South-east Africa
1978 100 centavos = 1 escudo
1980 100 centavos = 1 metical

1978

705 50c Violet-crested Turaco (*Gallirex porphyreolophus*)
706 1e Lilac-breasted Roller (*Coracias caudata*)
707 1e50 Red-headed Weaver (*Anaplectes rubriceps*)
708 2e50 Violet Starling (*Cinnyricinclus leucogastec*)
709 3e Peters's Twin-spot (*Hypargos niveoguttatus*)
710 15e European Bee Eater (*Merops apiaster*)

Set of 6 1.75 70

1980

832 1m Narina Trogon (*Apaloderma narina*)
833 1m50 South African Crowned Crane (*Balearica regulorum*)
834 2m50 Bare-throated Francolin (*Francolinus afer swynnertoni*)
835 5m Ostrich (*Struthio camelus australis*)
836 7m50 Spur-winged Goose (*Plectropterus gambensis*)
837 12m50 African Fish Eagle (*Haliaeetus vocifer*)

Set of 6 1.75 55

1981

861† 10m Marabou Stork (*Leptoptilos crumeniferus*) 40 30
862† 12m50 Saddle-bill Stork (*Ephippiorhynchus senegalensis*) 50 35
863† 15m Kori Bustard (*Ardeotis kori*) 60 45

1984

1048† 4m Secretary Bird 20 10

NAURU
Pacific
1954 12 pence = 1 shilling
1966 100 cents = 1 dollar

1954

51† 4d Great Frigate Bird ('Frigate Bird') 1.50 45

1963

57† 2d Micronesian Pigeon 1.00 1.00
62† 1s3d White Tern 4.00 2.75
64† 3s3d Finsch's Reed Warbler ('Reed Warbler').. .. .. 5.00 4.25

1966

73† 10c Great Frigate Bird ('Frigate Bird') 40 10
74† 15c White Tern 80 80
77† 35c Finsch's Reed Warbler ('Reed Warbler') 2.50 1.25
78† 50c Micronesian Pigeon 3.75 2.50

1968
Nos. 73/4 and 77/8 overprinted **REPUBLIC OF NAURU**
87† 10c Great Frigate Bird. 35 15
88† 15c White Tern 4.50 3.50
91† 35c Finsch's Reed Warbler 1.50 75
92† 50c Micronesian Pigeon 2.75 1.10

1973

108† 20c Great Frigate Bird 50 30
110† 30c Common Noddy 85 65
111† 50c Great Frigate Bird ('Frigate Bird').. .. 1.50 2.25

1976

145† 25c Finsch's Reed Warbler 55 55

1978

176† 3c White-capped Noddy 10 5
178† 5c Eastern Reef Heron 15 5
184† 30c Great Frigate Bird 40 35
185† 32c White-capped Noddy. 45 35
186† 40c Wandering Tattler 60 45
187† 50c Great Frigate Bird 55 55

1985

328   10c Common Noddy ('Brown Noddy')
329   20c Common Noddy ('Brown Noddy')
330   30c Common Noddy ('Brown Noddy')
331   50c Common Noddy ('Brown Noddy')
                      Set of 4   1.25   1.25

NEPAL
Central Asia
100 paisa = 1 rupee

1959

131†	1r Himalayan Monal Pheasant	..	..	3.00	1.25
132†	2r Himalayan Monal Pheasant	..	..	4.25	3.00
133†	5r Satyr Tragopan	..	..	20.00	5.00

1968

225   15p Himalayan Monal Pheasant..   25   15

1977

349   5p Great Indian Hornbill (*Buceros bicornis*)
350   15p Cheer Pheasant (*Catreus wellichii*)
351   1r Green Magpie (*Cissa chinensis*)
352   2r30 Spiny Babbler (*Turdoides nipalensis*)
                      Set of 4   1.25   80

1979

384   10p Great Grey Shrike (*Lanius excubitor*)
385   10r Fire-tailed Sunbird (*Aethopyga
      ignicauda*)

386   3r50 Himalayan Monal Pheasant
      (*Lophophorus impejanus*) (air)
                      Set of 3   4.25   4.25

1985

455   10r Himalayan Monal Pheasant 1.10   55

NETHERLANDS
North-west Europe
100 cents = 1 gulden

1938

486   12½c Carrion Crow
790a 25c Carrion Crow
                      Set of 2   3.50   2.00

1951

742   15g Gull sp
743   25g Gull sp
                      Set of 2   £350   £180

1961

907 4c+4c Herring Gull
908 6c+4c Oystercatcher
909 8c+4c Curlew
910 12c+8c Avocet
911 30c+10c Lapwing

Set of 5   8.25   5.25

1974

1184† 25c Northern Goshawk 1.90   40

1982

1403 50c Eider, Sandwich Tern
1404 70c Barnacle Goose

Set of 2   60   10

1410† 50c+30c Great Tit   40   15
1413† 70c+30c Palm Cockatoo   65   65

STAMP MONTHLY
— finest and most informative magazine for all collectors. Obtainable from your newsagent or by postal subscription — details on request.

1984

1435 50c+20c Lapwing
1436 60c+25c Ruff
1437 65c+25c Redshank
1438 70c+30c Black-tailed Godwit

Set of 4   1.75   1.60

NETHERLANDS ANTILLES
West Indies
100 cents = 1 gulden

1952

336† 1½c+1c Gull sp   65   75

1958

368 2½c+1c American Kestrel
369 7½c+1½c Yellow Oriole
370 15c+2½c Scaly-breasted Ground Dove
371 22½c+2½c Brown-throated Conure

Set of 4   2.40   1.90

372† 6c Greater Flamingo..   ..   ..   7.50   10
384† 50c Greater Flamingo   45   10
386† 65c Greater Flamingo   55   15
388† 75c Greater Flamingo   60   20
396† 10g Greater Flamingo 7.50   2.50

1965

467† 4c Greater Flamingo.. .. .. 25 10

1966

476 25c Budgerigar. 40 35

1972

553† 3c Greater Flamingo ('Bonaire Flamingos') 30 10

1980

734 25c White-fronted Dove (*Leptotila verreauxi*)
735 60c Tropical Mockingbird (*Mimus gilvus*)
736 85c Bananaquit (*Coereba flaveola*)
Set of 3 1.25 1.00

1984

863 45c Black-faced Grassquit (*Tiaris bicolor*)
864 55c Rufous-collared Sparrow (*Zonotrichia capensis*)
865 150c Blue-tailed Emerald (*Chlorostilbon mellisugus*)
Set of 3 3.00 2.50

1985

873 25c Greater Flamingo (*Phoenicopterus ruber ruber*)
874 45c Greater Flamingo (*Phoenicopterus ruber ruber*)
875 55c Greater Flamingo (*Phoenicopterus ruber ruber*)
876 100c Greater Flamingo (*Phoenicopterus ruber ruber*)
Set of 4 2.75 2.75

NETHERLANDS NEW GUINEA
South-east Asia
100 cents = 1 gulden

1954

25†	1c Lesser Bird of Paradise	25	10
26†	5c Lesser Bird of Paradise	25	10
60†	7c Blue Crowned Pigeon	35	20
27†	10c Greater Bird of Paradise	30	10
61†	12c Blue Crowned Pigeon	35	20
28†	15c Greater Bird of Paradise	35	10
62†	17c Blue Crowned Pigeon	35	15
29†	20c Greater Bird of Paradise	70	35

1955
Nos. 26/8 surcharged with cross and premium
38 5c + 5c Lesser Bird of Paradise
39 10c + 10c Greater Bird of Paradise
40 15c + 10c Greater Bird of Paradise
Set of 3 2.75 2.25

NEVIS
West Indies
100 cents = 1 dollar

1985

Broad-winged Hawk **20ᶜ**

265 20c Broad-winged Hawk
266 40c Red-tailed Hawk
267 60c Little Blue Heron
268 $3 Great Blue Heron (white phase) ('Great
    White Heron')

                    Set of 4 2.25 2.25

269 5c Eastern Bluebird
270 5c Common Cardinal ('Northern Cardinal')
271 55c Belted Kingfisher
272 55c Mangrove Cuckoo
273 60c Yellow Warbler
274 60c Cerulean Warbler
275 $2 Burrowing Owl
276 $2 Long-eared Owl

                    Set of 8 3.25 3.75

285 1c Painted Bunting
286 1c Golden-crowned Kinglet
287 40c Common Flicker
288 40c Western Tanager
289 60c Varied Thrush ('Sage Thrasher
    (Mountain Mocking Bird)' !)
290 60c Evening Grosbeak
291 $2.50 Blackburnian Warbler
292 $2.50 Northern Oriole

                    Set of 8 3.25 3.75

NEW CALEDONIA
South Pacific
100 centimes = 1 franc

1905

85†	1c Kagu	15	10
86†	2c Kagu	15	10
87†	4c Kagu	15	10
88†	5c Kagu (green)	20	10
112†	5c Kagu (blue)	15	10
113†	10c Kagu (green)	40	25
114†	10c Kagu (red)	20	15
90†	15c Kagu	30	15

1912
No. 90 surcharged in figures

124†	0.05 on 15c Kagu	25	25
125†	25c on 15c Kagu	20	20

1915
No. 114 surcharged with large red cross and **5 NCE**

107	10c†5c Kagu	30	35

Nos. 90 and 114 surcharged in figures and small red cross

109	10c + 5c Kagu		
110	15c + 5c Kagu		
	Set of 2	50	50

1918
No. 90 surcharged **5 CENTIMES**

111	5c on 15c Kagu	40	40

1942

267	5c Kagu	
268	10c Kagu	
269	25c Kagu	
270	30c Kagu	
271	40c Kagu	
272	80c Kagu	
273	1f Kagu	
274	1f50 Kagu	
275	2f Kagu	
276	2f50 Kagu	
277	4f Kagu	
278	5f Kagu	
279	10f Kagu	
280	20f Kagu	
	Set of 14	5.75 5.25

1945

Nos. 267, 269 and 276 surcharged

291 50c on 5c Kagu
292 60c on 5c Kagu
293 70c on 5c Kagu
294 1f20 on 5c Kagu
295 2f40 on 25c Kagu
296 3f on 25c Kagu
297 4f50 on 25c Kagu
298 15f on 2f50 Kagu

Set of 8 2.75 2.50

1948

306† 10c Kagu ('Kagous') 10 5
307† 30c Kagu ('Kagous') 15 5
308† 40c Kagu ('Kagous') 15 5

1960

358† 4f Kagu 60 30

1966

403 1f Red-throated Parrot Finch (Erythrura psittacea)
404 1f New Caledonian Grass Warbler (Megalurulus mariei)
405 2f New Caledonian Whistler (Pachycephala caledonica)
406 3f New Caledonian Pigeon (Ducula goliath)
407 3f White-throated Pigeon (Columba vitiensis hypoenochroa)
408 4f Kagu (Rhynochetus jubatus)
409 5f Horned Parakeet (Ennymphicus cornutus)
410 10f Red-faced Honeyeater (Gymnomyza aubryana)
411 15f New Caledonian Friarbird (Philemon diemenensis)
412 30f Sacred Kingfisher (Halcyon sanctus canacorum)

413 27f Horned Parakeet (Eunimphicus cornutus uveaensis) (air)
414 37f Scarlet Honeyeater (Myzomela sanguinolenta)
415 39f Emerald Dove (Chalcophaps indica chrysochlora)
416 50f Cloven-feathered Dove (Drepanoptila holosericea)
417 100f Whistling Hawk (Haliastur sphenurus)

Set of 15 50.00 22.00

1976

561 1f Brown Booby (Sula leucogaster)
562 2f Blue-faced Booby (Sula dactylatra)
563 8f Red-footed Booby (Sula sula)

Set of 3 1.40 70

1977

586 16f Great Frigate Bird (Fregate minor)
587 42f Great Frigate Bird (Fregate minor) (air)

Set of 2 3.00 1.40

1978

594 22f Black-naped Tern (Sterna sumatrana)
595 40f Sooty Tern (Sterna fuscata)

Set of 2 2.50 1.25

1982

767 220f Kagu ('Le Cagou') 2.50 1.75

682 100f Kagu 1.25 80

777 50f Purple Swamphen (*Porphyrio porphyrio
     caledonicus*)
778 60f Island Thrush (*Turdus poliocephalus
     xanthopus*)
      Set of 2 1.25 85

684 32f Grey's Fruit Dove ('Ptilope de Grey')
685 35f Rainbow Lory ('Loriquet Caledonien')
      Set of 2 1.60 80

1986

1983

791 110f Black-backed Magpie 1.25 1.00

718 34f Barn Owl (*Tyto alba lifuensis*)
719 37f Osprey (*Pandion haliaetus melvillensis*)
      Set of 2 1.50 80

NEWFOUNDLAND
North Atlantic
100 cents = 1 dollar

1897

1985

74† 12c Willow/Red Grouse ('Ptarmigan') 23.00 4.00

744 1f Kagu
745 2f Kagu
746 3f Kagu
747 4f Kagu
748 5f Kagu
749 35f Kagu
750 38f Kagu
751 40f Kagu
      Set of 8 1.40 1.40

NEW GUINEA
Australasia
12 pence = 1 shilling,
20 shillings = 1 pound

All bird stamps of New Guinea show Raggiana Bird of Paradise

1931

Dated '1921–1931'

150	1d green	
151	1½d red	
152	2d red	
153	3d blue	
154	4d olive	
155	5d green	
156	6d brown	
157	9d violet	
158	1s grey	
159	2s red	
160	5s brown	
161	10s red	
162	£1 grey	

Set of 13 £275 £425

Nos. 150/62 and additional value overprinted **AIR MAIL** *and biplane*

163	½d orange	
164	1d green	
165	1½d red	
166	2d red	
167	3d blue	
168	4d olive	
169	5d green	
170	6d brown	
171	9d violet	
172	1s grey	
173	2s red	
174	5s brown	
175	10s red	
176	£1 grey	

Set of 14 £200 £350

1932

Without dates

177	1d green	
178	1½d red	
179	2d red	
179a	2½d green	
180	3d blue	
180a	3½d red	
181	4d olive	
182	5d green	

183	6d brown	
184	9d violet	
185	1s grey	
186	2s red	
187	5s brown	
188	10s red	
189	£1 grey	

Set of 15 £190 £250

Nos. 177/89 and additional value overprinted **AIR MAIL** *and biplane*

190	½d orange	
191	1d green	
192	1½d red	
193	2d red	
193a	2½d green	
194	3d blue	
194a	3½d red	
195	4d olive	
196	5d green	
197	6d brown	
198	9d violet	
199	1s grey	
200	2s red	
201	5s brown	
202	10s red	
203	£1 grey	

Set of 16 £180 £200

1935

Nos. 177 and 179 overprinted **HIS MAJESTY'S JUBILEE. 1910 – 1935**

206	1d green	
207	2d red	

Set of 2 1.75 1.60

OFFICIAL STAMPS

1931
Nos. 150/60 overprinted **O S**

O10	1d green	
O11	1½d red	
O12	2d red	
O13	3d blue	
O14	4d olive	
O15	5d green	
O16	6d brown	
O17	9d violet	
O18	1s grey	
O19	2s red	
O20	5s brown	

Set of 11 £180 £300

1932
Nos. 177/87 overprinted **O S**

O21	1d green	
O22	1½d red	
O23	2d red	
O24	2½d green	
O25	3d blue	
O26	3½d red	
O27	4d olive	
O28	5d green	
O29	6d brown	
O30	9d violet	
O31	1s grey	
O32	2s red	
O33	5s brown	

Set of 13 £200 £325

NEW HEBRIDES

South Pacific
1908 100 centimes = 1 franc
1938 100 gold centimes = 1 gold franc
1977 100 centimes = 1 franc

'F' Nos. are inscribed in French; others in English

1908

Nos. 88 and 114 of New Caledonia overprinted **NOUVELLES HEBRIDES**

F1†	5c Kagu	75	75
F2†	10c Kagu	80	80

1910

Nos. 88 and 114 of New Caledonia overprinted **NOUVELLES HEBRIDES CONDOMINIUM**

F6†	5c Kagu	35	35
F7†	10c Kagu	40	40

1963

106†	1f Cardinal Honeyeater (Myzomela cardinalis)	2.50	1.75
107†	2f Buff-bellied Flycatcher (Neolalage banksiana)	2.75	2.00
108†	3f Thicket Warbler (Cichlornis grosvenori !)	10.00	8.00
109†	5f White-collared Kingfisher (Halcyon chloris)	18.00	14.00
F121†	1f Cardinal Honeyeater (as No. 106)	2.00	1.25
F122†	2f Buff-bellied Flycatcher (as No. 107)	6.50	3.75
F123†	3f Thicket Warbler (as No. 108) ('RF...ER')	11.00	11.00
F124†	3f Thicket Warbler (as No. 108) ('ER...RF')	5.50	5.00
F125†	5f White-collared Kingfisher (as No. 109)	15.00	13.00

1972

159†	10c Baker's Pigeon (Ducula bakeri)	10	10
161†	20c Red-headed Parrot Finch (Erythrura cyanovirens)	25	25
164†	35c Chestnut-bellied Kingfisher (Halcyon farquhari)	40	40
167†	2f Palm Lorikeet (Vini palmarum)	3.25	3.50
F174†	10c Baker's Pigeon (as No. 159)	35	12
F176†	20c Red-headed Parrot Finch (as No. 161)	50	25
F179†	35c Chestnut-bellied Kingfisher (as No. 164).	75	40
F182†	2f Palm Lorikeet (as No. 167)	4.50	4.50

1974

184†	25c Pacific Pigeon ('Pacific Dove')	95	55
F199†	25c Pacific Pigeon (as No.184) ('Nautou').	1.25	60

Nos. 164 and 167 overprinted **ROYAL VISIT 1974**

188	35c Chestnut-bellied Kingfisher		
189	2f Palm Lorikeet		
	Set of 2	1.25	1.75

Nos. F179 and F182 overprinted **VISITE ROYALE 1974**

F203	35c Chestnut-bellied Kingfisher		
F204	2f Palm Lorikeet		
	Set of 2	3.50	4.00

1977

Nos. 159, 161, 164 and 167 surcharged

221†	10f on 10c Baker's Pigeon	45	35
223†	20f on 20c Red-headed Parrot Finch	70	55
226†	35f on 35c Chestnut-bellied Kingfisher .	1.25	1.25
229†	70f on 2f Palm Lorikeet	2.50	2.50

Nos. F174, F176, F179 and F182 surcharged

F235†	10f on 10c Baker's Pigeon	40	35
F237†	20f on 20c Red-headed Parrot Finch	80	65
F240†	35f on 35c Chestnut-bellied Kingfisher	1.60	1.25
F243†	70f on 2f Palm Lorikeet .	3.25	2.50

1980

283	10f White-bellied Honeyeater (Phylidonyris notabilis)	
284	20f Scarlet Robin (Petroica multicolor similis)	
285	30f Yellow-fronted White Eye (Zosterops flavifrons flavifrons)	
286	40f Fan-tailed Cuckoo (Cacomantis pyrrhophanus schistaceigularis)	
	Set of 4	2.50	2.50

F296	10f White-bellied Honeyeater (as No. 283)		
F297	20f Scarlet Robin (as No. 284)		
F298	30f Yellow-fronted White Eye (as No. 285)		
F299	40f Fan-tailed Cuckoo (as No. 286)		
	Set of 4	4.00	3.25

STAMP MONTHLY

— finest and most informative magazine for all collectors. Obtainable from your newsagent or by postal subscription — details on request.

NEW SOUTH WALES
Australia
12 pence = 1 shilling,
20 shillings = 1 pound

1888

254†	2d Emu.	3.25	10
257†	8d Superb Lyrebird	8.50	1.50

1892

345a†	2s6d Superb Lyrebird	27.00	11.00

OFFICIAL STAMPS

1879
Nos. 254 and 257 overprinted **O S**

O40†	2d Emu	2.00	10
O43†	8d Superb Lyrebird	10.00	3.75

NEW ZEALAND
Australasia
1898 12 pence = 1 shilling,
20 shillings = 1 pound
1967 100 cents = 1 dollar

1898

23 mm wide

309†	3d Huia *	14.00	35
254†	6d Brown Kiwi (green)	48.00	22.00
265†	6d Brown Kiwi (red)	35.00	2.50
268a†	1s Kaka, Kea	30.00	3.25

1907

21 mm wide

438†	3d Huia *	45.00	8.00
430†	6d Brown Kiwi	45.00	7.00
440†	1s Kaka, Kea	£120	24.00

1935

577†	½d Collared Grey Fantail	25	5
578†	1d Brown Kiwi	25	5
588†	1s Tui	1.50	10

1956

754†	8d Takahe..	65	1.25

1958

769†	3d Australian Gannet ('Cape Kidnappers').	20	5

1959

771	3d Brown Kiwi..	12	5

776 2d + 1d Grey Teal ('Tete')
777 3d + 1d New Zealand Stilt ('Poaka')

Set of 2   30   30

1964

822 2½d + 1d Silver Gull ('Tarapunga')
823 3d + 1d Little Penguin ('Korora')

Set of 2   25   40

1960

803 2d + 1d Sacred Kingfisher ('Kotare')
804 3d + 1d New Zealand Pigeon ('Kereru')

Set of 2   60   65

1965

831 3d + 1d Kaka
832 4d + 1d Collared Grey Fantail
     ('Piwakawaka (Fantail)')

Set of 2   40   50

1961

806 2d + 1d Great Egret ('Kotuku')
807 3d + 1d New Zealand Falcon ('Karearea')

Set of 2   40   50

1966

839 3d + 1d New Zealand Bell Bird ('Bellbird')
840 4d + 1d Weka Rail ('Weka')

Set of 2   30   50

1962

812 2½d + 1d Red-fronted Parakeet ('Kakariki')
813 3d + 1d Saddleback ('Tieke')

Set of 2   40   50

1970

947† 2c Shy Albatross ('Chatham Islands
      Mollymawk')   15   25
                          (946/7 Set of 2)   25   40

1982

1288†	30c Kakapo	20	15
1289†	40c Mountain Duck ('blue duck')	25	15
1290†	45c New Zealand Falcon ('falcon')	25	20
1291†	60c New Zealand Teal ('brown teal')	35	25
1292†	$1 Kokako	60	30
1293†	$2 Chatham Island Robin ('black robin') ..	1.25	70
1294†	$3 Stitchbird..	1.75	1.40
1295†	$4 Saddleback	2.50	2.00

1984

1328†	40c Adelie Penguin..	35	35

OFFICIAL STAMPS

1907

Nos. 309, 265 and 268a overprinted **OFFICIAL.**

O63†	3d Huia *	35.00	2.50
O64†	6d Brown Kiwi	£110	15.00
O65†	1s Kaka, Kea..	85.00	15.00

1908

No. 430 overprinted **OFFICIAL.**

O71†	6d Brown Kiwi	£110	26.00

1936

Nos. 577/8 and 588 overprinted **Official**

O120†	½d Collared Grey Fantail	2.50	2.25
O115†	1d Brown Kiwi	60	10
O131†	1s Tui	4.00	85

NICARAGUA

Central America

100 centavos = 1 cordoba

1967

1575†	75c Mute Swan ('Los Cisnes')..	30	20

1971

1781	10c Montezuma Oropendola (*Gymnostinops montezuma*)
1782	15c Turquoise-browed Motmot (*Eumomota superciliosa*)
1783	20c White-throated Magpie-Jay (*Calocitta formosa*)
1784	25c Scissor-tailed Flycatcher (*Muscivora forficata*)
1785	30c Spotted-breasted Oriole (*Icterus pectoralis pectoralis*)
1786	35c Rufous-naped Wren (*Campylorhynchus rufinucha*)
1787	40c Great Kiskadee (*Pitangus sulphuratus*)
1788	75c Red-legged Honeycreeper (*Cyanerpes cyaneus*)
1789	1cor Great-tailed Grackle (*Cassidix mexicanus*)
1790	2cor Belted Kingfisher (*Megaceryle alcyon*)

Set of 10	2.75	1.50

1972

1829†	15c Gyrfalcon	15	5

1976

2088† 2c Mute Swan (on Western Australia
stamp No. 3)   25   10

1979

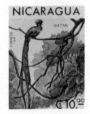

2202† 50c Broad-tailed Hummingbird   25   10

1981

MS2267   10cor Resplendent Quetzal ('Quetzal')..   1.75   1.75

2304   50c Lineated Woodpecker (*Dryocopus
      lineatus*)
2305   1cor20 Keel-billed Toucan (*Ramphastos
      sulfuratus*)
2306   1cor80 Finsch's Conure (*Aratinga finschi*)
2307   2cor Scarlet Macaw (*Ara macao*)

2308   3cor Slaty-tailed Trogon (*Trogon
      massena*) (air)
2309   4cor Violet Sabrewing (*Campylopterus
      hemileucurus*)
2310   6cor Blue-crowned Motmot (*Momotus
      momota*)
                         Set of 7   3.25   1.75

1985

2686†   50c Ring-necked Pheasant ('Faisan').. ..   10   5
2688†   1cor   Helmet   Guineafowl   ('Gallina
      guinea')   15   5
2690†   6cor Ocellated Turkey ('Pavo').   20   8

1986

2724   1cor Crimson Topaz ('Colibri Topacio')
2725   3cor Orange-billed Nightingale Thrush
      ('Paraulata Picodorado')
2726   3cor Troupial ('Trupial')
2727   5cor Painted Bunting ('Verderon Pintado')
2728   10cor Frantzius's Nightingale Thrush
      ('Tordo Ruisenor')
2729   21cor Great Horned Owl ('Buho Real')
2730   75cor Great Kiskadee ('Gran Kiskadee')
                         Set of 7   2.50   2.10

NIGER
West Africa
100 centimes = 1 franc

1959

100†   1f Crowned Crane ('Grues Couronnees') ..   25   10
101†   2f Crowned Crane ('Grues Couronnees') ..   25   10
102†   5f Saddle-bill Stork ('Jabirus')   25   10
103†   7f Saddle-bill Stork ('Jabirus')   30   15
109†   50f Ostrich ('Autruches') 1.75   60
110†   60f Ostrich ('Autruches') 2.00   85

113†   200f Carmine Bee Eater ('Guepier Rouge')
      (air) 6.50   2.75

1967

247 1f Red-billed Hornbill (*Tockus erythrorhynchus*)
248 2f Lesser Pied Kingfisher (*Ceryle rudis rudis*)
249 30f Common Gonolek (*Laniarius barbarus*)
249a 40f Red Bishop (*Euplectes orix franciscanus*)
250 45f Little Masked Weaver (*Ploceus luteolus*)
250a 65f Little Masked Weaver (*Ploceus luteolus*)
251 70f Chestnut-bellied Sandgrouse (*Pterocles exustus*)

251a 250f Splendid Glossy Starling (*Camprocolius splendidus*) (air)
                                        Set of 8   4.50   3.00

1968

Dated '1968'
292 5f African Grey Hornbill (*Tockus nasutus*)
293 10f Woodland Kingfisher (*Halcyon senegalensis*)
294 15f Senegal Coucal (*Centropus senegalensis*)
295 20f Rose-ringed Parakeet (*Psittacula krameri*)
296 25f Abyssinian Roller (*Coracias abyssinica*)
297 50f Cattle Egret (*Bulbucus ibis*)

298 100f Violet Starling (*Cinnyricinclus leucogaster*) (air)
                                        Set of 7   2.75   2.00

1971

Dated '1970', '1971' or '1972'
372 5f African Grey Hornbill (*Tockus nasutus*)
373 10f Woodland Kingfisher (*Halcyon senegalensis*)
374 15f Senegal Coucal (*Centropus senegalensis*)
375 20f Rose-ringed Parakeet (*Psittacula krameri*)

376 35f Broad-tailed Paradise Whydah (*Steganura paradisea orientalis*)
377 50f Cattle Egret (*Bulbucus ibis*)
                                        Set of 6   3.25   1.90
See also Nos. 714/15.

1972

453† 25f Raven ('Le Corbeau')   50   20

1975

567 25f Abyssinian Roller (*Coracias abyssinica*)

568 100f Violet Starling (*Cinnyricinclus leucogaster*) (air)
                                        Set of 2   1.25   60

1977

673† 80f Marabou Stork (*Leptoptilus crumeniferus*)   85   50
                                        (673/4 Set of 2)   1.25   95

STANLEY GIBBONS
STAMP COLLECTING SERIES
Introductory booklets on *How to Start, How to Identify Stamps* and *Collecting by Theme*. A series of well illustrated guides at a low price.
Write for details.

1978

As Nos. 376/7 but redrawn and background colour of 35f changed
to blue. 35f undated, 50f dated '1978'
714 35f Broad-tailed Paradise Whydah
      (*Steganura paradisea orientalis*)
715 50f Cattle Egret (*Bulbucus ibis*)
                                    Set of 2   70   35

733 100f Golden Eagle
734 100f Crowned Crane (on stamp No. 101)
                                    Set of 2   2.25   2.00

736† 50f Ostrich (*Struthio camelus*)   50   30

1981

839† 10f Ostrich ('Autruche')   25   10
842† 30f Arabian Bustard ('Grande Outarde') ..   30   15

1985

1021 110f Black-necked Stilt (*Himantopus
        mexicanus*)
1022 140f Greater Flamingo (*Phoenicopterus
        ruber*)
1023 200f Atlantic Puffin (*Fratercula arctica*)
1024 350f Arctic Tern (*Sterna paradisaea*)
                                    Set of 4   3.75   3.25

1045† 210f Sudan Golden Sparrow (*Passer
          luteus*).. .. ..   1.25   90
1046† 390f Red-billed Quelea (*Quelea quelea*) ..   2.25   1.75

NIGERIA
West Africa
1961 12 pence = 1 shilling,
20 shillings = 1 pound
1973 100 kobo = 1 naira

1961

96† 1s Yellow-casqued Hornbill ('Hornbill')   35   5

1965

NIGERIA

174† 1½d Splendid Sunbird.   25   1.40
175† 2d Village Weaver, Red-headed Malimbe
        ('Weavers')..   60   5

178†	6d Saddle-bill Stork	60	5
179†	9d Grey Parrot	65	30
180†	1s Blue-breasted Kingfisher ('Kingfishers')	70	5
181†	1s3d Crowned Crane ('Crown Bird')	2.75	15
185†	£1 Cattle Egret	15.00	8.50

See also Nos. 222/8.

1969

As Nos. 175 and 178/81 but additionally inscribed 'N.S.P. & M. CO. LTD' *at foot*

222†	2d Village Weaver, Red-headed Malimbe ..	80	5
225†	6d Saddle-bill Stork	1.00	25
226†	9d Grey Parrot	3.00	1.25
227†	1s Blue-breasted Kingfisher	1.75	20
228†	1s3d Crowned Crane	3.75	1.40

1984

484	10k Pin-tailed Whydah		
485	25k Spur-winged Plover		
486	30k Red Bishop		
487	45k Double-spurred Francolin ('Francolin')		
	Set of 4	2.75	2.75

NIUAFO'OU
South Pacific
100 seniti = 1 pa'anga

1983

27	1s Purple Swamphen		
28	2s White-collared Kingfisher		
29	3s Red-headed Parrot Finch		
30	5s Banded Rail		
31	6s Polynesian Scrub Hen ('Niuafo'ou Magapode')		
32	9s Green Honeyeater ('Giant Forest Honeyeater')		
33	10s Purple Swamphen		
34	13s Banded Rail		
35	15s Polynesian Scrub Hen ('Niuafo'ou Megapode')		
36	20s Banded Rail		
37	29s Red-headed Parrot Finch		
38	32s White-collared Kingfisher		

39	47s Polynesian Scrub Hen ('Niuafo'ou Megapode')		
40	1p Purple Swamphen		
41	2p Polynesian Scrub Hen ('Niuafo'ou Megapode')		
	Set of 15	3.25	3.75

1984

45†	1p50 Polynesian Scrub Hen ('Niuafo'ou Megapode')	1.50	2.00

1986

Nos. 32/9 surcharged

74	4s on 9s Green Honeyeater		
75	4s on 10s Purple Swamphen		
76	42s on 13s Banded Rail		
77	42s on 15s Polynesian Scrub Hen		
78	57s on 29s Red-headed Parrot Finch		
79	57s on 32s White-collared Kingfisher		
80	2p50 on 20s Banded Rail		
81	2p50 on 47s Polynesian Scrub Hen		
	Set of 8	4.50	5.00

NIUE
South Pacific
1902 12 pence = 1 shilling
1967 100 cents = 1 dollar

1902

Nos. 309, 265 and 268a of New Zealand surcharged **NIUE** *and value in native language*

13†	3d Huia *	4.50	4.50
14†	6d Brown Kiwi	3.25	8.00
16†	1s Kaka, Kea	16.00	17.00

1971

158	5c Spotted Triller ('Heahea')		
159	10c Purple-capped Fruit Dove ('Kulukulu')		
160	20c Blue-crowned Lory ('Henga')		
	Set of 3	1.50	60

1985

581 40c House Wren
582 70c Veery
583 83c Grasshopper Sparrow
584 $1.05 Henslow's Sparrow
585 $2.50 Vesper Sparrow
Set of 5   3.75   4.00
MS586 Five sheets. (a) $1.75 House Wren; (b)
$1.75 Veery; (c) $1.75 Grasshopper
Sparrow; (d) $1.75 Henslow's
Sparrow; (e) $1.75 Vesper Sparrow
Price for 5 sheets   6.50   6.75

1986

628 40c Great Egret (*Egretta alba*)
629 60c Painted Finch (*Emblema picta*)
630 75c Australian King Parrot (*Aprosmictus
    scapularis*)
631 80c Variegated Wren (*Malurus lamberti*)
632 $1 Peregrine Falcon (*Falco peregrinus*)
633 $1.65 Azure Kingfisher (*Halcyon azurea*)
634 $2.20 Budgerigar (*Melopsittacus undulatus*)
635 $4.25 Emu (*Dromaius novaehollandiae*)
Set of 8   7.50   8.25

NORFOLK ISLAND
Australasia
1953 12 pence = 1 shilling
1966 100 cents = 1 dollar

1953

26† 3d White Tern   90   30
32† 2s Solander's Petrel ('Providence Petrel') .. 5.50 1.75
36† 10s Red-tailed Tropic Bird 48.00 22.00

1966
Nos. 26, 32 and 36 surcharged in decimal currency
62† 3c on 3d White Tern   60   15
67† 20c on 2s Solander's Petrel 4.00   1.50
71† $1 on 10s Red-tailed Tropic Bird. 4.50   2.75

1970

103 1c Scarlet Robin ('Norfolk Island Robin')
104 2c Golden Whistler ('Norfolk Island
     Thickhead')
105 3c New Zealand Grey Flyeater ('Norfolk
     Island Fly Eater')
106 4c Long-tailed Koel ('Longtailed Cuckoo')
107 5c Red-fronted Parakeet ('Norfolk Island
     Green Parrot')
108 7c Long-tailed Triller ('Norfolk Island
     Caterpillar-catcher')
109 9c Island Thrush ('Grey-headed Blackbird')
110 10c Boobook Owl ('Norfolk Island Owl')
111 15 New Zealand Pigeon (subspecies *)
     ('Norfolk Island Pigeon')
112 20c White-chested White Eye ('White-
     breasted White-eye')
113 25c Norfolk Island Parrot * ('Philip Island
     Parrot')
114 30c Collared Grey Fantail ('Norfolk Island
     Fantail')
115 45c Norfolk Island Starling
116 50c Crimson Rosella ('Red Parrot')
117 $1 Sacred Kingfisher ('Norfolk Island
     Kingfisher')
Set of 15   30.00   18.00

1974

160† 35c Crimson Rosella, Sacred Kingfisher .. 1.10   1.40

STAMP MONTHLY
— finest and most informative magazine for all
collectors. Obtainable from your newsagent or by
postal subscription — details on request.

1976

175† 45c California Quail 85 70

1982

277† 24c Sooty Tern (*Sterna fuscata*). 25 25
282† 35c Blue-faced Booby (*Sula dactylatra*) .. 35 35

284† 24c Red-tailed Tropic Bird 35 35

176 18c Swallow-tailed Tern
177 25c Swallow-tailed Tern
178 45c Swallow-tailed Tern

Set of 3 1.60 1.10

1984

Norfolk Island 30c

338 30c Boobook Owl (with eggs)
339 30c Boobook Owl (fledgeling)
340 30c Boobook Owl (young owl on stump)
341 30c Boobook Owl (adult on branch)
342 30c Boobook Owl (in flight)

Set of 5 1.90 2.00

1980

254 15c Red-tailed Tropic Bird
255 22c White Tern
256 35c White-capped Noddy
257 60c White Tern

Set of 4 1.50 1.50

1981

NORFOLK ISLAND

Zosterops albogularis 35c

Inscribed 'White-breasted Silvereye, *Zosterops albogularis*'
269 35c White-chested White Eye (pair)
270 35c White-chested White Eye (on nest)
271 35c White-chested White Eye (with egg shell)
272 35c White-chested White Eye (parents with chicks)
273 35c White-chested White Eye (fledgelings)

Set of 5 2.25 2.00

NORTH BORNEO
South-east Asia
100 cents = 1 dollar

1894

72† 5c Great Argus Pheasant.. .. .. 5.50 9.50

1897
As No. 72 but with Malay inscriptions inserted
100† 5c Great Argus Pheasant 11.00 4.25

1899
No. 100 surcharged **4 CENTS**

112a†	4c on 5c Great Argus Pheasant	9.00	10.00

1901
No. 100 overprinted **BRITISH PROTECTORATE.**

131a†	5c Great Argus Pheasant	4.00	2.25

1904
No. 100 surcharged **4 cents**

146†	4c on 5c Great Argus Pheasant	9.50	17.00

1909

285†	12c Palm Cockatoo	3.50	80
174†	16c Rhinoceros Hornbill..	14.00	4.25
176†	24c Dwarf Cassowary	16.00	3.00

1916
No. 285 surcharged

188†	10c on 12c Palm Cockatoo	10.00	17.00

Nos. 285, 174 and 176 overprinted with a Maltese cross

197†	12c Palm Cockatoo	35.00	55.00
198†	16c Rhinoceros Hornbill..	35.00	55.00
200†	24c Dwarf Cassowary	50.00	60.00

1918
Nos. 285, 174 and 176 surcharged **RED CROSS TWO CENTS**

224†	12c + 2c Palm Cockatoo	4.00	14.00
225†	16c + 2c Rhinoceros Hornbill	6.00	19.00
226†	24c + 2c Dwarf Cassowary	7.50	19.00

Nos. 285, 174 and 176 surcharged **FOUR CENTS** *and cross*

243†	12c + 4c Palm Cockatoo	5.00	11.00
244†	16c + 4c Rhinoceros Hornbill	5.00	18.00
245†	24c + 4c Dwarf Cassowary	6.00	20.00

1922
Nos. 285, 174 and 176 overprinted **MALAYA–BORNEO EXHIBITION 1922.**

265†	12c Palm Cockatoo	4.50	20.00
267†	16c Rhinoceros Hornbill..	4.25	25.00
270†	24c Dwarf Cassowary	7.50	30.00

1939

304†	2c Palm Cockatoo	60	30

1941
No. 304 overprinted **WAR TAX**

319†	2c Palm Cockatoo	45	1.25
	(318/19 *Set of* 2)	55	1.75

1945
No. 304 overprinted **BMA**

321†	2c Palm Cockatoo	75	40

1947
No. 304 overprinted with 'GR' cypher and bars obliterating 'The State of' and 'British Protectorate'

336†	2c Palm Cockatoo	45	50

1961

404†	$2 Rhinoceros Hornbill ('Hornbill')	4.00	1.50
405†	$5 Crested Wood Partridge ('Crested Jungle Partridge')	14.00	6.50

POSTAGE DUE STAMPS

1895
No. 72 overprinted **POSTAGE DUE**

D4†	5c Great Argus Pheasant	7.50	15.00

1897
No. 100 overprinted **POSTAGE DUE**

D19†	5c Great Argus Pheasant	5.00	10.00

1902
No. 131a overprinted **POSTAGE DUE**

D39†	5c Great Argus Pheasant	3.25	2.50

1920
Nos. 285 and 174 overprinted **POSTAGE DUE**

D64†	12c Palm Cockatoo..	7.00	18.00
D56b†	16c Rhinoceros Hornbill	9.00	24.00

NORTH KOREA
See under Korea

NORTH VIETNAM
See under Vietnam

NORWAY
Northern Europe
100 ore = 1 krone

1956

462 35ore Whooper Swan
463 65ore Whooper Swan
Set of 2   1.60   1.25

1970

647† 100ore White-tailed Sea Eagle (*Haliaeetus albicilla*). 1.40   1.00

1980

856 1k Oystercatcher (*Haematopus ostralegus*)
857 1k Mallard (*Anas platyrhynchos*)
858 1k25 Dipper (*Cinclus cinclus*)
859 1k25 Great Tit (*Parus major*)
Set of 4   1.25   35

1981

869 1k30 Lesser White-fronted Goose (*Anser erythropus*)
870 1k30 Peregrine Falcon (*Falco peregrinus*)
871 1k50 Atlantic Puffin (*Fratercula arctica*)
872 1k50 Black Guillemot (*Cepphus grylle*)
Set of 4   1.40   35

1982

894 2k Bluethroat (*Luscinia svecica*)
895 2k European Robin (*Erithacus rubecula*)
Set of 2   80   40

1983

914 2k50 Barnacle Goose (*Branta leucopsis*)
915 2k50 Little Auk (*Alle alle*)
Set of 2   1.00   50

1985

964† 2k50 Bullfinch   50   10
(963/4 Set of 2)   90   20

1986

979† 2k50 European Robin   40   10
(979/80 Set of 2)   1.00   45

STANLEY GIBBONS
STAMP COLLECTING SERIES
Introductory booklets on *How to Start, How to Identify Stamps* and *Collecting by Theme*. A series of well illustrated guides at a low price.
Write for details.

OCEANIC SETTLEMENTS
South Pacific
100 centimes = 1 franc

1948

207†	50f Wandering Albatross.	10.00	6.00
209†	200f Wandering Albatross	23.00	10.00

OMAN
Arabia
1000 baizas = 1 rial

1982

267†	100b Arabian Chukar (*Alectoris melanocephala*)	60	40
268†	¼r Hoopoe (*Upupa epops*)	1.40	1.25

PAKISTAN
Indian Sub-continent
100 paisa = 1 rupee

1975

394	20p Black Partridge		
395	2r25 Black Partridge		
		Set of 2 2.40	2.50

1976

411	20p Common Peafowl ('Peacock')		
412	3r Common Peafowl ('Peacock')		
		Set of 2 2.40	2.50

1979

493	20p Himalayan Monal Pheasant		
494	25p Kalij Pheasant		
495	40p Koklass Pheasant		
496	1r Cheer Pheasant		
		Set of 4 90	45

1980
No. 496 overprinted **WORLD TOURISM CONFERENCE MANILA 80**

538	1r Cheer Pheasant.	10	12

1981

572	40p Western Tragopan		
573	2r Western Tragopan		
		Set of 2 80	50

1983

605	3r Great White Crane ('Siberian Crane')	30	35

1986

691 1r50 Peregrine Falcon ('Shaheen Falcon') .. 25 20

1987

707 5r Mistletoe Flowerpecker ('Defence)
708 5r Spotted Pardalote ('Education')
709 5r Black-throated Blue Warbler
    ('Agriculture')
710 5r Red-capped Manakin ('Industry')

Set of 2 1.40 1.50

PALAU
North Pacific
100 cents = 1 dollar

1983

5 20c Palau Fruit Dove
6 20c Morning Bird ('Palau Morningbird')
7 20c Palau White Eye ('Giant White-eye')
8 20c Palau Fantail

Set of 4 1.50 1.00

1984

52 40c White-tailed Tropic Bird
53 40c White Tern ('Fairy Tern')
54 40c White-capped Noddy ('Black Noddy')
55 40c Black-naped Tern

Set of 4 1.75 1.25

1985

68 22c Audubon's Shearwater (chick)
69 22c Audubon's Shearwater (head)
70 22c Audubon's Shearwater (flying)
71 22c Audubon's Shearwater (swimming)

72 44c Audubon's Shearwater (air)

Set of 5 1.25 1.00

1986

98 44c Palau Myiagra Flycatcher ('Mangrove
    Flycatcher')
99 44c Cardinal Honeyeater
100 44c Blue-faced Parrot Finch
101 44c Grey-brown White Eye ('Dusky White-
    eye'), Bridled White Eye

Set of 4 2.00 1.50

163† 22c White Tern 30 15

PANAMA
Central America
100 centesimos = 1 balboa

1965

915   1c Cuvier's Toucan (*Ramphastos
      sulfuratus* !)
916   2c Scarlet Macaw (*Ara macao*)
917   3c Black-cheeked Woodpecker (*Centurus
      rubricapillus* !)
918   4c Blue-grey Tanager (*Thraupis episcopis*)
919   5c Troupial (*Cacicus cela* !)
920   10c Crimson-backed Tanager
      (*Ramphocelus dimidiatus*)

                          Set of 6   1.50   50

1967

944   ¹⁄₂c American Anhinga (*Amhinga amhinga*)
945   1c Resplendent Quetzal (*Pharomachrus
      mocinno*)
946   3c Turquoise-browed Motmot ('Momotus
      de Corona Azul—Motmot')
947   4c Red-necked Aracari ('Pico Feo—Tucan')
948   5c Chestnut-fronted Macaw
      ('Guacamaya—Ara')
949   13c Belted Kingfisher (*Achloceoite
      amazona*)

                          Set of 6   1.25   45

COLLECT MAMMALS ON STAMPS
The second Stanley Gibbons thematic catalogue —
copies are available at £7.50 (p. + p. £1.50) from:
Stanley Gibbons Publications Ltd, 5 Parkside,
Christchurch Road, Ringwood, Hants BH24 3SH.

1981

1288   3c Crimson-backed Tanager
       (*Ramphocelus dimidiatus*)
1289   6c Chestnut-fronted Macaw (*Ara severa*)
1290   41c Violet Sabrewing (*Campylopterus
       hemileucurus*)
1291   50c Keel-billed Toucan (*Ramphastos
       sulfuratus*)

                          Set of 4   2.40   1.50

Appendix
The following stamps have either been issued in excess of
postal needs, or have not been made available to the public in
reasonable quantities at face value. Miniature sheets,
imperforate stamps etc. are excluded from this section.

1967
Goya's Paintings. 21c Magpie

PAPUA
Australasia
12 pence = 1 shilling,
20 shillings = 1 pound

1932

133†   2d Raggiana Bird of Paradise 4.00   30

1935
No. 133 overprinted **HIS MAJESTY'S JUBILEE. 1910 – 1935**
151†   2d Raggiana Bird of Paradise   95   65

PAPUA NEW GUINEA
Australasia
1952 12 pence = 1 shilling,
20 shillings = 1 pound
1966 100 cents = 1 dollar
1975 100 toea = 1 kina

1952

4† 2½d Greater Bird of Paradise 1.75   40

1957
No. 4 surcharged 4d
16† 4d on 2½d Greater Bird of Paradise 20   5

1963

42† 5d Raggiana Bird of Paradise 80   5

1964

61 1d Striped Gardener Bowerbird (Amblyornis subalaris)
62 3d Adelbert Bowerbird (Sericulus bakeri)
63 5d Blue Bird of Paradise (Paradisaea rudolphi)
64 6d Lawes's Parotia (Parotia lawesi)
65 8d Black-billed Sicklebill (Drepanornis albertsii)
66 1s Emperor of Germany Bird of Paradise (Paradisaea guilielmi)
67 2s Brown Sicklebill (Epimachus meyeri)
68 2s3d Lesser Bird of Paradise (Paradisaea minor)
69 3s Magnificent Bird of Paradise (Diphyllodes magnificus)
70 5s Twelve-wired Bird of Paradise (Seleucides melanoleuca)
71 10s Magnificent Riflebird (Ptiloris magnificus)
     Set of 11   30.00   9.50

1967

121 5c Papuan Lory (Charmosyna stellae)
122 7c Pesquet's Parrot (Psittrichas fulgidus)
123 20c Dusky Lory (Pseudeos fuscata)
124 25c Edwards's Fig Parrot (Psittaculirostris edwardsii)
     Set of 4   1.50   50

1970

173 5c King of Saxony Bird of Paradise (Pteridophora alberti)
174 10c King Bird of Paradise (Cicinnurus regius)
175 15c Raggiana Bird of Paradise (Paradisaea raggiana augustaevictoriae)
176 25c Sickle Crested Bird of Paradise (Cnemophilus macgregorii)
     Set of 4   6.50   3.50

185† 15c Dwarf Cassowary 75   30

1973

237 7c Queen Carola's Parotia (Parotia carolae)
238 14c Goldie's Bird of Paradise (Paradiseae decora)

239 21c Ribbon-tailed Bird of Paradise
  (*Astrapia mayeri*)
240 28c Princess Stephanie's Bird of Paradise
  (*Astrapia stephaniae*)

Set of 4　9.00　6.25

1974

270 7c Blyth's Hornbill (*Aceros plicatus*)
271 10c Double-wattled Cassowary (*Casuarius casuarius*)
272 30c New Guinea Harpy Eagle (*Harpyopsis novaeguineae*)

Set of 3　9.00　10.50

1975

284† 20t Dwarf Cassowary.　..　..　..　..　..　1.25　80

1977

333 5t White-breasted Ground Pigeon
  (*Gallicolumba jobiensis*)
334 7t Victoria Crowned Pigeon (*Goura victoria*)
335 15t Pheasant Pigeon (*Otidiphaps nobilis*)
336 30t Orange-fronted Fruit Dove (*Ptilinopus aurantiifrons*)
337 50t Banded Imperial Pigeon (*Ducula zoeae*)

Set of 5　2.40　2.10

COLLECT RAILWAYS ON STAMPS

A Stanley Gibbons thematic catalogue on this popular subject. Copies available at £7.50 (p.＋p. £1.50) from: Stanley Gibbons Publications Ltd, 5 Parkside, Christchurch Road, Ringwood, Hants BH24 3SH.

1981

401 3t White-headed Kingfisher (*Halcyon saurophaga*)
402 7t Forest Kingfisher (*Halcyon macheayii*)
403 20t Sacred Kingfisher (*Halcyon sancta*)
404 25t White-tailed Kingfisher (*Tanysiptera sylvia*)
405 60t Blue-winged Kookaburra (*Dacelo leachii*)

Set of 5　2.25　2.25

1982

452† 5k Raggiana Bird of Paradise (*Paradisaea raggiana*)　..　..　..　..　..　..　..　6.25　6.50

1985

500 12t New Britain Sparrow Hawk (*Accipiter brachyurus*) (close up)
501 12t New Britain Sparrow Hawk (*Accipiter brachyurus*) (in flight)
502 30t Doria's Goshawk (*Megatriorchis doriae*) (close up)
503 30t Doria's Goshawk (*Megatriorchis doriae*) (in flight)
504 60t Long-tailed Honey Buzzard (*Henicopernis longicauda*) (close up)
505 60t Long-tailed Honey Buzzard (*Henicopernis longicauda*) (in flight)

Set of 6　2.75　2.75

1986

525 15t Rufous Fantail (*Pitta erythrogaster* !)
526 35t Streaked Berrypecker (*Melanocharis striativentris*)
527 45t Red-breasted Pitta (*Rhipidura rufifrons* !)
528 70t Olive-yellow Robin (*Poecilodryas placens*)
                                   Set of 4   2.25   2.40
The inscriptions on Nos. 525 and 527 are interchanged.

POSTAGE DUE STAMPS

1960

No. 4 surcharged **POSTAL CHARGES 3s.**
D6† 3s on 2½d Greater Bird of Paradise 38.00 26.00

PARAGUAY
South America
1931 100 centavos = 1 peso
1944 100 centimos = 1 guarani

1931

427† 80c Yellow-headed Caracara (blue) 30 15
428† 80c Yellow-headed Caracara (green) . .. 40 20
428a† 80c Yellow-headed Caracara (red) 30 15

Appendix
The following stamps have either been issued in excess of postal needs, or have not been made available to the public in reasonable quantities at face value. Miniature sheets, imperforate stamps etc. are excluded from this section.

1968
Paraguayan Stamps from 1870–1970. Postage 25c Yellow-headed Caracara (on stamp No. 427)

1969
Latin American Wildlife. Postage 10c Green Aracari, 15c Red-breasted Plantcutter, 20c Purple Gallinule, 25c Sharpbill, 30c Ornate Hawk Eagle, 50c Greater Flamingo, 75c Yellow-crowned Amazon. Air 12g45 Blue and Yellow Macaw and Scarlet Macaw, 18g15 Sparkling Violetear

1971
'Philatokyo'71' Stamp Exhibition, Tokyo. Japanese Paintings. 50c Hill Myna

1972
Paintings of Animals and Birds. Postage 10c Manchurian Crane, 25c Silver Pheasant. Air 12g45 Red Junglefowl, 18g15 Mute Swan

South American Fauna. 75c Greater Rhea

1973
Birds. Postage 10c Swallow Tanager, 15c Common Piping Guan, 20c Vermilion Flycatcher, 25c Plate-billed Mountain Toucan, 30c Pompadour Cotinga, 50c Paradise Tanager, 75c White-tailed Goldenthroat. Air 5g Northern Royal Flycatcher, 10g Grey Gallito, 20g Lattice-tailed Trogon

1974
Famous Paintings from Gulbenkian Museum, New York. 30c Common Peafowl

1982
75th Anniv of Boy Scout Movement. 50c Greater Rhea

1983
South American Birds. 25c Spectacled Owl, 50c West Mexican Chachalaca, 1g Amazon Kingfisher, 2g White-tailed Trogon, 3g Red-breasted Blackbird, 4g Collared Puffbird, 5g Red-legged Honeycreeper

---

PENRHYN ISLAND
South Pacific
1902 12 pence = 1 shilling
1973 100 cents = 1 dollar

1902
Nos. 309, 265 and 268a of New Zealand surcharged **PENRHYN ISLAND.** *and value in native language*
14† 3d Huia * 8.00 11.00
15† 6d Brown Kiwi 13.00 19.00
17† 1s Kaka, Kea 35.00 45.00

1978

107† 20c Iiwi ('I'wii') 40 30
109† 30c Apapane 50 40
111† 35c Moorhen ('Alae') 60 45
113† 75c Hawaii O-o * ('O'o') 1.25 80

1985

373   20c Harlequin Duck
374   55c Sage Grouse
375   65c Solitary Sandpiper
376   75c Dunlin ('Red-backed Sandpiper')
                                    Set of 4   1.75   1.75
MS377 Four sheets. (a) 95c Harlequin Duck; (b)
       95c Sage Grouse; (c) 95c Solitary
       Sandpiper; (d) 95c Dunlin ('Red-
       backed Sandpiper')
                          Price for 4 sheets   3.25   3.50

PERU
South America
1936 100 centavos = 1 sol
1985 100 centimos = 1 inti

1933

504†   20c Guanay Cormorant, Brown Pelican   ..   4.75   25

1936

586†   2c Guanay Cormorant (brown)   90   15

1937
As No. 586

616†   2c Guanay Cormorant (green)   70   15

1938

656†   70c Andean Condor (grey) 1.50   15
736†   70c Andean Condor (blue)   65   10

1948
No. 656 surcharged **Habilitada S/o.** and value

718†   10c on 70c Andean Condor   40   15
719†   15c on 70c Andean Condor   40   15
720†   20c on 70c Andean Condor   40   15
721†   55c on 70c Andean Condor   60   15

1952

Imprint 'THOMAS DE LA RUE & CO. LTD.' at foot

785†   75c Guanay Cormorant ('Guanay')   60   25
785a†   80c Guanay Cormorant ('Guanay')   30   10

1960
As No. 785a but imprint 'JOH. ENCHEDE EN ZONEN–HOLLAND'
at foot

834†   80c Guanay Cormorant ('Guanay')   35   10

1962
As Nos. 785/a

873†   1s30 Guanay Cormorant ('Guanay')   65   25

1972

1131   2s White-tailed Trogon (*Trogon viridis*)
1132   2s50 Amazonian Umbrellabird
       (*Cephalopterus ornatus*)
1133   3s Andean Cock of the Rock (*Rupicola
       peruviana*)
1134   6s50 Cuvier's Toucan (*Ramphastos
       cuvieri*)
1135   8s50 Blue-crowned Motmot (*Momotus
       momota*)
                                    Set of 5   2.50   90

COLLECT RAILWAYS ON STAMPS
A Stanley Gibbons thematic catalogue on this
popular subject. Copies available at £7.50 (p. + p.
£1.50) from: Stanley Gibbons Publications Ltd, 5
Parkside, Christchurch Road, Ringwood, Hants
BH24 3SH.

1973

1185† 2s50 Lesser Rhea (*Pterocnemia pennata*) 40 10
1187† 4s Andean Condor (*Vultur gryphus*) 55 15
1189† 6s Chilian Flamingo (*Phoenicopterus ruber* !). 65 20

1196† 10s Brown Pelican, Peruvian Booby, Guanay Cormorant 1.25 25

1985

1622 1500s Humboldt Penguin (*Spheniscus humboldti*).. .. .. 35 12

1986

1657 2i White-winged Guan (*Penelope albipennis*) 30 12

PHILIPPINES
South-east Asia
100 sentimos = 1 piso

1967

1045 1s + 5s Stork-billed Kingfisher
1046 5s + 5s Rufous Hornbill ('Luzon Hornbill or Kalaw')
1047 10s + 5s Philippine Eagle ('Monkey-eating Eagle')
1048 30s + 5s Great-billed Parrot ('Large-billed Parrot or Loro')
                              Set of 4 1.25 75

1969

1113 1s + 5s Golden-backed Three-toed Woodpecker ('Three-toed Woodpecker')
1114 5s + 5s Philippine Trogon
1115 10s + 5s Johnstone's Lorikeet ('Mt. Apo Lorikeet')
1116 40s + 5s Scarlet Minivet ('Johnstone's Minivet')
                              Set of 4 1.25 75

1979

1504 30s Merrill's Fruit Dove
1505 1p20 Brown Tit-Babbler
1506 2p20 Mindoro Zone-tailed Pigeon ('Mindoro Imperial Pigeon')
1507 2p30 Steere's Pitta
1508 5p Koch's Pitta, Red-breasted Pitta
1509 5p Great Eared Nightjar ('Philippine Eared Nightjar')
                              Set of 6 6.25 3.25

1982

1708† 3p20 Philippine Eagle 1.40 75

1984

1793 40s Red-vented Cockatoo (*Kakatoe haematuropygia*)
1794 2p30 Guaiabero (*Bolbopsittacus lunulatus*)
1795 2p80 Mountain Racket-tailed Parrot (*Prioniturus montanus*)
1796 3p20 Great-billed Parrot (*Tanygnathus megalorynchos*)
1797 3p60 Muller's Parrot (*Tanygnathus sumatranus*)
1798 5p Philippine Hanging Parrot (*Loriculus philippinensis*)
Set of 6 3.00 1.40

PITCAIRN ISLANDS
South Pacific
1964 12 pence = 1 shilling
1968 100 cents = 1 dollar

1964

39† 3d Great Frigate Bird ('Frigate Bird') 40 20
40† 4d White Tern ('Fairy Tern') 40 20
41† 6d Pitcairn Warbler ('Pitcairn Sparrow'). .. 40 20
42† 8d Red-footed Booby ('Austin Bird').. .. .. 40 20
43† 10d Red-tailed Tropic Bird ('Bosun Birds') .. 40 20
44† 1s Henderson Island Crake ('Chicken Bird') 40 20
45† 1s6d Stephen's Lory ('Red Breast') 7.00 1.50
46† 2s6d Murphy's Petrel ('Ghost Bird').. .. .. 7.00 1.75
47† 4s Henderson Island Fruit Dove ('Wood Pigeon') 8.00 2.25

1967
Nos. 39/47 surcharged with Bounty anchor and value
72† 2¾c on 3d Great Frigate Bird 35 20
73† 3c on 4d White Tern 35 20
74† 5c on 6d Pitcairn Warbler 35 20
75† 10c on 8d Red-footed Booby 40 20
76† 15c on 10d Red-tailed Tropic Bird 80 50
77† 20c on 1s Henderson Island Crake 1.00 75
78† 25c on 1s6d Stephen's Lory 2.75 90
79† 30c on 2s6d Murphy's Petrel.. .. .. .. 3.50 1.40
80† 40c on 4s Henderson Island Fruit Dove.. .. 5.00 1.60

1972

124 4c Red-tailed Tropic Bird
125 20c Red-tailed Tropic Bird
Set of 2 1.25 1.75

1981

217† 35c Black-browed Albatross. 40 45

POLAND
Eastern Europe
100 groszy = 1 zloty

1960

1201 10g Great Bustard (*Otis tarda*)
1202 20g Raven (*Corvus corax*)
1203 30g Common Cormorant (*Phalacrocorax carbo*)
1204 40g Black Stork (*Ciconia nigra*)
1205 50g Eagle Owl (*Bubo bubo*)
1206 60g White-tailed Sea Eagle (*Haliaeetus albicilla*)
1207 75g Golden Eagle (*Aquila chrysaetos*)
1208 90g Short-toed Eagle (*Circaetus gallicus*)
1209 2z50 Rock Thrush (*Monticola saxatilis*)

1210 4z Common Kingfisher (*Alcedo atthis*)
1211 5z60 Wallcreeper (*Tichodroma muraria*)
1212 6z50 Common Roller (*Coracias garrulus*)

Set of 12 15.00 5.50

1703 4z Siskin (*Carduelis spinus*)
1704 6z50 Chaffinch (*Fringilla coelebs*)
1705 7z10 Great Tit (*Parus major*)

Set of 9 5.50 2.25

1964

1968

1876† 4z50 Mallard 1.40 40

1484 30g Lapwing (*Vanellus vanellus*)
1485 40g Bluethroat (*Luscinia svecica*)
1486 50g Black-tailed Godwit (*Limosa limosa*)
1487 60g Osprey (*Pandion haliaetus*)
1488 90g Grey Heron (*Ardea cinerea*)
1489 1z35 Little Gull (*Larus minutus*)
1490 1z55 Common Shoveler (*Spatula clypeata*)
1491 5z60 Black-throated Diver (*Gavia arctica*)
1492 6z50 Great Crested Grebe (*Podiceps cristatus*)

Set of 9 4.00 1.40

1970

1968 40g Mallard
1969 60g Ring-necked Pheasant
1970 1z15 Woodcock
1971 1z35 Ruff
1972 1z50 Wood Pigeon
1973 3z40 Black Grouse
1974 7z Grey Partridge
1975 8z50 Capercaillie

Set of 8 5.25 2.25

1966

1644† 2z50 Archaeopteryx * 25 5

2023† 1z15 White Stork. 25 10

1972

1697 10g Jay, Siskin, Chaffinch, Green Woodpecker, Hoopoe, Golden Oriole, Redstart, Great Tit
1698 20g Green Woodpecker (*Picus viridis*)
1699 30g Jay (*Garrulus glandarius*)
1700 40g Golden Oriole (*Oriolus oriolus*)
1701 60g Hoopoe (*Upupa epops*)
1702 2z50 Redstart (*Phoenicurus phoenicurus*)

2149† 60g Toco Toucan (*Rhampastos toco*) 25 10

1973

2343 1z50 Red-footed Falcon (*Falco vespertinus*, male)
2344 1z50 Red-footed Falcon (*Falco vespertinus*, female)
2345 2z European Hobby (*Falco subbuteo*)
2346 3z Common Kestrel (*Falco tunnunculus*, male)
2347 4z Merlin (*Falco columbarius*, male)
2348 8z Peregrine Falcon (*Falco peregrinus*)

                                         Set of 8 6.00 2.25

2235† 2z70 Capercaillie (*Tetrao urogallus*) 30 10

1976

2432† 90g Tawny Owl 25 10
2433† 1z White-tailed Sea Eagle 25 10
2434† 1z50 Gull sp 30 10

2252† 1z White Stork 35 10
2256† 5z Green Woodpecker 2.00 45

1977

2492† 1z50 Great Bustard (*Otis tarda*) 25 10
2493† 1z50 Common Kestrel (*Falco tinnunculus*) 25 10

2267 1z Adelie Penguin 25 10

1981

2756† 6z50 Mallard (*Anas platyrhynchos*) 85 30
2757† 6z50 Barnacle Goose (*Anser anser* !) . .. 85 30

1975

2341 1z Lesser Kestrel (*Falco naumanni*, male)
2342 1z Lesser Kestrel (*Falco naumanni*, female)

1983

6 ZŁ·POLSKA

2864†	6z Mute Swan	20	8
2865†	17z Hoopoe	55	25

1985

3011 5z Green-winged Teal (*Anas crecca*)
3012 5z Garganey (*Anas querquedula*)
3013 15z Tufted Duck (*Aythya fuligula*)
3014 15z Goldeneye (*Bucephala clangula*)
3015 25z Eider (*Somateria mollissima*)
3016 29z Red-crested Pochard (*Netta rufina*)
Set of 6   2.75   95

1986

3032†	5z Grey Partridge (*Perdix perdix*)..	5	5
3034†	10z Ring-necked Pheasant (*Phasianus colchicus*)	5	5

1987

3091†	10z Southern Fulmar (*Fulmarus glacialoides*)	5	5
3092†	10z Adelie Penguin (*Pigoscelis adeliae*) ..	5	5

PORTUGAL
South-east Europe
100 centavos = 1 escudo

1972

1483†	2e50 European Bee Eater	65	25

1976

1618†	3e Azure-winged Magpie (*Cyanopica cyanea*)	40	10
1620†	7e Blue Tit	1.00	30

1631†	10e Mallard	1.60	35

1980

1796†	6e50 Barn Owl (*Tyto alba*)..	40	10
1799†	20e Golden Eagle (*Aquila chrysaetus*) ..	1.40	45

1982

1887 10e Dunlin (*Calidris alpina*)
1888 19e Red-crested Pochard (*Netta rufina*)
1889 27e Greater Flamingo (*Phoenicopterus ruber*)
1890 33e50 Black-winged Stilt (*Himantopus himantopus*)

Set of 4	2.25	2.00

1985

2024†	20e Kittiwake, Common Guillemot.	20	12
2026†	46e Pintail	40	30
2027†	80e Purple Swamphen	75	65
	(2024/7 Set of 4)	1.50	1.25

PORTUGUESE GUINEA
West Africa
100 centavos = 1 escudo

1948

305†	10c Crowned Crane	2.50	1.50

STANLEY GIBBONS
STAMP COLLECTING SERIES
Introductory booklets on *How to Start, How to Identify Stamps* and *Collecting by Theme*. A series of well illustrated guides at a low price.
Write for details.

QATAR
Arabia
1961 100 naye paise = 1 rupee
1967 100 dirhams = 1 riyal

1961

31†	40np Peregrine Falcon	60	5
32†	50np Peregrine Falcon	75	5

1964

No. 32 overprinted **1964**, *Olympic rings and Arabic inscription*

38†	50np Peregrine Falcon	1.25	1.25

No. 32 overprinted **John F. Kennedy 1917 – 1963** *in English and Arabic*

43†	50np Peregrine Falcon	1.25	1.25

1966

Nos. 31/2 surcharged with new currency

145†	40d on 40np Peregrine Falcon	30	15
146†	50d on 50np Peregrine Falcon	40	20

1968

250†	1r50 Peregrine Falcon	1.60	60

1970

318†	2d Peregrine Falcon	40	10

1971

349†	1d Common Cormorant	25	10
351†	3d Greater Flamingo..	25	10

1972

391	1d Common Roller (*Coracias garrulus*)
392	2d Common Kingfisher (*Alcedo atthis*)
393	3d Rock Thrush (*Monticola saxatilis*)
394	4d Caspian Tern (*Hydroprogne tschegrava*)
395	5d Hoopoe (*Upupa epops*)
396	35d European Bee Eater (*Merops apiaster*)
397	75d Golden Oriole (*Oriolus oriolus*)
398	3r Peregrine Falcon (*Falco peregrinus*)

Set of 8   4.00   2.40

1974

530†	10d White-cheeked Tern, Hoopoe	55	10

1976

608	5d Kentish Plover
609	10d Common Cormorant
610	35d Osprey
611	80d Greater Flamingo
612	1r25 Rock Thrush
613	2r Saker Falcon

Set of 6   3.75   2.00

RAS AL KHAIMA
Arabia
100 dirhams = 1 riyal

Appendix

The following stamps have either been issued in excess of postal needs, or have not been made available to the public in reasonable quantities at face value. Miniature sheets, imperforate stamps etc. are excluded from this section.

1967

Arab Paintings. 10d Purple Heron

1970

'EXPO'70' World Fair, Osaka, Japan (2nd issue). Poatage 65d Japanese Pheasant. Air 25d Moorhen

1972

Birds. 50d Budgerigar, 55d Troupial, 80d Toucan Barbet, 100d Gouldian Finch, 105d African Pygmy Kingfisher, 190d Goldfinch

Parrots. 40d Eastern Rosella, 45d Scarlet Macaw, 70d Blue and Yellow Macaw, 95d Nyasa Lovebird, 1r35 Galah, 1r75 Sulphur-crested Cockatoo

---

REDONDA
A dependency of Antigua
100 cents = 1 dollar

Appendix

The following stamps were issued in anticipation of commercial and tourist development, philatelic mail being handled by a bureau in Antigua. Since at the present time the island is uninhabited, we do not list these items in full. It is understood that the stamps are valid for the prepayment of postage in Antigua. Miniature sheets, imperforate stamps etc. are excluded from this section.

1979

Nos. 472 and 474 of Antigua overprinted **REDONDA**. 3c Loggerhead Kingbird, 5c Rufous-throated Solitaire

1980

Marine Life. 25c Brown Pelican

Birds of Redonda. 8c Adelaide's Warbler, 10c Troupial, 15c Stolid Flycatcher, 25c Brown Trembler, 30c Purple-throated Carib, 50c Montserrat Oriole, $1 Blue-hooded Euphonia, $2 Carib Grackle, $5 American Kestrel

1985

Birth Bicentenary of John J. Audubon (1st issue). 60c Ivory-billed Woodpecker, 90c Ruby-crowned Kinglet, $1 Grey Kinkbird, $3 Eastern Wood Pewee

1986

Birth Bicentenary of John J. Audubon (2nd issue). 90c Barrow's Goldeneye, $1 Bufflehead, $1.50 Long-tailed Duck, $3 Harlequin Duck

REUNION
Indian Ocean
100 centimes = 1 franc

1972

| 479 | 45f King Penguin | .. .. | 1.60 | 85 |

RHODESIA
Central Africa
1966 12 pence = 1 shilling,
20 shillings = 1 pound
1967 100 cents = 1 dollar

1966
No. 104 of Southern Rhodesia overprinted **INDEPENDENCE** 11th
November 1965
| 371† | 10s Helmet Guineafowl .. | .. .. | 5.00 | 2.75 |

| 386† | 10s Helmet Guineafowl .. | .. .. | 6.00 | 5.00 |

1970

| 449† | 25c Bateleur .. .. | 3.25 | 1.25 |

COLLECT MAMMALS ON STAMPS
The second Stanley Gibbons thematic catalogue —
copies are available at £7.50 (p. + p. £1.50) from:
Stanley Gibbons Publications Ltd, 5 Parkside,
Christchurch Road, Ringwood, Hants BH24 3SH.

1971

459	2c Hoopoe ('African Hoopoe')
460	2½c Half-collared Kingfisher
461	5c Golden-breasted Bunting
462	7½c Carmine Bee Eater
463	8c Red-eyed Bulbul
464	25c Senegal Wattled Plover ('Wattled Plover')

Set of 6   23.00   15.00

1977

537	3c Common Bulbul ('Blackeyed Bulbul')
538	4c Yellow-mantled Whydah ('Yellow-mantled Wydah')
539	6c Cape Longclaw ('Orangethroated Longclaw')
540	8c Eastern Long-tailed Shrike ('Long-tailed Shrike')
541	16c Lesser Blue-eared Glossy Starling ('Lesser Blue-eared Starling')
542	24c Green Wood Hoopoe ('Redbilled Woodhoopoe')

Set of 6   2.50   2.00

RIO MUNI
West Africa
100 centimos = 1 peseta

1961

| 211† | 25c Grey Parrot | .. .. | 30 | 10 |

1964

58† 1p Helmet Guineafowl 25 10

1965

66† 50c Ring-necked Pheasant 25 10
68† 2p50 Ring-necked Pheasant 1.60 50

1966

69† 50c Grey Parrot 30 10
70† 1p Grey Parrot... ... ... 30 12

ROSS DEPENDENCY
Antarctica
100 cents = 1 dollar

1972

9a† 3c Great Skua ('Skua') 65 65

1982

15† 5c Adelie Penguin.. ... ... 5 5

RUMANIA
South-east Europe
100 bani = 1 leu

1956

2424† 20b Great Bustard ('Dropie') (black and
olive) 2.00 2.00
2427† 55b Ring-necked Pheasant ('Fazan')
(green and bistre) 2.50 2.00
2431† 1le75 Capercaillie ('Cocos de Munte')
(brown and green) 5.00 5.00
2433† 3le25 Pintail ('Rata Salbatica') (black and
green) 20.00 20.00

As Nos. 2424/33 but colours changed and imperforate
2475† 20b Great Bustard (black and blue) 5.00 5.00
2478† 55b Ring-necked Pheasant (black and
violet) 5.00 5.00
2482† 1le75 Capercaillie (purple and green) .. 5.00 5.00
2484† 3le25 Pintail (brown and green) 8.00 8.00

1957

2552† 5b Black-winged Stilt ('Piciorong'). 25 10
2553† 10b Great Egret ('Egreta') 30 10
2554† 20b White Spoonbill ('Lopator') 50 15
2557† 1le30 Eastern White Pelican ('Pelican') .. 2.10 20

2558† 3le30 Black-headed Gull ('Pescarus') (air) 4.00 65
2559† 5le White-tailed Sea Eagle ('Vultur
Codalb') 5.50 1.00

1959

2648 10b Rock Thrush (*Monticola sax.*)
2649 20b Golden Oriole (*Oriolus oriolus*)
2650 35b Lapwing (*Vanellus van.*)
2651 40b Barn Swallow (*Hirundo rustica*)
2652 55b Great Spotted Woodpecker
      (*Dendrocopus major*)
2653 55b Goldfinch (*Carduelis card.*)
2654 55b Great Tit (*Parus major*)
2655 1le Bullfinch (*Pyrrhula pyrrh.*)
2656 1le55 Long-tailed Tit (*Aegithalos caud.*)
2657 5le Wallcreeper (*Tichodroma muraria*)
                Set of 10 10.00 2.75

1960

2704† 1le20 Common Shelduck (*Tadorna*
      tadorna) 1.40 35

2705† 1le30 Golden Eagle (*Aquila chrysaetos*)
      (air). 1.50 35
2706† 1le75 Black Grouse (*Lirurus tetrix*) 1.75 35
2707† 2le Lammergeier (*Gypaetus barbatus*) .. 1.90 50

1964

3198† 10b Black Swan (*Chenopsis atrata*) 30 10
3199† 35b Ostrich (*Struthio camelus*). 40 10
3200† 40b Crowned Crane (*Balearica pavonina*) 50 15

COLLECT RAILWAYS ON STAMPS
A Stanley Gibbons thematic catalogue on this popular subject. Copies available at £7.50 (p. + p. £1.50) from: Stanley Gibbons Publications Ltd, 5 Parkside, Christchurch Road, Ringwood, Hants BH24 3SH.

1965

3303 5b Common Quail (*Coturnix*)
3304 10b Woodcock (*Scolopax rusticola*)
3305 20b Common Snipe (*Capella gallinago*)
3306 40b Turtle Dove (*Streptopelia turtur*)
3307 55b Mallard (*Anas platyrhinchos*)
3308 60b White-fronted Goose (*Anser albifrons*)
3309 1le Common Crane (*Grus grus*)
3310 1le20 Glossy Ibis (*Plegadis falcinellus*)
3311 1le35 Mute Swan (*Cygnus olor*)
3312 3le25 Eastern White Pelican (*Pelecanus*
      onocrotalus)
                Set of 10 6.00 1.25

3339† 40b Woodcock 45 8

1966

3369 5b Red-breasted Flycatcher (*Muscicapa*
      parva)
3370 10b Red Crossbill (*Loxia curvirostra*)
3371 15b Great Reed Warbler (*Acrocephalus*
      arundinaceus)
3372 20b Redstart (*Phoenicurus phoenicurus*)
3373 55b European Robin (*Erithacus rubecula*)

3374 1le20 Bluethroat (*Luscinia svecica*)
3375 1le55 Yellow Wagtail (*Motacilla flava*)
3376 3le20 Penduline Tit (*Remiz pendulinus*)

Set of 8   7.50   2.40

1967

3442 10b Barn Owl (*Tyto alba*)
3443 20b Eagle Owl (*Bubo bubo*)
3444 40b Saker Falcon (*Falco cherrug*)
3445 55b Egyptian Vulture (*Neophron percnopterus*)
3446 75b Osprey (*Pandion haliaetus*)
3447 1le Griffon Vulture (*Gyps fulvus*)
3448 1le20 Lammergeier (*Gypaetus barbatus*)
3449 1le75 European Black Vulture (*Aegypius monachus*)

Set of 8   5.75   1.90

1968

3598†	10b Mute Swan (*Cygnus olor*)	25	10

3598†	10b Mute Swan (*Cygnus olor*)	25	10
3599†	20b Black-winged Stilt (*Himantopus himantopus*)	30	10
3600†	40b Common Shelduck (*Tadorna tadorna*)	35	10
3601†	55b Great Egret (*Egretta alba*)	40	10
3602†	60b Golden Eagle (*Aquila chrysaetos*)	45	10
3603†	1le20 Great Bustard (*Otis tarda*)	60	25

1973

3979†	1le40 European Bee Eater (*Merops apiaster*)	40	10
3980†	1le85 Red-breasted Goose (*Branta ruficollis*)	50	12
3981†	2le75 Penduline Tit (*Remiz pendulinus*)	75	25

1977

4285†	1le Mute Swan (*Cygnus olor*)	25	10
4286†	1le50 Egyptian Vulture (*Neophron percnopterus*)	35	15
4288†	3le40 White-headed Duck (*Oxyura leucocephala*)	75	20
4289†	4le80 Common Kingfisher (*Alcedo atthis*)	85	40

4352†	4le80 White Stork, Eastern White Pelican.	1.75	80

1978

4386†	55b Eastern White Pelican	30	5

1980

4566†	55b Common Kingfisher (*Alcedo atthis*)	25	10
4567†	1le Great Egret (*Egretta alba*)	35	10
4568†	1le50 Red-breasted Goose (*Branta ruficollis*)	40	15
MS4572	10le Eastern White Pelican (*Pelecanus onocrotalus*)	4.00	4.00

1983

POSTA ROMANA

4795 50b Bluethroat (*Luscinia svecica*)
4796 1le Rose-coloured Starling (*Sturnus roseus*)
4797 1le50 Common Roller (*Coracias garrulus*)
4798 2le50 European Bee Eater (*Merops apiaster*)
4799 4le Reed Bunting (*Emberiza schoeniclus*)
4800 5le Lesser Grey Shrike (*Lanius minor*)
                                    Set of 6   4.50   2.50

POSTA ROMANA 1L

4817† 1le Middle Spotted Woodpecker (*Dendrocopos medius*)   65   25
4819† 1le Wallcreeper (*Tichodroma muraria*) ..   65   25

1984

4850† 4le Jay 1.40   35

4899 50b Dalmatian Pelican (*Pelecanus crispus*)
4900 1le Dalmatian Pelican (*Pelecanus crispus*) (on nest)
4901 1le Dalmatian Pelican (*Pelecanus crispus*) (on lake)
4902 2le Dalmatian Pelican (*Pelecanus crispus*)
                                    Set of 4   1.50   70

1985

POSTA ROMANA

4922† 1le Grey Partridge (*Perdix perdix*)   40   5
4923† 1le50 Snowy Owl (*Nyctea scandiaca*) . ..   55   15
4927† 4le Capercaillie (*Tetrao urogallus*) 1.40   35
4928† 5le Great Bustard (*Otis tarda*).. .. .. ..   1.60   50

POSTA ROMANA ∎50

4936 50b American Robin (*Turdus migratorius*)
4937 1le Brown Pelican (*Pelecanus occidentalis*)
4938 1le50 Yellow-crowned Night Heron (*Nyctanassa violacea*)
4939 2le Northern Oriole (*Icterus galbula*)
4940 3le Red-necked Grebe (*Podiceps grisegena*)
4941 4le Mallard (*Anas platyrhynchos*)
                                    Set of 6   3.50   1.25

POSTA ROMANA

4964† 5le Golden Eagle (*Aquila chrysaetos*). ..   1.60   50

1986

MS5020 Two sheets. (a) 3le Capercaillie (*Tetrao urogallus*) (sheet also contains 3 other stamps) (other sheet shows plants)
                     Price for 2 sheets   9.75   9.75

POSTA ROMANA

| 5059† | 1le Atlantic Puffin | .. .. | 30 | 8 |
| 5062† | 4le Penguin sp | .. .. | 1.40 | 35 |

RUSSIA

Eastern Europe and Northern Asia
100 kopeks = 1 rouble

1957

2057a†	10k Grey Partridge.	.. ..	60	25
2058†	15k Black Grouse ..	.. ..	60	15
2060†	30k Mallard .	.. ..	75	25
2063c†	60k Hazel Grouse ..	.. ..	2.00	30
2063d†	1r Mute Swan ..	.. ..	2.75	60

1959

| 2321† | 40k Woodcock | .. .. | 90 | 15 |

| 2373† | 40k Emperor Penguin | .. .. | 2.50 | 30 |

1961

| 2546† | 1k Mute Swan | .. .. | 35 | 5 |

1962

2783	3k Rose-coloured Starling
2784	4k Red-breasted Goose
2785	6k Snow Goose
2786	10k Great White Crane
2787	16k Greater Flamingo

Set of 5   3.00   70

1963

| 2894† | 3k Emperor Penguin | .. .. | 1.25 | 20 |

1964

| 3004† | 10k Eastern White Pelican .. | .. .. | 60 | 12 |
| 3006† | 16k Lammergeier | .. .. | 1.25 | 50 |

STANLEY GIBBONS
STAMP COLLECTING SERIES

Introductory booklets on *How to Start, How to Identify Stamps* and *Collecting by Theme*. A series of well illustrated guides at a low price.
Write for details.

1965

3217 1k Common Buzzard
3218 2k Common Kestrel
3219 3k Tawny Eagle
3220 4k Red Kite
3221 10k Peregrine Falcon
3222 12k Golden Eagle
3223 14k Lammergeier
3224 16k Gyrfalcon

Set of 8   5.00   1.25

1966

3251† 10k Adelie Penguin 1.75   35

3376† 16k Common Guillemot 2.25   50

1967

3450 16k Manchurian Crane   55   20

BIRDS   BIRDS   BIRDS

Hundreds of Birds sets from around the World at
attractive prices are available from Stanley
Gibbons. Write now for our current Birds offers,
with no obligation, to: Stanley Gibbons Promotions
(Birds Offers), Parkside, Ringwood, Hants
BH24 3SH. Tel: (04254) 2363.

1968

3609†	4k Purple Swamphen	15	10
3610†	6k Great Egret	20	10
3611†	6k Ostrich, Golden Pheasant	20	15
3613†	10k Glossy Ibis, White Spoonbill	35	20

1969

3729† 4k Black Stork   25   10

1970

3850† 4k Mandarin   25   10

1972

4025 4k Red-faced Cormorant
4026 6k Ross's Gull
4027 10k Barnacle Goose
4028 12k Spectacled Eider
4029 16k Mediterranean Gull

Set of 5   2.50   60

MS4129 50k Mute Swan 4.50   1.00

1973

4184† 4k Caucasian Snowcock 25 10

1976

4545	1k Cattle Egret
4546	3k Black-throated Diver
4547	4k Common Coot
4548	6k Atlantic Puffin
4549	10k Slender-billed Gull

Set of 5   1.25   45

4231† 4k Common Peafowl 12 5

1978

4784†	1k Snares Island Penguin	35	10
4785†	3k Snow Petrel	45	10
4786†	4k Emperor Penguin	55	10

1975

4418† 10k Long-tailed Duck 50 12

1979

4922	2k Golden Oriole (*Oriolus oriolus*)
4923	3k Lesser Spotted Woodpecker (*Dendrocopus minor*)
4924	4k Crested Tit (*Parus cristatus*)
4925	10k Barn Owl (*Tyto alba*)
4926	15k European Nightjar (*Caprimulgus europaeus*)

Set of 5   1.60   65

4433† 1k Ruff 25 10
4436† 10k Capercaillie.. .. .. 45 15

1981

COLLECT MAMMALS ON STAMPS
The second Stanley Gibbons thematic catalogue —
copies are available at £7.50 (p. + p. £1.50) from:
Stanley Gibbons Publications Ltd, 5 Parkside,
Christchurch Road, Ringwood, Hants BH24 3SH.

5158 6k Severtzov's Tit Warbler
5159 10k Asiatic Paradise Flycatcher

5160 15k Jankowski's Bunting
5161 20k Vinous-throated Parrotbill
5162 32k Hodgson's Bushchat
                      Set of 5   2.25   1.25

RWANDA
Central Africa
100 centimes = 1 franc

1965

98†   10c Marabou Stork ('Marabout')   25   10
101† 40c Crowned Crane ('Grue Couronnee'),
      Cattle Egret   25   10
106† 40f Reed Cormorant ('Comoran'), African
      Darter (*Anhinga rufa*)   90   40

1982

5235 2k Hooded Crane (*Grus monacha*)
5236 4k Steller's Sea Eagle (*Haliaeetus
      pelagicus*)
5237 6k Spoon-billed Sandpiper
      (*Eurynorhynchus pygmeus*)
5238 10k Bar-headed Goose (*Eulabeia indica*)
5239 15k Sociable Plover (*Chettusia gregaria*)
5240 32k White Stork (*Ciconia boyciana*)
                      Set of 6   2.40   90

1966

180† 10c Yellow-crested Helmet Shrike
      (*Prionops alberti*)   25   10

1984

5412† 5k South African Crowned Crane   30   10
5413† 20k Blue and Yellow Macaw   70   20

1967

239 20c Red Bishop ('Eveque Rouge')
240 40c Woodland Kingfisher ('Martin-
    Pecheur')
241 60c Red-billed Quelea ('Travailleur a Bec
    Rouge')
242 80c Double-toothed Barbet ('Barbu a Bec
    Dente')
243 2f Pin-tailed Whydah ('Veuve Dominicaine')
244 3f Red-chested Cuckoo ('Coucou Solitaire')
245 18f Green Wood Hoopoe ('Moqueur
    Pourpre')
246 25f Cinnamon-chested Bee Eater ('Guepier
    des Montagnes')
247 80f Regal Sunbird ('Souimanga Royal')
248 100f Fan-tailed Whydah ('Veuve a
    Epaulettes Rouges')
                Set of 10   5.50   2.00

5465† 5k Mute Swan   15   5

1970

361† 20c Green Peafowl 25 10

1972

463† 32f Helmet Guineafowl ('Pintades') 90 60

469 20c Common Waxbill ('Astrild Ondule')
470 30c Collared Sunbird ('Souimanga a
 Collier')
471 50c Variable Sunbird ('Souimanga a Ventre
 Feu')
472 1f Greater Double-collared Sunbird
 ('Souimanga de Grauer')
473 4f Ruwenzori Puff-back Flycatcher ('Gobe-
 Mouches des Montagnes')
474 6f Red-billed Fire Finch ('Senegali Rouge')
475 10f Scarlet-chested Sunbird ('Souimanga a
 Gorge Rouge')
476 18f Red-headed Quelea ('Travailleur a Tete
 Rouge')
477 60f Black-headed Gonolek ('Gonolek a
 Dessous Rouge')
478 100f African Golden Oriole ('Loriot Dore')
 Set of 10 4.50 3.00

1975

660 20c Eastern White Pelican ('Pelican Blanc')
661 30c Malachite Kingfisher ('Martin-Pecheur
 Malachite')

662 50c Goliath Heron ('Heron Goliath')
663 1f Saddle-bill Stork ('Jabiru d'Afrique')
664 4f African Jacana ('Jacana d'Afrique')
665 10f African Darter ('Anhinga Rouge')
666 34f Sacred Ibis ('Ibis')
667 80f Hartlaub's Duck ('Canard de Hartlaub')
 Set of 8 3.75 2.75
MS668 40f Greater Flamingo ('Flamant Roses');
 60f Crowned Crane ('Grues
 Couronnees') 3.75 3.00

1977

833 20c Long-crested Eagle (*Lophaetus
 occipitalis*)
834 30c African Harrier Hawk (*Gymnogenys
 typicus*)
835 50c African Fish Eagle (*Haliaetus vocifer
 vocifer*)
836 1f Hooded Vulture (*Necrosyrtes monachus
 pileatus*)
837 3f Augur Buzzard (*Buteo rufofuscus
 augur*)
838 5f Black Kite (*Milvus aegyptius tenebrosus*)
839 20f Black-shouldered Kite (*Elanus
 caeruleus*)
840 100f Bateleur (*Terathopius ecaudatus*)
 Set of 8 3.50 3.00

1978

898 30f Great Spotted Woodpecker
899 30f Red Bishop (on stamp No. 239)
 Set of 2 2.00 1.90

903† 20c Spur-winged Goose, Mallard 25 10
908† 15f Common Turkey 40 35

1980

1141 20c Northern Double-collared Sunbird (*N. preussi kikuyuensis*)

956 20c Strange Weaver (*Ploceus alienus*)
957 30c Regal Sunbird (*Nectarinia regia*)
958 50c White-spotted Crake (*Sarothrura pulchra*)
959 3f Crowned Hornbill (*Tockus alboterminatus*)
960 10f Barred Owlet (*Glaudidium castaneum*)
961 26f African Emerald Cuckoo (*Chrysococcyx cupreus*)
962 60f Black-crowned Waxbill (*Estrilda nonnula*)
963 100f Crowned Eagle (*Stephanoaetus coronatus*)

1142 30c Regal Sunbird (*N. regia kivuensis*)
1143 50c Red-tufted Malachite Sunbird (*N. johnstoni dartmouthi*)
1144 4f Bronze Sunbird (*N. kilimensis kilimensis*)
1145 5f Collared Sunbird (*Anthreptes collaris garguensis*)
1146 10f Blue-headed Sunbird (*N. alinae tanganjicae*)
1147 20f Purple-breasted Sunbird (*N. purpureiventris*)
1148 40f Coppery Sunbird (*N. cuprea septentrionalis*)
1149 50f Olive-bellied Sunbird (*N. chloropygia orphogaster*)
1150 70f Red-chested Sunbird (*N. erythroceria*)

       Set of 8 4.50 3.75

       Set of 10 3.50 2.50

1015† 20c South African Crowned Crane   30 10

1985

1237 10f Barn Owl ('Chouette effraie')
1238 20f White-faced Scops Owl ('Petit duc a face blanche')
1239 40f Ruby-throated Hummingbird ('Colibri a gorge rubis')
1240 80f Eastern Meadowlark ('Sturnelle des pres')

       Set of 4 2.75 2.25

1982

1130† 40f Crowned Crane..   75 60
1131† 50f African Fish Eagle ..   95 75

No. 1134 overprinted 1910/1985 and guide emblem
1246† 30c Northern Double-collared Sunbird 5 5

1983

1986

1134† 30c Northern Double-collared Sunbird 10 5

1274† 7f Whale-headed Stork ('Bec en sabot') .. 15 5
1279† 100f Heuglin's Masked Weaver ('Tisserins') 1.90 1.50
1280† 100f Eastern White Pelican ('Pelican') .. 1.90 1.50

RYUKYU ISLANDS
Northern Pacific
100 cents = 1 dollar

1960

103	3c Little Egret	5.50	1.75

1963

144	3c Black Kite	1.75	1.00

1966

175†	3c Pryer's Woodpecker	50	45

178	3c Pacific Swallow.	45	35

1972

263†	5cShort-tailed Albatross..	80	70

SABAH
South-east Asia
100 cents = 1 dollar

1964
Nos. 404/5 of North Borneo overprinted **SABAH**

421†	$2 Rhinoceros Hornbill	3.25	2.75
422†	$5 Crested Wood Partridge	7.50	7.00

ST. HELENA
South Atlantic
1953 12 pence = 1 shilling,
20 shillings = 1 pound
1971 100 pence = 1 pound

1953

158†	3d St. Helena Sand Plover ('Wire Bird') ..	70	15

1961

177†	1½d Yellow Canary ('Cape Canary').	30	12
181†	6d Madagascar Red Fody ('Red Bird').. ..	80	25
185†	1s6d White Tern ('Fairy Tern')	5.00	3.00

1965
Nos. 181 and 185 overprinted **FIRST LOCAL POST 4th JANUARY**
1965

195†	6d Madagascar Red Fody	10	8
196†	1s6d White Tern	15	10

1972

289	2p St. Helena Sand Plover, White Tern		
290	16p St. Helena Sand Plover, White Tern		
	Set of 2	85	90

1975

312† 12p St. Helena Sand Plover (*Aegialitis sanctae-helenae*) 90 1.25

1982

395† 25p Ring-necked Pheasant, Chukar Partridge 75 75

1983

419 7p Java Sparrow (*Padda oryzivora*)
420 15p Madagascar Red Fody (*Foudia madagascariensis*)
421 33p Common Waxbill (*Estrilda astrild*)
422 59p Yellow Canary (*Serinus flaviventris*)
Set of 4 2.40 2.50

1984

443† 15p St. Helena Sand Plover ('Wire Bird') .. 40 40

COLLECT RAILWAYS ON STAMPS

A Stanley Gibbons thematic catalogue on this popular subject. Copies available at £7.50 (p. + p. £1.50) from: Stanley Gibbons Publications Ltd, 5 Parkside, Christchurch Road, Ringwood, Hants BH24 3SH.

1985

465† 15p Moorhen ('Common Gallinule'). 40 35
466† 25p White-tailed Tropic Bird ('Tropic Bird') 60 55
467† 60p Common Noddy ('Noddy Tern') 1.40 1.40
(464/7 *Set of* 4) 2.40 2.25

ST. KITTS
West Indies
100 cents = 1 dollar

1981

53 1c Magnificent Frigate Bird ('Frigatebird')
54 4c Wied's Crested Flycatcher ('Rusty-tailed Flycatcher')
55 5c Purple-throated Carib
56 6c Burrowing Owl
57 8c Caribbean Martin
58 10c Yellow-crowned Night Heron
59 15c Bananaquit
60 20c Scaly-breasted Thrasher
61 25c Grey Kingbird
62 30c Green-throated Carib
63 40c Turnstone ('Ruddy Turnstone')
64 45c Black-faced Grassquit
65 50c Cattle Egret
66 55c Brown Pelican
67 $1 Lesser Antillean Bullfinch
68 $2.50 Zenaida Dove
69 $5 American Kestrel ('Sparrow Hawk')
70 $10 Antillean Crested Hummingbird
Set of 18 9.50 10.00

1983

Nos. 55, 59/63 and 66/70 overprinted **INDEPENDENCE 1983**
118 5c Purple-throated Carib
119 15c Bananaquit
120 20c Scaly-breasted Thrasher
121 25c Grey Kingbird
122 30c Green-throated Carib
123 40c Turnstone
124 55c Brown Pelican
125 $1 Lesser Antillean Bullfinch
126 $2.50 Zenaida Dove
127 $5 American Kestrel
128 $10 Antillean Crested Hummingbird
Set of 11 8.75 9.00

1984

139† 45c Parrot sp 15 10

OFFICIAL STAMPS

1981

Nos. 59/70 overprinted **OFFICIAL**

O11 15c Bananaquit
O12 20c Scaly-breasted Thrasher
O13 25c Grey Kingbird
O14 30c Green-throated Carib
O15 40c Turnstone
O16 45c Black-faced Grassquit
O17 50c Cattle Egret
O18 55c Brown Pelican
O19 $1 Lesser Antillean Bullfinch
O20 $2.50 Zenaida Dove
O21 $5 American Kestrel
O22 $10 Antillean Crested Hummingbird
Set of 12 7.50 8.00

ST. KITTS-NEVIS
West Indies
100 cents = 1 dollar

1963

139† 25c White-crowned Pigeon 50 12

1964

No. 139 overprinted **ARTS FESTIVAL ST KITTS 1964**
146† 25c White-crowned Pigeon 10 5
(145/6 *Set of 2*) 15 10

1972

256 20c Brown Pelican
257 25c Brown Pelican
Set of 2 40 45

1978

391† $1 Brown Pelican ('Pelican') 35 45

ST. LUCIA
West Indies
100 cents = 1 dollar

1969

256 10c Purple-throated Carib ('Humming Bird
(Colibri)')
257 15c St. Lucia Amazon ('St. Lucia Parrot')
258 25c Purple-throated Carib ('Humming Bird
(Colibri)')
259 35c St. Lucia Amazon ('St. Lucia Parrot')
Set of 4 1.10 45

1972

343 15c St. Lucia Amazon
344 35c St. Lucia Amazon
Set of 2 40 30

1976

415 1c Laughing Gull
416 2c Little Blue Heron
417 4c Belted Kingfisher
418 5c St. Lucia Amazon ('St. Lucia Parrot')
419 6c St. Lucia Oriole
420 8c Brown Trembler ('Trembler')
421 10c American Kestrel ('Sparrow Hawk')
422 12c Red-billed Tropic Bird
423 15c Moorhen ('Common Gallinule')
424 25c Common Noddy ('Brown Noddy')
425 35c Sooty Tern
426 50c Osprey
427 $1 White-breasted Trembler ('White-
     breasted Thrasher')
428 $2.50 St. Lucia Black Finch
429 $5 Red-necked Pigeon ('Ramier')
430 $10 Caribbean Elaenia

Set of 16	16.00	12.00

1981

572†	50c St. Lucia Amazon ('St. Lucia Parrot') ..	30	20
573†	$2 Purple-throated Carib.	80	90

1985

820 10c Magnificent Frigate Bird ('Frigate
     Bird')
821 35c Mangrove Cuckoo
822 65c Lesser Yellowlegs ('Yellow Sandpiper')
823 $3 Audubon's Shearwater

Set of 4	2.40	2.50

ST. PIERRE ET MIQUELON
North Atlantic
100 centimes = 1 franc

1909

86†	25c Glaucous Gull (?) (blue).	80	50
112†	25c Glaucous Gull (green and brown)	25	20
87†	30c Glaucous Gull (brown and orange) ..	50	40
113†	30c Glaucous Gull (red)	25	10
114†	30c Glaucous Gull (blue and red)	25	10
115†	30c Glaucous Gull (green and olive)	12	15
88†	35c Glaucous Gull (brown and green)	30	12
89†	40c Glaucous Gull (green and brown)	1.40	75
90†	45c Glaucous Gull (green and violet)	30	12
91†	50c Glaucous Gull (green and brown)	55	45
116†	50c Glaucous Gull (blue).	50	40
117†	50c Glaucous Gull (mauve and brown). ..	30	25
118†	60c Glaucous Gull (red and blue)	30	12
119†	65c Glaucous Gull (brown and mauve). ..	50	45
92†	75c Glaucous Gull (olive and brown)	50	45
120†	90c Glaucous Gull (red)	10.00	8.50

1924
Nos. 90, 92 and additional value surcharged

127†	65c on 45c Glaucous Gull	45	45
128†	85c on 75c Glaucous Gull	45	45
129†	90c on 75c Glaucous Gull (red)	80	80

1941
No. 114 overprinted **FRANCE LIBRE F. N. F. L.**

246†	30c Glaucous Gull	£600	£600

1963

422 50c Eider (*Somateria mollissima*)
423 1f Rock Ptarmigan (*Lagopus mutus*)
424 2f Semipalmated Plover (*Charadrius
     hiaticula* !)
425 6f Blue-winged Teal (*Anas discors*)

Set of 4	1.40	90

1973

507†	6c Long-tailed Duck ('Haralde de		
	Miquelon')	20	20
508†	10c Atlantic Puffin ('Macareux Moine') ..	30	30
509†	20c Snowy Owl ('Harfang des Neiges') ..	40	30
510†	40c Long-tailed Duck ('Haralde de		
	Miquelon')	60	40
511†	70c Atlantic Puffin ('Macareux Moine') ..	70	70
512†	90c Snowy Owl ('Harfang des Neiges') ..	2.00	1.50

1974

525	70c Northern Gannet		
526	90c Northern Gannet		
	Set of 2	2.00	1.50

531†	6c Caspian Tern, Kittiwake, Great Auk * ..	30	30

1975

539†	6c Brunnich's Guillemot, Double-crested		
	Cormorant	40	15
540†	10c Atlantic Puffin, Pintail	40	20
	(539/41 Set of 3)	90	50

ST. THOMAS AND PRINCE ISLANDS
Off West Africa
100 cents = 1 dobra

Appendix
The following stamps have either been issued in excess of postal needs, or have not been made available to the public in reasonable quantities at face value. Miniature sheets, imperforate stamps etc. are excluded from this section.

1978
1st Anniv of New Currency. 5d, 8d Grey Parrot

1979
Birds. Postage 50c Principe Seedeater, 50c Golden-backed Bishop, 1d White-bellied Kingfisher, 7d Sao Thome Giant Sunbird, 8d Giant Weaver. Air 100d Black-capped Speirops

ST. VINCENT
West Indies
100 cents = 1 dollar

1965

244†	$2.50 St. Vincent Amazon ('St. Vincent		
	Parrot')	9.00	5.00

1970

285	½c House Wren
286a	1c Green Heron
287	2c Lesser Antillean Bullfinch ('Bullfinch')
288	3c St. Vincent Amazon ('St. Vincent
	Parrot')
289	4c Rufous-throated Solitaire ('Soufriere
	Bird')
364	5c Red-necked Pigeon ('Ramier')
291	6c Bananaquit
292	8c Purple-throated Carib ('Humming
	Bird')
293	10c Mangrove Cuckoo

294 12c Common Black Hawk ('Black Hawk')
295 20c Bare-eyed Thrush
296 25c Hooded Tanager ('Prince')
297 50c Blue-hooded Euphonia
298 $1 Barn Owl
299 $2.50 Yellow-bellied Elaenia ('Crested
Elaenia')
300 $5 Ruddy Quail Dove

Set of 16 24.00 16.00

1985

1971

322† 12c St. Vincent Amazon 30 10
324† 40c St. Vincent Amazon 65 40

854 15c Brown Pelican
855 15c Green Heron
856 40c Pileated Woodpecker
857 40c Common Flicker
858 60c Painted Bunting (female)
859 60c White-winged Crossbill
860 $2.25 Red-shouldered Hawk
861 $2.25 Common Caracara ('Crested
Caracara')

Set of 8 4.25 4.25

1973

Nos. 292 and 297/8 surcharged
380 30c on 50c Blue-hooded Euphonia
381 40c on 8c Purple-throated Carib
382 $10 on $1 Barn Owl

Set of 3 15.00 7.50

SAMOA
South Pacific
1952 12 pence = 1 shilling,
20 shillings = 1 pound
1967 100 sene = 1 tala (or dollar)

1974

396 30c Royal Tern
397 40c Brown Pelican
398 $10 Magnificent Frigate Bird ('Frigatebird')

Set of 3 17.00 11.00

1952

223† 5d Tooth-billed Pigeon 1.25 80

1976

1965

263† 8d Red-tailed Tropic Bird 40 5
(263/4 Set of 2) 1.25 30

1967

487 5c Blue-headed Hummingbird
488 10c Antillean Crested Hummingbird
('Crested Hummingbird')
489 35c Purple-throated Carib
490 45c Blue-headed Hummingbird
491 $1.25 Green-throated Carib

Set of 5 12.00 7.50

280 1s Carunculated Honeyeater ('Wattled
Honey-eater')
281 2s Pacific Pigeon

282	3s Samoan Starling	
283	5s White-vented Flycatcher ('Samoan Broadbill')	
284	7s Red-headed Parrot Finch	
285	10s Purple Swamphen	
286	20s Barn Owl	
287	25s Tooth-billed Pigeon	
288	50s Island Thrush	
289	$1 Samoan Fantail	
289a	$2 Black-breasted Honeyeater ('Mao')	
289b	$4 Savaii White Eye ('Samoan White-Eye')	
	Set of 12	45.00 48.00

1968

No. 285 *surcharged* **1928–1968 KINGSFORD-SMITH TRANS-PACIFIC FLIGHT 20 SENE**

305	20s on 10s Purple Swamphen	12	10

1978

510†	26s Pacific Pigeon	35	40

SAN MARINO
Southern Europe
100 centesimi = 1 lira

1959

564	5li Mediterranean Gull ('Gabbiano')	
565	10li Common Kestrel ('Falco')	
566	15li Mallard ('Germano')	
567	120li Rock Dove ('Colombo')	
568	250li Barn Swallow ('Rondine')	
	Set of 5	3.00 1.25

1960

593	1li Golden Oriole ('Rigogolo')
594	2li Nightingale ('Usignuolo')

595	3li Woodcock ('Beccaccia')
596	4li Hoopoe ('Upupa')
597	5li Red-legged Partridge ('Pernice')
598	10li Goldfinch ('Cardellino')
599	25li Common Kingfisher ('Martin Pescatore')
600	60li Ring-necked Pheasant ('Fagiano')
601	80li Green Woodpecker ('Picchio')
602	110li Red-breasted Flycatcher ('Pettirosso')

	Set of 10	8.50 3.00

1962

684†	15li Lapwing	5	5

1972

938	1li House Sparrow (*Passer italiae*)
939	2li Firecrest (*Regulus ignicapillus*)
940	3li Blue Tit (*Parus caeruleus*)
941	4li Ortolan Bunting (*Emberiza hortulana*)
942	5li Bluethroat (*Luscinia svecica*)
943	10li Bullfinch (*Pyrrhula pyrrhula*)
944	25li Linnet (*Carduelis cannabina*)
945	50li Black-eared Wheatear (*Oenanthe hispanica*)
946	90li Sardinian Warbler (*Sylvia melanocephala*)
947	220li Greenfinch (*Carduelis chloris*)

	Set of 10	1.10 60

1978

1095	120li Slender-billed Gull
1096	170li Slender-billed Gull

	Set of 2	40 20

Nos. 1095/6 also depict an unidentifiable bird of prey.

STAMP MONTHLY
— finest and most informative magazine for all collectors. Obtainable from your newsagent or by postal subscription — details on request.

1979

1121†	10li Golden Eagle	15	5
1124†	70li Hoopoe	15	5

1986

1270†	650li Common Kestrel	85	45
	(1269/70 Set of 2)	1.25	85

SARAWAK
South-east Asia
100 cents = 1 dollar

1955

191†	6c Malabar Pied Hornbill ('Hornbill')	40	10

SAUDI ARABIA
Arabia
20 piastres = 1 riyal

1968

1022	1p Saker Falcon
1023	4p Saker Falcon
1024	10p Saker Falcon
1025	20p Saker Falcon
	Set of 4 90.00 8.75

SEIYUN
See under Aden Protectorate States

SENEGAL
West Africa
100 centimes = 1 franc

1960

234	50f Carmine Bee Eater ('Guepier de Nubie')
235	100f Abyssinian Roller ('Rollier')
236	200f Violet Turaco ('Touraco Violet')
237	250f Red Bishop ('Franciscain')
238	500f African Fish Eagle ('Aigle Pecheur')
	Set of 5 35.00 13.00

1966

344†	25f Gull sp	30	15

1968

376	5f Lesser Pied Kingfisher (*Ceryle rudis*)
377	15f African Jacana (*Actophilornis africana*)
378	70f African Darter (*Anhinga rufa*)
379	250f Village Weaver (*Ploceus cucullatus*) (air)
380	300f Comb Duck (*Sarkidiornis melanotos*)
381	500f Bateleur (*Terathopius ecaudatus*)
	Set of 6 20.00 8.00

1974

545 1f Peters's Finfoot ('Grebifoulques')
546 2f White Spoonbill ('Spatules Blanches')
547 3f Crowned Crane ('Grues Couronnees')
548 4f Little Egret ('Aigrettes')
549 250f Greater Flamingo ('Flamants Roses')
      (gold value)
550 250f Greater Flamingo ('Flamants Roses')
      (black value)
                              Set of 6   7.00   2.75

1976

585† 3f Bar-tailed Godwit ('Barge Rouge')   25   10
587† 5f African Fish Eagle ('Aigle Pecheur'). ..   30   15

1978

658 5f Caspian Tern ('Sternes Caspiennes'),
      Royal Tern ('Sternes Royales')
659 10f Pink-backed Pelican ('Pelican Gris')
660 15f Grey Heron ('Heron Cendre')
661 20f Greater Flamingo ('Nidification de
      Flaments')
662 150f Grey Heron ('Heron Cendre'), Royal
      Tern ('Sternes Royales')
663 150f Abyssinian Ground Hornbill ('Calaos
      d'Abyssinie')
                              Set of 6   2.75   1.40

681 100f Capercaillie
682 100f Violet Turaco (on stamp No. 236)
                              Set of 2   2.25   2.00

1979

697 500f Abyssinian Roller (on stamp No. 235) ..   2.50   1.60

1981

729† 50f Caspian Tern ('Sterne Caspienne'),
      Grey-headed Gull ('Mouettes'), Eastern
      White Pelican   40   15
730† 70f Slender-billed Gull ('Goelands
      Railleurs'), Gull-billed Tern ('Sterne
      Hansel')   45   25
732† 150f Red-billed Tropic Bird ('Phaeton
      Ethere'), White-breasted Cormorant
      ('Cormoran') 1.00   50
                        (729/32 Set of 4)   2.00   1.00
MS733 125f Caspian Tern, Grey-headed Gull,
      Eastern White Pelican; 125f Slender-
      billed Gull, Gull-billed Tern; 125f Red-
      billed Tropic Bird, White-breasted
      Cormorant (sheet also contains one
      other stamp).. .. ..   2.25   2.25

1982

753 45f Black-tailed Godwit ('Barge')
754 75f Saddle-bill Stork ('Jabiru')
755 80f White-throated Francolin ('Francolin')
756 500f Tawny Eagle ('Aigle')
                              Set of 4   3.50   2.40

1986

862†	50f Ostrich ('Autruches')	30	15
865†	100f Ostrich	60	50

1987

882†	70f Ostrich ('L'Autruche')	35	20

SEYCHELLES
Indian Ocean
100 cents = 1 rupee

1962

196†	5c Black Parrot	5	5

1968

255†	85c Black Parrot	35	20

1969

264†	15c Sacred Ibis	25	10

1970

280†	20c White Tern	15	10

1972

308	5c Seychelles Brush Warbler	
309	20c Bare-legged Scops Owl ('Seychelles Scops Owl')	
310	50c Seychelles Blue Pigeon	
311	65c Seychelles Magpie Robin	
312	95c Seychelles Paradise Flycatcher ('Black Paradise Flycatcher')	
313	3r50 Seychelles Kestrel	
	Set of 6	10.00 10.50

1976

369	20c Seychelles Paradise Flycatcher	
370	1r25 Seychelles Sunbird	
371	1r50 Seychelles Brown White Eye ('The Seychelles White-Eye')	
372	5r Black Parrot ('The Seychelles Black Parrot')	
	Set of 4	3.25 3.25

1977

Inscribed 'Re.' or 'Rs.'
412† 1r Madagascar Red Fody ('Madagascar
      Fody')   45   5
413† 1r25 White Tern ('Fairy Tern')   50   15
For these stamps inscribed 'R' see Nos. 487 and 489.

1978

434† 1r25 Seychelles Magpie Robin ('Magpie
      Robin')   40   25
435† 1r50 Seychelles Paradise Flycatcher   45   35

1979

441 2r Seychelles Fody
442 2r Green Heron ('Green-backed Heron')
443 2r Thick-billed Bulbul ('Seychelles Bulbul')
444 2r Seychelles Cave Swiftlet
445 2r Grey-headed Lovebird
                          Set of 5   2.25   2.25

451† 2r25 Seychelles Blue Pigeon (on stamp
      No. 310)..   25   30

1980

463 2r Seychelles Kestrel (male)
464 2r Seychelles Kestrel (pair)
465 2r Seychelles Kestrel (with eggs)
466 2r Seychelles Kestrel (on nest with chicks)
467 2r Seychelles Kestrel (chicks in nest)
                          Set of 5   2.25   2.25

468† 40c Red-footed Booby   5   5

1981

As Nos. 412/13 but inscribed 'R'
487† 1r Madagascar Red Fody ('Madagascar
      Fody')   20   25
489† 1r25 White Tern ('Fairy Tern')   25   30

500 2r White Tern ('Male Fairy Tern')
501 2r White Tern ('Pair Fairy Terns')
502 2r White Tern ('Female Fairy Tern')
503 2r White Tern ('Female Fairy Tern (nest
     and egg)')
504 2r White Tern ('Fairy Tern and chick')
                          Set of 5   3.00   3.00

COLLECT MAMMALS ON STAMPS
The second Stanley Gibbons thematic catalogue —
copies are available at £7.50 (p. + p. £1.50) from:
Stanley Gibbons Publications Ltd, 5 Parkside,
Christchurch Road, Ringwood, Hants BH24 3SH.

1982

523 3r Chinese Little Bittern ('Chinese Bittern (male)')
524 3r Chinese Little Bittern ('Chinese Bittern (female)')
525 3r Chinese Little Bittern ('Chinese Bittern (hen on nest)')
526 3r Chinese Little Bittern ('Chinese Bittern (nest and eggs)')
527 3r Chinese Little Bittern ('Chinese Bittern (hen with chicks)')

Set of 5   3.50   3.00

1983

568† 40c Moorhen   15   5

1985

605 50c Bare-legged Scops Owl
606 2r Bare-legged Scops Owl
607 3r Bare-legged Scops Owl
608 10r Bare-legged Scops Owl

Set of 4   4.00   4.00

COLLECT RAILWAYS ON STAMPS
A Stanley Gibbons thematic catalogue on this popular subject. Copies available at £7.50 (p.+p. £1.50) from: Stanley Gibbons Publications Ltd, 5 Parkside, Christchurch Road, Ringwood, Hants BH24 3SH.

610† 2r White Tern ('Fairy Tern')..   45   50

As No. 489 but additionally inscribed 'AIR SEYCHELLES FIRST AIRBUS'
623 1r25 White Tern ('Fairy Tern')   30   35

1986

As No. 610 but without 'Expo'85 inscription and emblem
MS650 2r White Tern (sheet also contains 3 other stamps) 2.40   2.60

No. 487 overprinted **LAZOURNEN ENTERNASYONAL KREOL**
653 1r Madagascar Red Fody   20   25

SHARJAH
Arabia
1965 100 naye paise = 1 rupee
1966 100 dirhams = 1 riyal

1965

101 30np Rock Dove
102 40np Red Junglefowl ('Jungle Fowl')
103 75np Hoopoe
104 150np Rock Dove
105 2r Red Junglefowl ('Jungle Fowl')
106 3r Hoopoe

Set of 6   7.50   5.25

Appendix
The following stamps have either been issued in excess of postal needs, or have not been made available to the public in reasonable quantities at face value. Miniature sheets, imperforate stamps etc. are excluded from this section.

1967
Post Day. Japanese Paintings. 1r Japanese Pheasant

1972
Birds (1st series). Postage 20d Black Grouse, 25d Stock Dove, 75d Little Bittern. Air 1r Hazel Grouse, 2r Tree Sparrow

Birds (2nd series). 25d Great Tit, 25d Grey Partridge, 35d Jay, 35d White-tailed Sea Eagle, 50d Great Spotted Woodpecker, 50d Black Stork, 65d Common Kingfisher, 65d Great Bustard, 1r Red Crossbill, 1r Bean Goose, 1r Mute Swan, 1r Common Turkey, 1r Red Junglefowl, 3r Nightingale, 3r Rock Ptarmigan

13th World Jamboree. Postage 2d Lesser Kestrel. Air 35d Lesser Kestrel

	Nos. 632 *and* 635 *overprinted* **AUSIPEX 84**		
818	50c Black Crake		
819	5le Barrow's Bustard		
	Set of 2	2.75	2.75

1985

853	40c Fischer's Whydah ('Straw-tailed Whydah')		
854	90c Spotted Flycatcher		
855	1le30 Garden Warbler		
856	3le Speke's Weaver		
	Set of 4	3.00	2.75
MS857	5le Great Grey Shrike..	2.00	2.50

SIERRA LEONE
West Africa
100 cents = 1 leone

1980

622	1c Knysna Turaco ('Sierra Leone Touraco')		
623	2c Olive-bellied Sunbird		
624	3c Western Black-headed Oriole ('Sierra Leone Black-headed Oriole')		
625	5c Spur-winged Goose		
626	7c Didric Cuckoo ('White-bellied Didric Cuckoo')		
627	10c Grey Parrot ('Sierra Leone Grey Parrot')		
766	15c Blue Quail ('African Blue Quail')		
767	20c African Wood Owl ('West African Wood Owl')		
768	30c Great Blue Turaco ('Blue Plantain Eater')		
631	40c Blue-breasted Kingfisher ('Nigerian Blue-breasted Kingfisher')		
632	50c Black Crake		
633	1le Hartlaub's Duck		
634	2le Black Bee Eater		
635	5le Barrow's Bustard ('Denham's Bustard')		
	Set of 14	8.00	10.00

1984

800†	60c Greater Flamingo	20	25

	Nos. 625, 627 *and* 634 *surcharged*		
811	25c on 10c Grey Parrot		
812	40c on 10c Grey Parrot		
813	50c on 2le Black Bee Eater		
814	70c on 5c Spur-winged Goose		
815	10le on 5c Spur-winged Goose		
	Set of 5	6.00	6.00

SINGAPORE
South-east Asia
100 cents = 1 dollar

1962

70a†	15c Black-naped Tern (*Sterna*)..	80	5
74†	50c White-rumped Shama (*Copsychus malabaricus*)	95	5
75†	$1 White-breasted Kingfisher (*Halcyon smyrnensis*)	7.00	20
76†	$2 Yellow-bellied Sunbird (*Leptocoma jugularis*)	13.00	1.00
77†	$5 White-bellied Sea Eagle (*Haliaeetus leucogaster*)	26.00	2.75

1970

130†	75c Helmeted Hornbill, Greater Flamingo..	4.75	3.75

1973

193† 15c Sacred Ibis, Palm Cockatoo, White-
bellied Sea Eagle, Major Mitchell's
Cockatoo, Toco Toucan, Greater
Flamingo 45 12

1975

260 5c South African Crowned Crane
(Balearica pavonina !)
261 10c Great Indian Hornbill (Buceros
bicornis)
262 35c White-breasted Kingfisher (Halcyon
smyrnensis), White-collared Kingfisher
(Halcyon chloris)
263 $1 Sulphur-crested Cockatoo (Cacatua
galerita), Blue and Yellow Macaw (Ara
ararauna)
Set of 4 10.00 9.00

1978

322 10c Red-whiskered Bulbul
323 35c Oriental White Eye ('White Eye')
324 50c White-rumped Shama
325 75c White-crested Laughing Thrush,
Hwamei ('China Thrush')
Set of 4 2.75 1.75

STANLEY GIBBONS
STAMP COLLECTING SERIES
Introductory booklets on How to Start, How to
Identify Stamps and Collecting by Theme. A series
of well illustrated guides at a low price.
Write for details.

1984

467 10c Blue-breasted Banded Rail ('Slaty-
breasted Rail')
468 35c Black Bittern
469 50c Brahminy Kite
470 75c Moorhen ('Common Moorhen')
Set of 4 1.60 1.60

SOLOMON ISLANDS
Pacific Ocean
1939 12 pence = 1 shilling,
20 shillings = 1 pound
1966 100 cents = 1 dollar

1939

70† 2s6d Common Scrub Hen 17.00 6.00

1961

97 2d Great Frigate Bird
98 3d Great Frigate Bird
99 9d Great Frigate Bird
Set of 3 25 15

1965

115† 2d Blyth's Hornbill ('Hornbill') 35 12
119† 9d Lesser Frigate Bird ('Frigate Bird').. .. 40 15
122† 2s Sanford's Sea Eagle ('Sanford's Eagle') 5.00 2.75
125† 10s Ducorp's Cockatoo ('White Cockatoo'). 10.00 4.50

1966

Nos. 115, 119, 122 and 125 surcharged with new currency

138†	4c on 2d Blyth's Hornbill.	12	5
142†	8c on 9d Lesser Frigate Bird	15	5
147†	20c on 2s Sanford's Sea Eagle	75	25
149†	35c on 2d Blyth's Hornbill	2.25	40
151†	$1 on 10s Ducorp's Cockatoo	4.00	2.50

1973

233a†	$5 Great Frigate Bird	10.00	10.00

1974

263†	9c Great Frigate Bird (on stamp No. 98) ..	15	10
264†	15c Great Frigate Bird (on stamp No. 98) ..	25	25

1975

Inscribed 'British Solomon Islands'

267	1c Golden Whistler		
268	2c Common Kingfisher ('River Kingfisher')		
269	3c Red-bibbed Fruit Dove ('Red-throated Fruit Dove')		
270	4c Little Button Quail ('Button-Quail')		
271	$2 Duchess Lorikeet		
	Set of 5	12.00	12.00

Nos. 267/71 and 233a with obliterating bar over 'British'

285†	1c Golden Whistler	20	25
286†	2c Common Kingfisher	25	25
287†	3c Red-bibbed Fruit Dove	25	25
288†	4c Little Button Quail.	25	25
299†	$2 Duchess Lorikeet..	8.00	8.00
300†	$5 Great Frigate Bird.	15.00	18.00

1976

Inscribed 'Solomon Islands'

305†	1c Golden Whistler	20	20
306†	2c Common Kingfisher ('River Kingfisher')	25	25
307†	3c Red-bibbed Fruit Dove ('Red-throated Fruit Dove')	25	25
308†	4c Little Button Quail ('Button-Quail')	30	25
309†	5c Willie Wagtail	30	25
312†	12c Rainbow Lory ('Coconut Lory')	60	40
319†	$2 Duchess Lorikeet..	5.50	4.75
320†	$5 Great Frigate Bird.	7.50	7.50

1978

359†	45c Sanford's Sea Eagle ('Sandford Eagle')	40	50

1982

461	12c Sanford's Sea Eagle (constructing nest)		
462	12c Sanford's Sea Eagle (egg and chick)		
463	12c Sanford's Sea Eagle (hen feeding chicks)		
464	12c Sanford's Sea Eagle (fledgelings)		
465	12c Sanford's Sea Eagle (young bird in flight)		
466	12c Sanford's Sea Eagle (pair of birds in village)		
	Set of 6	1.40	1.40

1984

533 12c Little Pied Cormorant
534 18c Spotbill Duck ('Australian Grey Duck')
535 35c Rufous Night Heron ('Nankeen Night-
Heron')
536 $1 Eastern Broad-billed Roller
('Dollarbird')

| | | Set of 4 | 2.00 | 2.10 |

1985

MS556 50c x 2 Osprey (sheet also contains one
other stamp).. .. .. 1.50 1.75

1950

234†	5c Ostrich..	..	..	..	..	..	..	..	25	5
238†	20c Ostrich	..	..	..	..	..	..	45	5
241†	60c Ostrich	..	..	..	..	..	..	60	10

1959

334 5c White Stork (*Ciconia ciconia*)
335 10c Saddle-bill Stork (*Ephippiorynchus
senegalensis*)
336 15c Sacred Ibis (*Threskiornis aethiopicus*)
337 25c Pink-backed Pelican (*Pelecanus
rufescens*)
338 1s20 Marabou Stork (*Leptiptilos
crumeniferus*) (air)
339 2s Great Egret (*Casmerodius albus*)

| | | Set of 6 | 1.10 | 75 |

SOMALIA
East Africa
1932 100 centesimi = 1 lira
1950 100 centesimi = 1 somalo
1961 100 centesimi = 1 Somali shilling

1932

1960

| 352† | 1s50 White Stork .. | .. | .. | .. | .. | .. | 35 | 12 |

1965

| 174† | 2li55 Ostrich | .. | .. | .. | .. | .. | .. | .. | 5.50 | 9.00 |
| 175a† | 5li Ostrich | .. | .. | .. | .. | .. | .. | 2.75 | 60 |

1934
As No. 175a *but in different colour overprinted* **ONORANZE AL
DUCA DEGLI ABRUZZI**
183† 5li Ostrich.. .. .. 1.10 3.25

| 433† | 1s Greater Flamingo.. | .. | .. | .. | .. | .. | 40 | 10 |
| 434† | 1s30 Ostrich | .. | .. | .. | .. | .. | .. | 55 | 15 |

1966

436 25c Narina Trogon ('Narina')
437 35c Bateleur ('Falco Giocoliere')
438 50c Ruppell's Griffon ('Avvoltoio')
439 1s30 Common Roller ('Ghiandaia Marina')
440 2s Vulturine Guineafowl ('Faraona
     Vulturina')

| | | Set of 5 | 1.50 | 55 |

1968

491 35c Great Egret ('Airone Bianco
     Maggiore')
492 1s Carmine Bee Eater ('Gruccione
     Scarlatto')
493 1s30 Yellow-bellied Green Pigeon
     ('Colombo Pappagallo')
494 1s80 Paradise Whydah ('Vedovella Nera')

| | | Set of 4 | 1.50 | 60 |

1980

658 1s Pygmy Puff-back Flycatcher (*Batis
     perkeo*)
659 2s25 Golden-winged Grosbeak
     (*Rynchostruthus socotranus louisae*)
660 5s Red-crowned Bush Shrike (*Laniarius
     ruficeps*)

| | | Set of 3 | 2.00 | 1.25 |

BIRDS   BIRDS   BIRDS

SOMALILAND PROTECTORATE
East Africa
100 cents = 1 shilling

1953

142†	35c Somali Stock Dove ('Somali Rock Pigeon')	.. ..	45	10
143†	50c Martial Eagle.		45	10
146†	2s Somali Stock Dove ('Somali Rock Pigeon')		4.00	2.25
147†	5s Martial Eagle		4.50	6.00

SOUTH AFRICA
Southern Africa
100 cents = 1 rand

1961

238†	½c African Pygmy Kingfisher ('Natal Kingfisher')..	5	5
243†	3c Burchell's Gonolek ('Shrike')	30	5
249†	20c Secretary Bird ('Sekretarisvoel')	3.50	15

1969

276†	½c African Pygmy Kingfisher.	10	5

1974

352†	5c Cape Gannet (*Morus capensis*) (blue & multicoloured)	20	5
358†	15c Greater Double-collared Sunbird (*Nectarinia afer*)	30	5
359†	20c Yellow-billed Hornbill (*Tockus flavirostris*)..	45	5
361†	30c Bokmakierie Shrike (*Malaconotus zeylonus*)	6.00	35

362† 50c Stanley Crane (*Tetrapterys paradisea*) 2.00   35
363† 1r Bateleur (*Terathopius ecaudatus*) 6.00 2.50

As No. 352 but colours changed
372† 5c Cape Gannet (*Morus capensis*) (black
and blue)   55   20

SOUTH GEORGIA
South Atlantic
1963 12 pence = 1 shilling,
20 shillings = 1 pound
1971 100 pence = 1 pound

1963

4† 2½d King Penguin, Chinstrap Penguin 1.50   65
8† 6d Light-mantled Sooty Albatross ('Sooty
Albatross')   75   25
12† 2s6d Wandering Albatross 12.00 7.00
16† £1 King Penguin 15.00 22.00

1971
Nos. 4, 8 and 12 surcharged in new currency
22† 2½p on 2½d King Penguin, Chinstrap Penguin 1.00   50
25† 5p on 6d Light-mantled Sooty Albatross. ..   90   40
64† 15p on 2s6d Wandering Albatross 6.00 10.00

1972

36 5p King Penguin
37 10p King Penguin
Set of 2 2.40 1.10

1979

72† 11p King Penguin 1.60 1.90

SOUTH GEORGIA AND SOUTH SANDWICH ISLANDS
South Atlantic
100 pence = 1 pound

1987

161 1p Southern Black-backed Gull
('Dominican Gull')
162 2p Blue-eyed Cormorant
163 3p Snowy Sheathbill ('Wattled Sheathbill')
164 4p Great Skua ('Brown Skua')
165 5p Pintado Petrel ('Cape Pigeon')
166 6p Georgian Diving Petrel ('South Georgia
Diving Petrel')
167 7p South Georgia Pipit
168 8p Georgian Teal ('South Georgia Pintail')
169 9p Fairy Prion
170 10p Chinstrap Penguin
171 20p Macaroni Penguin
172 25p Light-mantled Sooty Albatross
173 50p Giant Petrel ('Southern Giant Petrel')
174 £1 Wandering Albatross
175 £3 King Penguin
Set of 15 8.50 8.75

SOUTH KOREA
See under Korea

SOUTH VIETNAM
See under Vietnam

SOUTH WEST AFRICA
Southern Africa
1931 12 pence = 1 shilling,
20 shillings = 1 pound
1961 100 cents = 1 rand

1931

74† ½d Kori Bustard (pair of stamps, one
inscribed in English, the other in
Afrikaans) 70   90

1961

176† 3c Greater Flamingo.. .. .. 1.75 10
178† 5c Greater Flamingo.. .. .. 2.25 5

1974

260 4c Chat-Shrike (*Lanioturdus torquatus*)
261 5c Peach-faced Lovebird (*Agapornis roseicollis*)
262 10c Damaraland Rock Jumper (*Achaetops pycnopygius*)
263 15c Ruppell's Parrot (*Poicephalus rupellii*)
Set of 4 16.00 11.00

1975

270 4c Peregrine Falcon (*Falco peregrinus*)
271 5c Verreaux's Eagle (*Aquila verreauxii*)
272 10c Martial Eagle (*Polemaetus bellicosus*)
273 15c Egyptian Vulture (*Neophron percnopterus*)
Set of 4 13.00 8.50

1978

315† 4c Ostrich.. .. .. 15 10

1979

330 4c Greater Flamingo (*Phoenicopterus ruber*)
331 15c White-breasted Cormorant (*Phalacrocorax carbo* !
332 20c Chestnut-banded Sand Plover (*Charadrius pallidus*)
333 25c Eastern White Pelican (*Pelecanus onocrotalus*)
Set of 4 1.40 1.10

1982

396† 25c Southern Black-backed Gull, White-breasted Cormorant 35 35

1985

439 11c Ostrich (*Struthio camelus australis*)
440 25c Ostrich (*Struthio camelus australis*)
441 30c Ostrich (*Struthio camelus australis*)
442 50c Ostrich (*Struthio camelus australis*)
Set of 4 80 85

OFFICIAL STAMPS

1931

No. 74 *overprinted alternately* **OFFICIAL** *or* **OFFISIEEL** *in small capital letters*
O13† ½d Kori Bustard (pair) 1.40 6.00

1938

No. 74 *overprinted alternately* **OFFICIAL** *or* **OFFISIEEL** *in large capital letters*
O23† ½d Kori Bustard (pair) 1.50 3.50

SOUTHERN RHODESIA
Central Africa
12 pence = 1 shilling

1953

72† 1d Cattle Egret.. .. .. 15 5

1964

104† 10s Helmet Guineafowl 12.00 8.00

SPAIN
South-west Europe
100 centimos = 1 peseta

1961

1465† 5p Great Bustard 3.75 1.25

1971

2094† 1p Great Bustard (Otis tarda) 60 10
2097† 5p Red-legged Partridge (Alectoris rufa).. 1.50 20

COLLECT MAMMALS ON STAMPS
The second Stanley Gibbons thematic catalogue —
copies are available at £7.50 (p.+p. £1.50) from:
Stanley Gibbons Publications Ltd, 5 Parkside,
Christchurch Road, Ringwood, Hants BH24 3SH.

1973

2192 1p Black-bellied Sandgrouse (Pterocles
orientalis)
2193 2p Black Stork (Ciconia nigra)
2194 5p Azure-winged Magpie (Cyanopica
cyanus)
2195 7p Imperial Eagle (Aquila heliaca)
2196 15p Red-crested Pochard (Netta rufina)
Set of 5 3.50 90

1978

2518† 5p Red-breasted Merganser 25 10
2521† 20p Audouin's Gull ('Gaviota de
Audouin') 40 25

1985

2792 17p Andean Condor 30 5

2849 6p Subalpine Warbler (Sylvia cantillans)
2850 7p Rock Thrush (Monticola saxatilis)
2851 12p Spotless Starling (Sturnis unicolor)
2852 17p Bearded Reedling (Panurus
biarmicus)
Set of 4 60 25

SPANISH GUINEA
West Africa
100 centimos = 1 peseta

1952

371	5c + 5c Brown-cheeked Hornbill		
372	10c + 5c Brown-cheeked Hornbill		
373	60c + 15c Brown-cheeked Hornbill		
	Set of 3	1.40	80

1957

418	5c + 5c Grey Parrot (*Psittacus erithacus*)		
419	15c + 5c Grey Parrot (*Psittacus erithacus*)		
420	70c Grey Parrot (*Psittacus erithacus*)		
	Set of 3	65	40

1944

269†	1c Cattle Egret	25	10
276†	30c Cattle Egret	40	10

1950

355†	90c + 10c White Stork.	90	50

1954

420†	5c + 5c White Stork	30	10

SPANISH MOROCCO
North Africa
100 centimos = 1 peseta

1938

204†	10c White Stork	30	25
210†	1p50 White Stork	1.10	50

SPANISH SAHARA
North-west Africa
100 centimos = 1 peseta

1943

72†	5c Ostrich ('Avestruces')	30	15
74†	50c Ostrich ('Avestruces').	50	25
76†	1p40 Ostrich ('Avestruces')	50	25
78†	5p Ostrich ('Avestruces')	2.50	1.60

1952

95   5c + 5c Ostrich
96   10c + 5c Ostrich
97   60c + 15c Ostrich

Set of 3   90   55

150   10c + 5c Hoopoe Lark
151   25c + 10c Hoopoe Lark
152   50c + 10c Fulvous Babbler

Set of 3   65   40

1959

1957

131†   15c Ostrich   25   10
134†   80c Ostrich 1.25   20

157   25c Grey Heron
158   50c European Sparrow Hawk
159   75c Herring Gull
160   1p Grey Heron
161   1p50 European Sparrow Hawk
162   2p Herring Gull
163   3p Grey Heron
164   5p European Sparrow Hawk
165   10p Herring Gull

Set of 9   16.00   7.00

136   5c + 5c Golden Eagle (*A. chrysaetus*)
137   15c + 5c Tawny Eagle (*Aquila noevia*)
138   70c Golden Eagle (*A. chrysaetus*)

Set of 3   65   50

1960

175†   30c + 10c Golden Eagle   35   15

1958

143   10c + 5c White Stork
144   15c + 10c White Stork
145   50c + 10c White Stork

Set of 3   65   45

1961

177   25c Houbara Bustard
178   50c Rock Dove
179   75c Houbara Bustard
180   1p Rock Dove
181   1p50 Houbara Bustard
182   2p Rock Dove
183   3p Houbara Bustard
184   5p Rock Dove
185   10p Houbara Bustard

Set of 9   9.00   2.50

1967

259   1p Ruddy Shelduck (Tadorna ferruginea)
260   1p50 Greater Flamingo (Phoenicopterus
        ruber)
261   3p50 Rufous Bushchat (Erythropygia
        galactotes)

Set of 3   70   50

1971

290   1p50 Trumpeter Finch (Rhodopechys
        githaginea)
291   2p Trumpeter Finch (Rhodopechys
        githaginea)
292   5p Cream-coloured Courser (Cursorius
        cursor)
293   24p Lanner Falcon (Falco biarmicus)

Set of 4   2.40   85

1974

314   2p Eagle Owl (Bubo desertorum)
315   5p Lappet-faced Vulture (Torgos
        tracheliotus)

Set of 2   65   35

SPANISH WEST AFRICA
North-west Africa
100 centimos = 1 peseta

EXPRESS LETTER STAMP

1951

E26   25c Ostrich..   75   35

SRI LANKA
Indian Ocean
100 cents = 1 rupee

1979

684   10c Ceylon Blue Magpie
685   15c Ceylon Hanging Parrot ('Ceylon
        Lorikeet')
686   75c Ceylon Whistling Thrush ('Ceylon
        Arrenga')
687   1r Ceylon Spurfowl
688   5r Yellow-fronted Barbet
689   10r Yellow-tufted Bulbul ('Yellow-eared
        Bulbul')

Set of 6   1.40   1.40

1983

827 25c Sri Lanka Wood Pigeon ('Ceylon Wood Pigeon')
828 35c Large Sri Lanka White Eye ('Ceylon White-Eye')
829 2r Sri Lanka Dusky Blue Flycatcher ('Dusky-Blue Flycatcher')
830 20r Ceylon Coucal

Set of 4   1.10   1.25

1986

No. 828 surcharged

921† 7r on 35c Large Sri Lanka White Eye   35   40

SUDAN

North-east Africa
1000 milliemes = 100 piastres = 1 Sudanese pound

1951

124† 2m Whale-headed Stork ('Shoebill')   10   5

1967

262† 55m Whale-headed Stork   55   40

OFFICIAL STAMPS

1951

No. 124 overprinted S.G.

O68† 2m Whale-headed Stork.   10   5

SURINAM

South America
100 cents = 1 gulden

1953

414† 15c Blue and Yellow Macaw ('Ara') 1.25   30

1966

575 1c Red-breasted Blackbird (*Leistes militaris*)
576 2c Great Kiskadee (*Pitangus sulphuratus*)
577 3c Silver-beaked Tanager (*Ramphocelus carbo*)
578 4c Ruddy Ground Dove (*Columbigallina talpacotti*)
579 5c Blue-grey Tanager (*Thraupis virens*)
580 6c Straight-billed Hermit (*Amazilia fimbriata* !)
581 8c Turquoise Tanager (*Tanagra mexicana*)
582 10c Pale-breasted Thrush (*Turdus leucomelas*)

Set of 8   1.40   85

1971

689 15c Cocoi Heron
690 20c Greater Flamingo
691 25c Scarlet Macaw

Set of 3   1.75   1.40

1977

860 20c Red-breasted Blackbird ('Soldatenspreeuw')
861 25c Green Honeycreeper ('Zwartkap Suikervogel')
862 30c Paradise Tanager ('Paradijstangara')
863 40c Spot-tailed Nightjar ('Vlekstaart Nachtzwaluw')

864 45c Yellow-backed Tanager
     ('Geelrugtanager')
865 50c White-tailed Goldenthroat
     ('Witstaartgoudkeelkolibri')
866 55c Grey-breasted Sabrewing
     ('Grijsborstsabelvleugelkolibri')
867 60c Caica Parrot ('Zwartkappapegaai')
868 65c Cuvier's Toucan ('Roodsnaveltoekan')
869 70c Crimson-hooded Manakin
     ('Roodkapmanneke')
870 75c Hawk-headed Parrot ('Kraagpapegaai')
871 80c Spangled Cotinga ('Cayenne Cotinga')
872 85c Black-tailed Trogon
     ('Zwartstaarttrogon')
873 95c Black-banded Owl ('Zwartgestreepte
     Tropenbosuil')

Set of 14   11.00   9.00

1979

946 5g Black Curassow (*Crax alector*) 7.50   6.00

1983

SURINAME 80c

1134† 80c Blue-grey Tanager..   90   90

1985

suriname

1214 90c Orange-winged Amazon
      ('venezolaanse amazone') 1.25   95

SURINAME   f1.-

1248 1g Purple Gallinule ('amerikaans
      purperhoen')
1249 1g50 Rufescent Tiger Heron ('tigrifowroe
      – tijgervogel')
1250 2g50 Scarlet Ibis ('kori kori – rode ibis')
                          Set of 3   4.75   4.50

1986

SURINAME   f5.-

1268 5g Guianan Cock of the Rock ('guiana
      rotshaan') 3.50   3.00

SURINAME   f10.-

1291 10g Harpy Eagle ('gonini – harpij-arend') ..   7.50   7.00

No. 862 surcharged
1292 15c on 30c Paradise Tanager   35   25

SWAZILAND
Southern Africa
1962 100 cents = 1 rand
1976 100 cents = 1 emalangeni

1962

96†   5c Long-tailed Whydah ('Widowbird')   25   5
98†   10c Secretary Bird   20   5
103† 50c Southern Ground Hornbill ('Ground
      Hornbill') 3.00   2.25

1968
No. 96 surcharged
136   3c on 5c Long-tailed Whydah.   5   5

Nos. 96, 98 and 103 overprinted **INDEPENDENCE 1968**
149† 5c Long-tailed Whydah   30   5
151† 10c Secretary Bird   30   5
156† 50c Southern Ground Hornbill 1.50   1.75

STAMP MONTHLY
— finest and most informative magazine for all
collectors. Obtainable from your newsagent or by
postal subscription — details on request.

1976

236 1c African Black-headed Oriole ('Black-
   headed Oriole')
237 2c African Green Pigeon ('Green Pigeon')
238 3c Green-winged Pytilia ('Melba Finch')
239 4c Violet Starling ('Plum-coloured
   Starling')
240 5c Black-headed Heron
241 6c Stonechat
242 7c Chorister Robin Chat ('Chorister
   Robin')
243 10c Four-coloured Bush Shrike
   ('Gorgeous Bush Shrike')
244 15c Black-collared Barbet
245 20c Grey Heron
246 25c Giant Kingfisher
247 30c Verreaux's Eagle ('Black Eagle')
248a 50c Red Bishop
249a 1e Pin-tailed Whydah
250a 2e Lilac-breasted Roller
                           Set of 15   10.00   10.50

1982

399 35c Pel's Fishing Owl ('Male Fishing Owl')
400 35c Pel's Fishing Owl ('Female Fishing Owl
   at nest')
401 35c Pel's Fishing Owl ('Pair of Fishing
   Owls')
402 35c Pel's Fishing Owl ('Fishing Owl nest
   and eggs')
403 35c Pel's Fishing Owl ('Adult Fishing Owl
   with youngster')
                           Set of 5   2.75   2.75

STANLEY GIBBONS
STAMP COLLECTING SERIES
Introductory booklets on *How to Start, How to
Identify Stamps* and *Collecting by Theme.* A series
of well illustrated guides at a low price.
Write for details.

1983

SWAZILAND

425 35c Lammergeier ('Male Lammergeyer')
426 35c Lammergeier ('Pair of Lammergeyers')
427 35c Lammergeier ('Lammergeyer nest and
   egg')
428 35c Lammergeier ('Female Lammergeyer
   at nest')
429 35c Lammergeier ('Adult Lammergeyer
   with fledgeling')
                           Set of 5   2.75   2.75

1984

SWAZILAND

448 35c Bald Ibis ('Male')
449 35c Bald Ibis ('Male & Female')
450 35c Bald Ibis ('nest and egg')
451 35c Bald Ibis ('Female at nest')
452 35c Bald Ibis ('Adult & fledgeling')
                           Set of 5   3.00   2.75

1985

SWAZILAND

481 25c Southern Ground Hornbill ('Male
   Ground Hornbill')
482 25c Southern Ground Hornbill ('Male &
   Female Ground Hornbill')
483 25c Southern Ground Hornbill ('Female
   Ground Hornbill at nest')
484 25c Southern Ground Hornbill ('Ground
   Hornbill nest & egg')
485 25c Southern Ground Hornbill ('Ground
   Hornbill with fledgeling')
                           Set of 5   1.90   1.90

SWEDEN
Northern Europe
100 ore = 1 krona

1942

257a 20k Mute Swan 3.25 40

1956

376 25ore Whooper Swan
377 40ore Whooper Swan

Set of 2 3.00 50

1967

543† 1k Common Crane 25 5

1968

569† 30ore Great Black-backed Gull 30 30
571† 30ore Golden Eagle, Carrion Crow 30 30

1969

581 35ore Eagle Owl
582 55ore Eagle Owl

Set of 2 35 20

1970

630 30ore Blackbird (*Turdus merula*)
631 30ore Great Tit (*Parus major*)
632 30ore Bullfinch (*Pyrrhula pyrrhula*)
633 30ore Greenfinch (*Carduelis chloris*)
634 30ore Blue Tit (*Parus caeruleus*)

Set of 5 2.25 2.25

1971

642 40ore Arctic Tern
643 55ore Arctic Tern

Set of 2 70 25

1973

756† 20ore Peregrine Falcon (*Falco peregrinus*) 25 10
760† 75ore White-tailed Sea Eagle (*Haliaeetus albicilla*). 35 12

1974

806† 65ore Lesser Black-backed Gull 30 30

1975

848† 1k70 Capercaillie.. .. .. 40 10

1976

878† 85ore Common Guillemot, Razorbill 30 10

1977

913† 45ore Tawny Owl 25 12

928† 95ore Black-headed Gull. 30 20

1978

960† 1k30 Avocet (*Recurvirostra avosetta*) 1.00 30

966† 1k15 Common Crane 40 20

1981

1067 50k Gyrfalcon (*Falco rusticolus*) 7.50 2.75

1984

1208 1k60 Hawfinch (*Coccothraustes*
       coccothraustes)
1209 1k60 Bohemian Waxwing (*Bombycilla*
       garrulus)
1210 1k60 Great Spotted Woodpecker
       (*Dendrocopos major*)
1211 1k60 European Nuthatch (*Sitta europaea*)
                              Set of 4   1.50   1.40

1985

1266† 2k70 Manchurian Crane 70 45

1986

1272 2k10 Eider (*Somateria mollissima*)
1273 2k10 Whimbrel (*Numenius phaeopus*)
1274 2k30 Black-throated Diver (*Gavia arctica*)
                              Set of 3   1.40   1.25

SWITZERLAND
Central Europe
100 centimes = 1 franc

1966

731† 10c Common Kingfisher.. .. .. 15 5

1976

919† 20c Barn Swallow 25 10

'PRO JUVENTUTE' CHARITY STAMPS

1968

J221 10c + 10c Capercaillie
J222 20c + 10c Bullfinch
J223 30c + 10c Woodchat Shrike
J224 50c + 20c Firecrest
　　　　　　　　Set of 4　1.25　70

1969

J225 10c + 10c Goldfinch
J226 20c + 10c Golden Oriole
J227 30c + 10c Wallcreeper
J228 50c + 20c Jay
　　　　　　　　Set of 4　1.10　75

1970

J229 10c + 10c Blue Tit
J230 20c + 10c Hoopoe
J231 30c + 10c Great Spotted Woodpecker
J232 50c + 20c Great Crested Grebe
　　　　　　　　Set of 4　1.40　1.00

COLLECT MAMMALS ON STAMPS
The second Stanley Gibbons thematic catalogue —
copies are available at £7.50 (p. + p. £1.50) from:
Stanley Gibbons Publications Ltd, 5 Parkside,
Christchurch Road, Ringwood, Hants BH24 3SH.

1971

J233 10c + 10c Redstart
J234 20c + 10c Bluethroat
J235 30c + 10c Peregrine Falcon
J236 40c + 20c Mallard
　　　　　　　　Set of 4　2.10　1.00

SYRIA
Middle East
100 centimes = 1 piastre

1978

1371 10p Goldfinch
1372 20p Peregrine Falcon
1373 25p Rock Dove
1374 35p Hoopoe
1375 60p Chukar Partridge
　　　　　　　　Set of 5　9.00　4.25

TAIWAN
See under China

TANZANIA
East Africa
100 cents = 1 shilling

1981

342 50c Ostrich
343 1s Secretary Bird
344 5s Kori Bustard
345 10s Saddle-bill Stork
　　　　　　　　Set of 4　2.50　2.50

1986

464 5s Mallard
465 10s Eider ('American Eider')
466 20s Scarlet Ibis
467 30s Roseate Spoonbill

                           Set of 4   2.25   2.25

THAILAND
South-east Asia
100 satangs = 1 baht

1967

562 20s Great Indian Hornbill ('Great Hornbill')
563 25s Hill Myna ('Talking Myna')
564 50s White-rumped Shama
565 1b Siamese Fireback Pheasant ('Diard's
     Fireback Pheasant')
566 1b50 Spotted Dove ('Spotted-necked Dove')
567 2b Sarus Crane
568 3b White-breasted Kingfisher
569 5b Asian Open-bill Stork ('Open-billed
     Storks')

                           Set of 8   8.50   4.75

1975

829 75c White-eyed River Martin
     (*Pseudochelidon sirintarae*)
830 2b Asiatic Paradise Flycatcher
     (*Terpsiphone paradise*)
831 2b75 Long-tailed Broadbill (*Psarisomus
     dalhousiae*)
832 5b Sultan Tit (*Melanochlora sultanea*)

                           Set of 4   2.00   85

1976

891 1b Golden-backed Three-toed Woodpecker
     (*Dinopium javanense*)
892 1b50 Greater Green-billed Malcoha
     (*Phaenicophaeus tristis*)
893 3b Long-billed Scimitar Babbler
     (*Pomatorhinus hypoleucos*)
894 4b Green Magpie (*Cissa chinensis*)

                           Set of 4   1.75   90

1980

1017 75c Golden-fronted Leafbird (*Chloropsis
      aurifrons*)
1018 2b Chinese Yellow Tit (*Parus spilonotus*)
1019 3b Chestnut-tailed Minla (*Minla strigula*)
1020 5b Scarlet Minivet (*Pericrocotus
      flammeus*)

                           Set of 4   1.40   65

TIBET
Central Asia
12 pies = 1 anna,
16 annas = 1 Indian rupee

1911

Nos. 131/2 *of China surcharged in Indian currency and with
Chinese characters*

C10† 1r on $1 Bean Goose £100   £120
C11† 2r on $2 Bean Goose £275   £375

TOGO
West Africa
100 centimes = 1 franc

1957

213† 500f Great Egret 14.00   8.00

1959

235† 500f Great Egret 11.00   3.50

1960

261† 500f Palm-nut Vulture 7.50   2.40

1961

272 1f South African Crowned Crane ('Grues
       Couronnees')
273 10f South African Crowned Crane ('Grues
       Couronnees')
274 25f South African Crowned Crane ('Grues
       Couronnees')
275 30f South African Crowned Crane ('Grues
       Couronnees')
                           Set of 4   1.60   60

1963

325† 100f Palm-nut Vulture (on stamp No. 261) ..   2.00   70

1964

361† 50f Black-bellied Seedcracker (*Pirenestes
       ostrinus*). 2.00   65
362† 100f Black & White Mannikin (*Spermestes
       bicolor*). 3.25   90
363† 200f Red-faced Lovebird (*Agapornis
       pullaria*). 7.00   2.50
364† 250f Grey Parrot (*Psittacus erithacus*) 15.00   3.00
365† 500f Yellow-breasted Barbet
       (*Trachyphonus margaritaceus*) 21.00   4.50

1967

545† 10f Montagu's Harrier (*Circinae pygargus*)   25   12
547† 20f Montagu's Harrier (*Circinae pygargus*)   60   15
549† 30f Montagu's Harrier (*Circinae pygargus*)   1.00   30

1972

893 25f Pin-tailed Whydah (*Vidua macroura*)
894 30f Broad-tailed Paradise Whydah
      (*Steganura paradisaea*)
895 40f Yellow-mantled Whydah (*Coliuspasser
      macrocercus*)

896 60f Long-tailed Whydah (*Diatropura progne*)

897 90f Rose-ringed Parakeet (*Psittacula cyanocephala*) (air)

                 Set of 5   2.75   1.00

1973

964† 100f Black-bellied Seedcracker (on stamp No. 361).. .. .. 1.10   45

1975

1098† 90f Eastern White Pelican 90   35

1978

1314 100f Jay
1315 100f Black-bellied Seedcracker (on stamp No. 361)
                 Set of 2   2.25   1.75

1981

1529 30f Grey-necked Bald Crow (*Picathartes oreas*)

1530 40f Splendid Sunbird (*Nectarinia coccinigaster*)
1531 60f Violet Starling (*Cinnyricinclus leucogaster*)
1532 90f Red-collared Whydah (*Coliuspasser ardens*)

1533 50f Violet-backed Sunbird (*Anthreptes longuemarei*) (air)
1534 100f Red Bishop (*Euplectus orix*)
                 Set of 6   2.00   1.10

1985

1819 120f Brown Pelican (*Pelecanus occidentalis*)
1820 270f Golden Eagle (*Aquila chrysaetos*)
1821 90f Bonaparte's Gull (*Larus bonapartii*) (air)
1822 135f Great-tailed Grackle (*Cassidix mexicanus*)
1823 500f Red-headed Woodpecker (*Picus erythrocephalus*)
                 Set of 5   4.75   4.00
MS1824 1000f Yellow Warbler (*Dendroica petechia*) 5.00   4.75

1986

1912† 70f Spur-winged Goose ('Canards sauvages') 40   25

TOKELAU
Pacific Ocean
100 cents = 1 dollar

1977

57 8c White Tern ('Akiaki')
58 10c Turnstone ('Vahavaha')
59 15c White-capped Noddy ('Lakia')
60 30c Common Noddy ('Gogo')

Set of 4   2.50   2.50

TONGA
South Pacific
1897 12 pence = 1 shilling,
20 shillings = 1 pound
1967 100 seniti = 1 pa'anga

1897

81† 2s6d Red Shining Parrot 10.00   12.00

1923
No. 81 surcharged TWO PENCE PENI-E-UA
69† 2d on 2s6d Red Shining Parrot 5.50   6.00

1974

479 7s Red Shining Parrot
480 9s Red Shining Parrot
481 12s Red Shining Parrot
482 14s Red Shining Parrot
483 17s Red Shining Parrot

484 29s Red Shining Parrot
485 38s Red Shining Parrot
486 50s Red Shining Parrot
487 75s Red Shining Parrot

Set of 9   4.75   4.75

1978

693†   28s Red Shining Parrot   50   35

698†   39s Red Shining Parrot (air).   70   50

1984

890   32s Laughing Kookaburra (on Australia stamp No. 19)
891   1p50 Red Shining Parrot (on stamp No. 81)
Set of 2   1.75   1.75
MS892   32s Laughing Kookaburra; 1p50 Red Shining Parrot (as Nos. 891/2 but without exhibition emblem and with colour change) 1.90   2.25

1986

MS955   50s Red Shining Parrot (on stamp No. 81) (sheet also contains seven other stamps) 3.50   3.75

OFFICIAL STAMPS

1979

O193	5s Blue-crowned Lory (with foliage)		
O194	11s Blue-crowned Lory		
O195	14s Blue-crowned Lory		
O196	15s Blue-crowned Lory		
O197	17s Blue-crowned Lory		
O198	18s Blue-crowned Lory		
O199	22s Blue-crowned Lory		
O200	31s Blue-crowned Lory		
O201	39s Blue-crowned Lory		
O202	75s Blue-crowned Lory		
O203	1p Blue-crowned Lory		
	Set of 11	3.75	4.25

1980

O213	5s Blue-crowned Lory (without foliage)	..	£100

TRANSKEI
Southern Africa
100 cents = 1 rand

1980

75	5c Red-chested Cuckoo (*Cuculus solitarius*)		
76	10c Cape Puff-back Flycatcher (*Batis capensis*)		
77	15c South African Crowned Crane (*Balearica pavonina* !)		
78	20c Spectacled Weaver (*Ploceus ocularius*)		
	Set of 4	1.50	85

STANLEY GIBBONS
STAMP COLLECTING SERIES
Introductory booklets on *How to Start, How to Identify Stamps* and *Collecting by Theme.* A series of well illustrated guides at a low price.
Write for details.

TRIESTE
Southern Europe
100 centesimi = 1 lira

Zone A, Allied Military Government

1947

Nos. 671, 952 and 676 of Italy overprinted **A.M.G. F.T.T.** *in two lines*

19†	2li Barn Swallow	5	10
20†	5li Barn Swallow	25	30
22†	25li Barn Swallow..	25	30

1948

No. 676 of Italy overprinted **A.M.G. F.T.T. 1948 TRIESTE** *and posthorn*

81†	25li Barn Swallow..	20	20

1949

No. 676 of Italy overprinted **AMG-FTT** *in one line*

116†	25li Barn Swallow	10	10

1954

No. 867 of Italy overprinted **AMG-FTT**

291	25li Golden Eagle	30	15

Zone B, Yugoslav Military Government

1949

B13†	100li Mediterranean Gull	1.50	85

No. B13 surcharged **DIN 30**

B32†	30d on 100li Mediterranean Gull	1.90	60

1954

Nos. 770/1 of Yugoslavia with colour changed overprinted **STT VUJNA**

B124†	25d Eastern White Pelican	40	5
B125†	30d Lammergeier	50	10

TRINIDAD AND TOBAGO
West Indies
100 cents = 1 dollar

1960

292†	25c Scarlet Ibis	35	5
296†	$1.20 Copper-rumped Hummingbird ('Humming Bird')	4.00	1.00

1962

303† 35c Greater Bird of Paradise ('Bird of
Paradise')   15   5
304† 60c Scarlet Ibis   25   25

1969

341† 5c Rufous-vented Chachalaca ('Cocrico') ..   15   5
344† 10c Green Hermit.   25   5
350† 40c Scarlet Ibis 1.25   15

1970

No. 341 *overprinted* **NATIONAL COMMERCIAL BANK
ESTABLISHED 1.7.70**
382 5c Rufous-vented Chachalaca   5   5

1979

551† 25c Scarlet Ibis (on stamp No. 304).   15   10

1980

563 50c Scarlet Ibis (male)
564 50c Scarlet Ibis (male and female)
565 50c Scarlet Ibis (hen and nest)
566 50c Scarlet Ibis (nest and eggs)
567 50c Scarlet Ibis (chick in nest)
                           Set of 5 1.75 1.75

1981

587† $3 Scarlet Ibis. 1.50 1.60

TRIPOLITANIA
North Africa
100 centesimi = 1 lira

1933

158† 10c Ostrich 10.00   5.50
162† 1li25 Golden Eagle 11.00 18.00

TRISTAN DA CUNHA
South Atlantic
1954 12 pence = 1 shilling,
20 shillings = 1 pound
1971 100 pence = 1 pound

1954

16† 1½d Rockhopper Penguin   75   30
18† 2½d Yellow-nosed Albatross ('Mollymauk') .. 1.50   50
26† 5s Inaccessible Island Rail ('Flightless Rail') 40.00 25.00

1963

Nos. 177, 181 *and* 185 *of St. Helena overprinted* **TRISTAN DA
CUNHA RESETTLEMENT 1963**
56† 1½d Yellow Canary   20   12
60† 6d Madagascar Red Fody.   55   20
64† 1s6d White Tern 1.25   70

1968

113 4d Wandering Albatross
114 1s Wilkin's Finch ('Big-billed Bunting')
115 1s6d Tristan Thrush
116 2s6d Greater Shearwater ('Great Shearwater')

Set of 4   2.50   70

1972

164†	5p Sooty Albatross	45	15
165†	7½p Yellow-nosed Albatross..	75	30
168†	50p Rockhopper Penguin	3.50	3.00

174 2½p Tristan Thrush, Wandering Albatross
175 7½p Tristan Thrush, Wandering Albatross

Set of 2   70   90

1974

188 2½p Rockhopper Penguin ('Rockhopper and egg')
189 5p Rockhopper Penguin ('Rockhopper colony')
190 7½p Rockhopper Penguin ('Rockhoppers fishing')
191 25p Rockhopper Penguin ('Rockhopper and fledgling')

Set of 4   13.50   7.00

MS192 35p Rockhopper Penguin, Wandering Albatross 1.50   2.75

1977

220 1p Great-winged Petrel ('Black Haglet')
221 2p White-faced Storm Petrel ('White-faced Skipjack')
222 3p Hall's Giant Petrel ('Stinker')
223 4p Soft-plumaged Petrel ('Littlest White-breasted Haglet')
224 5p Wandering Albatross ('Gony (Tristan Wandering Albatross)')
225 10p Kerguelen Petrel ('Blue Nighthawk')
226 15p Swallow-tailed Tern ('King Bird')
227 20p Greater Shearwater ('Petrel (Great Shearwater)')
228 25p Broad-billed Prion ('Nightbird')
229 50p Great Skua ('Sea Hen')
230 £1 Common Diving Petrel ('Flying Pinnamin')
231 £2 Yellow-nosed Albatross ('Molly')

Set of 12   9.00   9.00

1979

257† 15p Tristan Thrush   45   30
258† 20p Nightingale Finch ('Tristan Bunting') ..   60   40

265† 10p Inaccessible Island Rail (on stamp No. 26)   25   25
MS267 50p Rockhopper Penguin   75   90

271† 20p Rockhopper Penguin   30   30

1981

The Nest

315 10p Inaccessible Island Rail ('The Nest')
316 10p Inaccessible Island Rail ('The Eggs')
317 10p Inaccessible Island Rail ('The Chicks')
318 10p Inaccessible Island Rail (*Atlantisia rogersi*)

Set of 4   1.10   1.10

1982

Nos. 224 *and* 228 *overprinted* **1ST PARTICIPATION COMMONWEALTH GAMES 1982**
335 5p Wandering Albatross
336 25p Broad-billed Prion

Set of 2   65   50

1986

417† 5p Wandering Albatross..   10   12
420† 25p Wilkin's Finch ('Wilkins' Bunting')   50   55
421† 50p White-chinned Petrel ('Ring-Eye') 1.00   1.10

1987

424† 35p Inaccessible Island Rail ('Flightless Rail').   70   75
425† 50p Gough Island Coot ('Gough Island Moorhen') 1.00   1.10

STAMP MONTHLY
— finest and most informative magazine for all collectors. Obtainable from your newsagent or by postal subscription — details on request.

Tristan da Cunha

Eudyptes chrysocome moseleyi 10^P

430 10p Rockhopper Penguin
431 20p Rockhopper Penguin
432 30p Rockhopper Penguin
433 50p Rockhopper Penguin

Set of 4   2.25   2.40

TUNISIA
North Africa
1000 milliemes = 1 dinar

1959

479† ½m Common Snipe   25   10

1965

601 25m Fulvous Babbler (*Alaemon alaudipes* !)
602 55m Great Grey Shrike (*Lanius excubitor*)
603 55m Cream-coloured Courser (*Cursorius cursor*)
604 100m Chaffinch (*Fringilla coelebs spodiogenys*)
605 150m Greater Flamingo (*Phoenicopterus ruber roseus*)
606 200m Barbary Partridge (*Alectoris barbara*)
607 300m Common Roller (*Coracias garrulus*)
608 500m Houbara Bustard (*Chlamydotis ondulata*)

Set of 8   28.00   13.00

1967

638† 155m Greater Flamingo (*Phoenicopterus ruber roseus*) 1.00 35

1979

938† 30m Common Peafowl (*Pavo cristatus*) .. 25 10

1980

963† 100m Golden Eagle (*Aquila chrysaetos*) .. 60 15

1986

1118† 380m Greylag Goose ('Oie Cendree') . .. 70 55

TURKEY
South-east Europe and Asia Minor
100 kurus = 1 lira

1959

1843† 40k Barn Swallow 25 10
1845† 85k Gull sp 45 20
1847† 125k House Martin 80 25
1848† 155k Demoiselle Crane 90 30
1850† 245k Turtle Dove 1.50 80
Birds on the 65k, 105k, 195k values are too stylised for identification.

1967

2208 10k Common Kestrel ('Kerkenez')
2209 60k Imperial Eagle? ('Kartal')
2210 130k Pallid Harrier? ('Docan')
2211 220k European Sparrow Hawk? ('Atmaca')
2212 270k Common Buzzard? ('Sahin')
Set of 5 5.00 1.40

1976

2553† 150k Greater Flamingo.. .. .. 1.25 50

2569 100k + 25k White Spoonbill (*Platalea leucorida*)
2570 150k + 25k Common Roller (*Corasias garrulus*)
2571 200k + 25k Greater Flamingo (*Phoenicopterus ruber*)
2572 400k + 25k Waldrapp (*Geronticus eremita*)
Set of 4 1.75 1.40

1979

2679† 5li + 1li Black Partridge (*Francolinus*) . .. 30 15
2680† 5li + 1li Great Bustard (*Otis tarda*). 30 15
2681† 5li + 1li Demoiselle Crane (*Anthropoides virgo*) 30 15

TURKS AND CAICOS ISLANDS
West Indies
1955 12 pence = 1 shilling,
20 shillings = 1 pound
1971 100 cents = 1 dollar

462   $1 Bananaquit ('Bahama Bananaquit')
463   $2 Cedar Waxwing
464   $5 Painted Bunting

Set of 16   17.00   15.00

1955

236† 8d Greater Flamingo ('Flamingoes on North Caicos')   35   10

1957

245† 8d Greater Flamingo ('Flamingoes')   50   10
253† £1 Brown Pelican ('Pelican') 22.00   23.00

1971

349† 15c Oystercatcher ('Common Oyster Catcher')   30   5

1973

381   ¼c Sooty Tern
382   1c Magnificent Frigate Bird
453   2c Common Noddy ('Noddy Tern')
454   3c Blue-grey Gnatcatcher
385   4c Little Blue Heron ('Blue Heron')
386   5c Catbird
387   7c Black-whiskered Vireo
388   8c Osprey
457   10c Greater Flamingo ('Flamingo')
390   15c Brown Pelican
459   20c Parula Warbler
460   30c Northern Mockingbird ('Mockingbird')
461   50c Ruby-throated Hummingbird

1979

534† 6c Osprey   25   10

1980

592   20c Pied-billed Grebe
593   25c Ovenbird
594   35c Hen Harrier ('Marsh Hawk')
595   55c Yellow-bellied Sapsucker
596   $1 Blue-winged Teal

Set of 5   3.50   2.10
MS597 $2 Glossy Ibis 2.75   2.50

1983

783B† $5 White-tailed Tropic Bird 6.00   6.25

1984

820† 50c Rainbow Lory ('Rainbow Lorikeet') ..   1.00   1.00

1985

829 25c Magnolia Warbler
830 45c Short-eared Owl
831 70c Mourning Dove
832 85c Caribbean Martin ('Purple Martin')
                                    Set of 4   4.00   3.50
MS833 $2 Oystercatcher 3.75   4.00

1985

301 1c Common Flicker
302 1c Say's Phoebe
303 25c Townsend's Warbler
304 25c Bohemian Waxwing
305 50c Prothonotary Warbler
306 50c Worm-eating Warbler
307 70c Broad-winged Hawk
308 70c Hen Harrier ('Northern Harrier (Marsh Hawk)')
                                    Set of 8   3.00   3.25

TUVA
Central Asia
100 kopeks = 1 rouble

1934

53† 10k Capercaillie 1.50   45

309 15c Black-naped Tern
310 40c White-capped Noddy ('Black Noddy')
311 50c White-tailed Tropic Bird
312 60c Sooty Tern
                                    Set of 4   1.60   1.75

Niutao

Appendix
The following stamps have either been issued in excess of postal needs, or have not been made available to the public in reasonable quantities at face value. Miniature sheets, imperforate stamps etc. are excluded from this section.

TUVALU
Central Pacific
100 cents = 1 dollar

1978

81 8c Pacific Pigeon
82 20c Eastern Reef Heron ('Reef Heron')
83 30c White Tern ('Fairy Tern')
84 40c Lesser Frigate Bird
                                    Set of 4   8.00   4.50

1985
Leaders of the World. Birth Bicentenary of John J. Audubon. Birds. 5c Purple Finch, 5c White-throated Sparrow, 15c Anna's Hummingbird, 15c Smith's Longspur, 25c White-tailed Kite, 25c Harris's Hawk, $1 Northern Oriole, $1 Great Crested Flycatcher

UGANDA
East Africa
100 cents = 1 shilling

1965

111 30c South African Crowned Crane
112 1s30 South African Crowned Crane

Set of 2   30   10

113 5c Black Bee Eater
114 10c African Jacana
115 15c Orange Weaver
116 20c Narina Trogon
117 30c Sacred Ibis
118 40c Blue-breasted Kingfisher
119 50c Whale-headed Stork
120 65c Red-crowned Bishop ('Black-winged
        Red Bishop')
121 1s Ruwenzori Turaco
122 1s30 African Fish Eagle
123 2s50 Great Blue Turaco
124 5s Lilac-breasted Roller
125 10s Black-collared Lovebird
126 20s South African Crowned Crane

Set of 14   28.00   26.00

1979

298† 1s South African Crowned Crane (on
       stamp No. 126)..   15   5

1980
No. 298 overprinted LONDON 1980

317† 1s South African Crowned Crane   15   5

1982

378 1s Yellow-billed Hornbill ('Hornbill')
379 20s Superb Starling
380 50s Bateleur ('Bateleur Eagle')
381 100s Saddle-bill Stork

Set of 4   2.75   2.75

MS382 200s Laughing Dove 3.25   3.25

1985

480 115s Sedge Warbler
481 155s Cattle Egret
482 175s Crested Lark
483 500s Tufted Duck

Set of 4   2.25   2.25

MS484 1000s Tawny Owl 3.00   3.25

494 5s Rock Ptarmigan
495 155s Sage Grouse
496 175s Lesser Yellowlegs
497 500s Brown-headed Cowbird

Set of 4   2.50   2.50

MS498 1000s Whooping Crane 3.00   3.25

COLLECT MAMMALS ON STAMPS
The second Stanley Gibbons thematic catalogue —
copies are available at £7.50 (p. + p. £1.50) from:
Stanley Gibbons Publications Ltd, 5 Parkside,
Christchurch Road, Ringwood, Hants BH24 3SH.

1986

526† 100s Emperor Penguin 15 12

UMM AL QIWAIN
Arabian Peninsula
1964 100 naye paise = 1 rupee
1967 100 dirhams = 1 riyal

1964

7†	15np White Stork	10	5
8†	20np White Stork	15	5
9†	30np White Stork	20	8
16†	3r White Stork	1.75	55
17†	5r White Stork	2.50	90
18†	10r White Stork.	4.00	1.50

1965
As Nos. 16/18 but inscribed 'AIR MAIL'

40†	2r White Stork	1.25	30
41†	3r White Stork	1.75	50
42†	5r White Stork	2.50	90

1967
Nos. 7/9, 16/18 and 40/2 with currency names changed by overprinting

86†	15d on 15np White Stork	10	5
87†	20d on 20np White Stork	20	12
88†	30d on 30np White Stork	25	15
95†	3r on 3r White Stork	1.75	1.50
96†	5r on 5r White Stork	2.75	2.25
97†	10r on 10r White Stork.	4.50	4.25
104†	2r on 2r White Stork (air)	80	65
105†	3r on 3r White Stork	1.25	90
106†	5r on 5r White Stork	2.50	2.00

OFFICIAL STAMPS

1965
As Nos. 16/18 but additionally inscribed 'ON STATE'S SERVICE'

O55†	2r White Stork	90	40
O56†	3r White Stork	1.25	60
O57†	5r White Stork	1.90	90

1967
Nos. O55/7 with currency name changed by overprinting

O113†	2r on 2r White Stork	1.25	90
O114†	3r on 3r White Stork	1.50	1.25
O115†	5r on 5r White Stork	2.50	1.90

Appendix
The following stamps have either been issued in excess of postal needs, or have not been made available to the public in reasonable quantities at face value. Miniature sheets, imperforate stamps etc. are excluded from this section.

1968
Falcons and Hawks. Postage 15d Gyrfalcon, 25d Red-shouldered Hawk, 50d Red-tailed Hawk, 75d Peregrine Falcon with Blue Jay, 1r Ferruginous Hawk. Air 1r50 Ferruginous Hawk, 3r Gyrfalcon, 5r Red-shouldered Hawk

1972
Penguins. Postage 5d Gentoo Penguin, 10d Emperor Penguin, 15d Rockhopper Penguin and Macaroni Penguin, 20d Magellanic Penguin. Air 50d Emperor Penguin, 4r Emperor Penguin

Exotic Birds (1st series). Air 1r x 16 Ruddy Ground Dove, Golden Pheasant, Red-crested Cardinal, Yellow Cardinal, Red Bishop, Painted Bunting, Rose-ringed Parakeet, Nanday Conure, Orange-chinned Parakeet, Peach-fronted Conure, Bourke's Parrot, Red-capped Parrot, Pale-headed Rosella, Crimson Rosella, Mulga Parrot, Red & White Crake

Exotic Birds (2nd series). Air 1r x 16 Lesser Sulphur-crested Cockatoo, Black-winged Lovebird, Peach-faced Lovebird, Black-cheeked Lovebird, Masked Lovebird, Red-crested Turaco, Toco Toucan, Black-headed Starling, Purple Glossy Starling, Hill Myna, Peters's Twin-Spot, Paradise Sparrow, Double-barred Finch, Gouldian Finch, Red Munia, Dusky Twin-Spot

---

UNITED ARAB EMIRATES
Arabian peninsula
100 fils = 1 dirham

1982

153†	75f American Bald Eagle	70	45
155†	3d American Bald Eagle	2.40	2.00

1986

198 50f Saker Falcon
199 75f Saker Falcon
200 125f Saker Falcon

Set of 3   1.50   95

1954

A1066 4c American Bald Eagle
A1067 5c American Bald Eagle

Set of 2   30   15

UNITED NATIONS

Geneva Headquarters

Switzerland
100 centimes = 1 franc

1986

G141 5c Herring Gull   5   5

1956

1079† 3c Common Turkey ('Wild Turkey')   25   5

1957

1100 3c Whooping Crane   25   5

UNITED STATES OF AMERICA
North America
100 cents = 1 dollar

1938

A845 6c American Bald Eagle.   50   5

1947

949 3c Great Blue Heron   25   5

1963

A1215† 6c American Bald Eagle   30   8

1223 5c Collie's Magpie-Jay   25   5

1967

1971

1431† 8c California Condor 25 10

A1304 20c Collie's Magpie-Jay 1.00 15

1968

1448† 8c Chukar Partridge. 25 10

1347 6c Wood Duck. 25 10

1972

1969

1453† 2c Bonaparte's Gull (value at left). 25 10
1454† 2c Bonaparte's Gull (value at right) 25 10

1362 6c Common Flicker 25 10

1970

1470† 8c Common Cardinal ('Cardinal') 25 10
1471† 8c Brown Pelican 25 10

1978

1377† 6c American Bald Eagle 30 10

MS1726 13c Common Cardinal ('Cardinal'); 13c
Mallard; 13c Canada Goose; 13c
Blue Jay (sheet also contains 4 other
stamps).. .. .. 2.00 2.00

1409† 6c Western Gull.. .. .. 60 10

1731 15c Great Grey Owl
1732 15c Saw-whet Owl
1733 15c Barred Owl
1734 15c Great Horned Owl
                    Set of 4   70   20

1980

1804 15c American Bald Eagle   25   10

1981

1895† 18c Great Blue Heron   25   20
1898† 18c Ruffed Grouse   25   20

1982

1930 20c Common Flicker ('Yellowhammer',
      Alabama)
1931 20c Willow/Red Grouse ('Willow
      Ptarmigan', Alaska)
1932 20c Cactus Wren (Arizona)
1933 20c Northern Mockingbird ('Mockingbird',
      Arkansas)

1934 20c California Quail (California)
1935 20c Lark Bunting (Colorado)
1936 20c American Robin ('Robin',
      Connecticut)
1938 20c Northern Mockingbird ('Mockingbird',
      Florida)
1939 20c Brown Thrasher (Georgia)
1940 20c Hawaiian Goose (Hawaii)
1941 20c Mountain Bluebird (Idaho)
1942 20c Common Cardinal ('Cardinal', Illinois)
1943 20c Common Cardinal ('Cardinal',
      Indiana)
1944 20c American Goldfinch (' Eastern
      Goldfinch', Iowa)
1945 20c Western Meadowlark (Kansas)
1946 20c Common Cardinal ('Cardinal',
      Kentucky)
1947 20c Brown Pelican (Louisiana)
1948 20c Black-capped Chickadee
      ('Chickadee', Maine)
1949 20c Northern Oriole ('Baltimore Oriole',
      Maryland)
1950 20c Black-capped Chickadee
      (Massachusetts)
1951 20c American Robin ('Robin', Michigan)
1952 20c Great Northern Diver ('Common
      Loon', Minnesota)
1953 20c Northern Mockingbird ('Mockingbird',
      Mississippi)
1954 20c Eastern Bluebird (Missouri)
1955 20c Western Meadowlark (Montana)
1956 20c Western Meadowlark (Nebraska)
1957 20c Mountain Bluebird (Nevada)
1958 20c Purple Finch (New Hampshire)
1959 20c American Goldfinch (New Jersey)
1960 20c Roadrunner (New Mexico)
1961 20c Eastern Bluebird (New York)
1962 20c Common Cardinal ('Cardinal', North
      Carolina)
1963 20c Western Meadowlark (North Dakota)
1964 20c Common Cardinal ('Cardinal', Ohio)
1965 20c Scissor-tailed Flycatcher (Oklahoma)
1966 20c Western Meadowlark (Oregon)
1967 20c Ruffed Grouse (Pennsylvania)
1969 20c Carolina Wren (South Carolina)
1970 20c Ring-necked Pheasant (South Dakota)
1971 20c Northern Mockingbird ('Mockingbird',
      Tennessee)
1972 20c Northern Mockingbird ('Mockingbird',
      Texas)
1973 20c California Gull (Utah)
1974 20c Hermit Thrush (Vermont)
1975 20c Common Cardinal ('Cardinal',
      Virginia)
1976 20c American Goldfinch (Washington)
1977 20c Common Cardinal (West Virginia)
1978 20c American Robin ('Robin', Wisconsin)
1979 20c Western Meadowlark (Wyoming)
                    Sheet of 50   11.25   9.00

The sheet of 50 includes No. 1937 (Delaware) and No. 1968
(Rhode Island), which show poultry.

COLLECT RAILWAYS ON STAMPS

A Stanley Gibbons thematic catalogue on this
popular subject. Copies available at £7.50 (p. + p.
£1.50) from: Stanley Gibbons Publications Ltd, 5
Parkside, Christchurch Road, Ringwood, Hants
BH24 3SH.

1983

2044 $9.35 American Bald Eagle..   ..   ..   13.00   4.00

1984

2077   20c American Golden Plover   25   5

Freshwater as a source of Life

2083   20c Canada Goose, American Anhinga,
Louisiana Heron, Prothonotary Warbler.   25   5

2089   20c Mallard   25   5

1985

2185 $10.75 American Bald Eagle 15.00   14.00

REGISTERED LETTER STAMP

1911

R404   10c American Bald Eagle 50.00   3.00

UPPER VOLTA
West Africa
100 centimes = 1 franc

1964

150   250f Grey Woodpecker (*Mesopicos goertae*)   7.00   3.50

1965

154   10f Pygmy Sunbird (*Hedydipna platura*)
155   15f Olive-bellied Sunbird (*Cinnyris
chloropygius*)
156   20f Splendid Sunbird (*Cinnyris
coccinigaster*)
157   500f Abyssinian Roller (*Coracias
abyssinica*) (air)
                                    Set of 4   16.00   6.50

1970

303† 50f Manchurian Crane 60 25
(303/4 *Set of 2*) 1.75 1.00

1971

327† 100f Purple Heron ('Les Herons') 75 40
(327/8 *Set of 2*) 2.75 1.25

1972

REPUBLIQUE DE HAUTE-VOLTA

393† 10f Spur-winged Goose 25 15

1977

452† 55f Bean Goose 40 15

1978

498 100f Common Kingfisher
499 100f Cattle Egret, Grey Woodpecker (on
stamp No. 150)
Set of 2 2.25 2.00

1979

537 5f King Vulture (*Sarcorhampus papa*)
538 10f Hoopoe (*Upupa*)
539 15f Ruppell's Griffon ('Charognard')
540 25f Intermediate Egret ('Grandes
Aigrettes')
541 35f Ostrich ('Autruche')
542 45f Crowned Crane ('Grue Couronnee')
543 125f Cassin's Hawk Eagle ('Aigle')
Set of 7 1.75 1.00

1981

622† 90f Helmet Guineafowl ('Pintade') 60 40

1984

701 90f Greater Flamingo (*Phoenicopterus roseus*)
702 185f Kori Bustard (*Choriotis kori*)
703 200f Red-billed Oxpecker (*Buphagus erythrorhynchus*)
704 300f Southern Ground Hornbill (*Bucorvus leadbeateri*)

Set of 4   3.25   2.75

728† 400f Marabou Stork, African White-backed Vulture (*Gyps bengalensis* !) 1.90 1.60

Appendix
The following stamps have either been issued in excess of postal needs, or have not been made available to the public in reasonable quantities at face value. Miniature sheets, imperforate stamps etc. are excluded from this section.

1975

Birth Centenary of Dr. Albert Schweitzer. Postage 5f Eastern White Pelican, 15f Bateleur. Air 150f Red-billed Hornbill, 175f Vulturine Guineafowl, 200f King Vulture

UPPER YAFA
Arabian Peninsula
1000 fils = 1 dinar

Appendix
The following stamps have either been issued in excess of postal needs, or have not been made available to the public in reasonable quantities at face value. Miniature sheets,imperforate stamps etc. are excluded from this section.

1967

Paintings by Old Masters. 20f Goldfinch

Persian Miniatures. 20f Raven, 30f Golden Pheasant

Portraits by Old Masters. 75f Magpie

URUGUAY
South America
1000 milesimos = 100 centesimos = 1 peso

1923

453 5m Chilian Lapwing
422 1c Chilian Lapwing (yellow)
454 1c Chilian Lapwing (pink)
477 1c Chilian Lapwing (mauve)
528 1c Chilian Lapwing (violet)
423 2c Chilian Lapwing (mauve)
529 2c Chilian Lapwing (pink)
456 3c Chilian Lapwing
457 5c Chilian Lapwing
458 8c Chilian Lapwing
459 10c Chilian Lapwing
460 12c Chilian Lapwing
461 15c Chilian Lapwing
462 20c Chilian Lapwing
429 36c Chilian Lapwing (green)
463 36c Chilian Lapwing (pink)
430 50c Chilian Lapwing (orange)
464 50c Chilian Lapwing (olive)
431 1p Chilian Lapwing (red)
465 1p Chilian Lapwing (buff)
432 2p Chilian Lapwing (green)
466 2p Chilian Lapwing (lilac)

Set of 22   70.00   42.00

1928

No. 460 surcharged **Inauguracion Ferrocarril SAN CARLOS a ROCHA 14/1/928** *and value*
537 2c on 12c Chilian Lapwing
538 5c on 12c Chilian Lapwing
539 10c on 12c Chilian Lapwing
540 15c on 12c Chilian Lapwing

Set of 4   2.50   1.40

1962

1205 2c Rufous-bellied Thrush ('Zorzal')
1206 50c Rufous Hornero ('Hornero')
1207 1p Chalk-browed Mockingbird ('Calandria')
1208 2p Rufous-collared Sparrow ('Chingolo')
1209 20c Red-crested Cardinal ('Cardenal Colorado) (air)
1210 45c Diademed Tanager ('Cardenal Azul')
1211 90c Vermilion Flycatcher ('Churrinche')
1212 1p Common Cowbird ('Tordo')
1213 1p20 Great Kiskadee ('Benteveo')
1214 1p40 Fork-tailed Flycatcher ('Tijereta')
1215 2p Yellow Cardinal ('Cardenal Amarillo')

1216 3p Hooded Siskin ('Cabecita Negra')
1217 5p Sayaca Tanager ('Cielito')
1218 10p Blue & Yellow Tanager ('Naranjero')
1219 20p Scarlet-headed Blackbird ('Federal')
Set of 15   8.00   6.50

1963

1220 20c Greater Rhea
1221 40c Greater Rhea
Set of 2   20   10

1966

1292 100p Crested Screamer (*Chauna torquata*)   4.00   2.50

1967
No. 1210 *surcharged*
1343† 5p90 on 45c Diademed Tanager   30   15

1968

1363 1p Great Horned Owl (*Virginianus nacurutu*)
1364 2p Cocoi Heron (*Ardea cocoi*)
1365 3p Brown-hooded Gull (*Larus ridibundis maculipennis*)
1366 4p White-faced Whistling Duck (*Dendrocygna viduata*)
1367 4p Black-tailed Stilt (*Himantopus mexicanus* !)
1368 5p Wattled Jacana (*Jacana spinosa*)
1369 10p Snowy Egret (*Ardea thula*)
Set of 7   1.00   35

1970

1415† 20p Greater Rhea (*Rhea americana*).. ..   30   15

1975

1604 1p Common Cowbird (on stamp No. 1212).   1.25   70

1976

1639† 1c Chilian Lapwing ('Terutero')   25   10

1978

1687 45c Greater Rhea.   30   10

OFFICIAL STAMPS

1924
Nos. 423, 429/32, 457/60 and 462/3 overprinted **OFICIAL** in oval.
(a) Perforated
O439 2c Chilian Lapwing
O440 5c Chilian Lapwing
O593 8c Chilian Lapwing
O594 10c Chilian Lapwing
O441 12c Chilian Lapwing
O442 20c Chilian Lapwing
O443 36c Chilian Lapwing (green)
O444 50c Chilian Lapwing
O445 1p Chilian Lapwing
O446 2p Chilian Lapwing
Set of 10   20.00   14.00

(b) Imperforate

O499 2c Chilian Lapwing
O500 5c Chilian Lapwing
O501 8c Chilian Lapwing
O502 12c Chilian Lapwing
O503 20c Chilian Lapwing
O504 36c Chilian Lapwing (pink)

Set of 6   2.75   1.75

VANUATU
South Pacific
1981 100 centimes = 1 franc
1981 vatus

1981

307 10f Blue-faced Parrot Finch (*Erythrura
    trichroa cyanofrons*)
308 20f Emerald Dove (*Chalcophaps indica
    sandwichensis*)
309 30f Golden Whistler (*Pachycephala
    pectoralis cucullata*)
310 40f Silver-shouldered Fruit Dove
    (*Ptilinopus tannensis*)

Set of 4   2.00   1.60

1982

327 15v New Caledonian Myiagra Flycatcher
    (*Myiagra caledonica*)
328 20v Rainbow Lory (*Trichoglossus
    haematodus*)
329 25v Buff-bellied Flycatcher (*Neolalage
    banksiana*)
330 45v Collared Grey Fantail (*Rhipidura
    fuliginosa*)

Set of 4   1.75   1.60

1985

402 20v Peregrine Falcon
403 35v Peregrine Falcon
404 45v Peregrine Falcon
405 100v Peregrine Falcon

Set of 4   3.00   3.00

VATICAN CITY
Southern Europe
100 centesimi = 1 lira

1947

133† 15li Barn Swallow   65   35
135† 50li Barn Swallow 5.00   1.50
136† 100li Barn Swallow 12.00   2.00

VENDA
Southern Africa
100 cents = 1 rand

1981

38 5c Collared Sunbird (*Anthreptes collaris*)
39 15c Mariqua Sunbird (*Nectarinia
    mariquensis*)
40 20c Southern White-bellied Sunbird
    (*Nectarinia talatala*)
41 25c Scarlet-chested Sunbird (*Nectarinia
    senegalensis*)

Set of 4   1.25   1.00

1983

71 8c European Bee Eater
72 20c Tawny Eagle ('Steppe Eagle')
73 25c Violet Starling ('Plum-coloured Starling')
74 40c Abdim's Stork ('White-bellied Stork')
                                    Set of 4   1.40   1.25

1984

91 11c White Stork
92 20c African Paradise Flycatcher ('Paradise
      Flycatcher')
93 25c Black Kite ('Yellow-billed Kite')
94 30c Wood Sandpiper
                                    Set of 4   80   80

1985

103 11c White-browed Robin Chat ('Heuglin's
       Robin')
104 25c Black-collared Barbet
105 30c African Black-headed Oriole ('Black-
       headed Oriole')
106 50c Kurrichane Thrush
                                    Set of 4   80   80

COLLECT MAMMALS ON STAMPS
The second Stanley Gibbons thematic catalogue —
copies are available at £7.50 (p. + p. £1.50) from:
Stanley Gibbons Publications Ltd, 5 Parkside,
Christchurch Road, Ringwood, Hants BH24 3SH.

1987

151 14c Comb Duck (*Sarkidiornis melanotos*)
152 20c White-faced Whistling Duck
       (*Dendrocygna viduata*)
153 25c Spur-winged Goose (*Plectropterus
       gambensis*)
154 30c Egyptian Goose (*Alopochen
       aegyptiacus*)
                                    Set of 4   50   50

VENEZIA GIULIA AND ISTRIA
Southern Europe
100 centesimi = 1 lira

1945

Nos. 671, 675/6 and 952 of Italy overprinted **A.M.G. V.G.** in two
lines

49†	2li Barn Swallow	8	8
50†	5li Barn Swallow	25	30
52†	25li Barn Swallow (blue)	35	55
53†	25li Barn Swallow (brown)	1.25	1.60

VENEZUELA
South America
100 centimos = 1 bolivar

1961

1694 30c Yellow-crowned Amazon (*Amazona
        ochrocephala*)
1695 40c Snowy Egret (*Leucophoyx thula*)
1696 50c Scarlet Ibis (*Eudocimus rubra*)
1697 5c Troupial (*Icterus icterus*) (air)
1698 10c Guianan Cock of the Rock (*Rupicola
        rupicola*)
1699 15c Tropical Mockingbird (*Mimus glivus*)
                                    Set of 6   4.25   3.00

1962

1973

2233† 10c Scarlet Macaw 25 10

1748 5c Vermilion Cardinal (*Richmondena phoenicea*)
1749 10c Great Kiskadee (*Pitangus sulphuratus*)
1750 20c Glossy-black Thrush (*Turdus serranus*)
1751 25c Collared Trogon (*Trogon collaris*)
1752 30c Swallow Tanager (*Tersina viridis*)
1753 40c Long-tailed Sylph (*Aglaiocerus kingi*)
1754 3b Black-necked Stilt (*Himantopus himantopus* !)

1755 5c American Kestrel (*Falco sparverius*) (air)
1756 20c Red-billed Whistling Duck (*Dendrocygna autumnalis*)
1757 25c Amazon Kingfisher (*Chloroceryle amazona*)
1758 30c Rufous-vented Chachalaca (*Ortalis ruficauda*)
1759 50c Oriole Blackbird (*Gymnomystax mexicanus*)
1760 55c Pauraque (*Nyctidromus albicollis*)
1761 2b30 Red-crowned Woodpecker (*Melanerpes rubricapillus*)
1762 2b50 White-faced Quail Dove (*Geotrygon linearis*)
                                Set of 15 17.00 9.25

1965

Nos. 1754, 1760/62 *surcharged* **RESELLADO VALOR** *and new value*
1845† 20c on 3b Black-necked Stilt 30 15

1877† 20c on 55c Pauraque (air) 55 25
1878† 20c on 2b30 Red-crowned Woodpecker .. 30 15
1879† 20c on 2b50 White-faced Quail Dove 50 25

1968

2053† 15c Marbled Wood Quail 30 10
2054† 20c Scarlet Ibis, Jabiru, Great Blue Heron (white phase), Red-billed Whistling Duck 40 12
2058† 1b Red-eyed Vireo, Common Cowbird (young). 85 40

1982

2474† 3b Oilbird (*Steatornis caripensis*).. .. .. 1.40 60

VIETNAM
South-east Asia

South Vietnam
100 cents ·1 piastre

1970

S353 2p Asian Golden Weaver, Baya Weaver ('Chim Dong Doc')
S354 6p Chestnut Mannikin ('Chim Ao Da')
S355 7p Great Indian Hornbill ('Hong-Hoang')
S356 30p Tree Sparrow ('Chim Se Se')
                                Set of 4 3.50 1.60

North Vietnam
100 xu = 1 dong

1963

N277 12x Chinese Francolin (*Francolinus stephenson*)

N278 12x Chinese Jungle Mynah (*Acridotheres cristatellus brevipennis*)
N279 12x White-breasted Kingfisher (*Halcyon smyrneusis*)
N280 20x Siamese Fireback Pheasant (*Diardigallus diardi*)
N281 30x Eastern Reef Heron (*Egretta*)
N282 40x Slaty-headed Parakeet (*Psittacula alexandri* !)

	Set of 6	15.00	8.50
MSN282a 50x Eastern Reef Heron (*Egretta*) . ..		6.00	6.00

1966

N453 12x Moluccan Pitta (*Pitta moluccensis*)
N454 12x Black-naped Oriole (*Oriolus chinensis*)
N455 12x Common Kingfisher (*Alcedo atthis*)
N456 12x Long-tailed Broadbill (*Psarisomus dalhousiae*)
N457 20x Hoopoe (*Upupa epops*)
N458 30x Maroon Oriole (*Oriolus traillii*)

	Set of 6	6.25	3.50

1972

N706 12x Falcated Teal (*Anas falcata*)
N707 12x Red-wattled Lapwing (*Lobivanellus indicus*)
N708 30x Cattle Egret (*Bubulcus ibis*)
N709 40x Water Cock (*Gallicrex cinerea*)
N710 50x Purple Swamphen (*Porphyrio porphyrio*)
N711 1d Greater Adjutant Stork (*Leptoptilos dubius*)

	Set of 6	3.50	1.75

1973

N740 12x Striated Canegrass Warbler (*Megalurus palustris*)

N741 12x Red-whiskered Bulbul (*Pycnonotus jocosus*)
N742 20x Magpie Robin (*Copsychus saularis*)
N743 40x White-browed Fantail (*Rhipidura albicollis* !)
N744 50x Great Tit (*Parus major*)
N745 1d Japanese White Eye (*Zosterops japonica*)

	Set of 6	3.50	1.50

Vietnam Republic
100 xu = 1 dong

1977

135 12x Great Indian Hornbill
136 12x Tickell's Hornbill (*Ptiloleamus tickelli*)
137 20x Long-crested Hornbill (*Berenicornis comatus*)
138 30x Wreathed Hornbill (*Aceros undulatus*)
139 40x Indian Pied Hornbill (*Anthracoceros malabaricus*)
140 50x Black Hornbill (*Anthracoceros malayanus*)
141 60x Great Indian Hornbill (*Buceros bicornis*)
142 1d Rufous-necked Hornbill (*Aceros nipalensis*)

	Set of 8	2.10	1.10

1978

184 12x Hill Myna (*Gracula religiosa*)
185 20x Spotted Dove (*Streptopelia chinensis*)
186 20x Hwamei (*Garrulax canorus*)
187 30x Black-headed Shrike (*Linius schach*)
188 40x Crimson-winged Laughing Thrush (*Garrulax formosus*)
189 50x Black-throated Laughing Thrush (*Garrulax chinensis*)
190 60x Chinese Jungle Mynah (*Acridotheres cristatellus*)
191 1d Yersin's Laughing Thrush (*Garrulax yersini*)

	Set of 8	5.25	2.10

1979

280 12x Siamese Fireback Pheasant (*Lophura diardi*)
281 12x Temminck's Tragopan (*Tragopan temminckii*)
282 20x Ring-necked Pheasant (*Phasianus colchicus*)
283 30x Edwards's Pheasant (*Lophura edwardsi*)
284 40x Silver Pheasant (*Lophura nycthemera*)
285 50x Germain's Peacock-Pheasant (*Polyplectron germaini*)
286 60x Rheinard's Pheasant (*Rheinartia ocellata*)
287 1d Green Peafowl (*Pavo muticus*)

Set of 8   2.10   1.00

1980

359† ·50x Magpie Robin   35   15

1981

404 12x Green Imperial Pigeon (*Ducula aenea*)
405 12x White-bellied Wedge-tailed Green Pigeon (*Treron sieboldi*)
406 20x Red Turtle Dove (*Streptopelia tranquebarica*)
407 30x Bar-tailed Cuckoo Dove (*Macropygia unchall*)
408 40x Mountain Imperial Pigeon (*Ducula badia*)
409 50x Pin-tailed Green Pigeon (*Treron apicauda*)

410 60x Emerald Dove (*Chalcophaps indica*)
411 1d White-bellied Pin-tailed Green Pigeon (*Seimun treron seimundi*)

Set of 8   2.50   1.75

412 20x Yellow-backed Sunbird (*Aethopyga siparaja*)
413 20x Ruby-cheeked Sunbird (*Antreptes singalensis*)
414 30x Black-throated Sunbird (*Aethopyga saturata*)
415 40x Mrs Gould's Sunbird (*Aethopyga gouldiae*)
416 50x Macklot's Sunbird (*Nectarinia chalcostethia*)
417 50x Blue-naped Sunbird (*Nectarinia hypogrammica*)
418 60x Van Hasselt's Sunbird (*Nectarinia sperata*)
419 1d Green-tailed Sunbird (*Aethopyga nipalensis*)

Set of 8   2.75   1.75

1982

477 30x Common Kestrel (*Falco tinnunculus*)
478 30x Pied Falconet (*Microhierax melanoleucos*)
479 40x Black Baza (*Aviceda leuphotes*)
480 50x Black Kite (*Milvus korschun*)
481 50x Lesser Fishing Eagle (*Icthyophaga nana*)
482 60x Fieldens Falconet (*Neohierax harmandi*)
483 1d Black-shouldered Kite (*Elanus caeruleus*)
484 1d Short-toed Eagle (*Circaetus gallicus*)

Set of 8   3.75   3.25

1983

MS599 10d Toco Toucan (*Rhamphastos toco*) .. 2.25 90

649 50x Grey Heron (*Ardea cinerea*)
650 50x Painted Stork (*Ibis leucocephalus*)
651 50x Black Stork (*Ciconia nigra*)
652 50x Purple Heron (*Ardea purpurea*)
653 1d Common Crane (*Grus grue*)
654 2d Black-faced Spoonbill (*Platalea minor*)
655 5d Black-crowned Night Heron (*Nycticorax nycticorax*)
656 10d Asian Open-bill Stork (*Anastomus oscitans*)

Set of 8 5.75 1.90

1984

MS687 10d White Stork (*Ciconia ciconia*) 2.25 90

780† 1d Eastern White Pelican (*Pelecanus onocrotalus*) 40 15
785† 10d Great Indian Hornbill (*Rhytidoceros bicornis*). 2.25 90

1985

836† 1d King Penguin (*Aptenodytes pennati*) .. 10 5
840† 3d Lesser Rhea (*Peterocnemia pennata*) .. 15 5
842† 6d Andean Condor (*Voltur gryphus*) 25 5

VIRGIN ISLANDS
See British Virgin Islands

WALLIS AND FUTUNA ISLANDS
South Pacific
100 centimes = 1 franc

1920

Nos. 85/8, 90 and 112/14 of New Caledonia overprinted ILES
WALLIS ET FUTUNA

1 1c Kagu
2 2c Kagu
3 4c Kagu
4 5c Kagu (No. 88)
18 5c Kagu (No. 112)
5 10c Kagu (No. 114)
19 10c Kagu (No. 113)
6 15c Kagu

Set of 8 90 65

1922

No. 6 surcharged

29† 0.01f on 15c Kagu 10 20
30† 0.02f on 15c Kagu 10 20
31† 0.04f on 15c Kagu 10 20
32† 0.05f on 15c Kagu 10 20

1978

294 17f Eastern Reef Heron ('Aigrette Sacree Grise')

295	18f Red-footed Booby ('Fou a Pieds Rouges')		
296	28f Brown Booby ('Fou Brun')		
297	35f White Tern ('Sterne Blanche')		
	Set of 4	2.50	1.90

WEST BERLIN
See under Germany

WEST GERMANY
See under Germany

WEST IRIAN
South-east Asia
100 sen = 1 rupiah

1963

25†	60s Greater Bird of Paradise .	55	35
26†	75s Greater Bird of Paradise .	70	40

1968

32†	75s One-wattled Cassowary (Casuarii). .	75	75
34†	3r Blue Crowned Pigeon (Goura coronata). .	1.60	1.60
35†	5r Black-capped Lory (Domicella lory rubiensis)	60	50
36†	10r Greater Bird of Paradise (Paradisea apoda)	1.50	1.10

STANLEY GIBBONS
STAMP COLLECTING SERIES
Introductory booklets on *How to Start, How to
Identify Stamps* and *Collecting by Theme*. A series
of well illustrated guides at a low price.
Write for details.

WEST NEW GUINEA
South-east Asia
100 cents = 1 gulden

1962

Nos. 25/9 and 60/2 of Netherlands New Guinea overprinted
UNTEA

20†	1c Lesser Bird of Paradise	80	75
3†	5c Lesser Bird of Paradise	85	90
23†	7c Blue Crowned Pigeon . .	95	95
5†	10c Greater Bird of Paradise .	85	90
6†	12c Blue Crowned Pigeon	1.10	1.25
7†	15c Greater Bird of Paradise .	1.10	1.25
8†	17c Blue Crowned Pigeon	1.10	1.25
9†	20c Greater Bird of Paradise .	1.10	1.25

WESTERN AUSTRALIA
Australia
12 pence = 1 shilling,
20 shillings = 1 pound

1854

Imperforate or rouletted

1	1d Mute Swan (black) . .	£1200	£250
25	2d Mute Swan (orange, as 1d) .	80.00	60.00
3	4d Mute Swan (blue) .	£325	£225
26	4d Mute Swan (blue, as 1d)	£250	£500
28	6d Mute Swan (green, as 1d) . .	£1300	£600
4c	1s Mute Swan (brown) . .	£450	£350

1857

Imperforate or rouletted

15	2d Mute Swan	£2500	£800
18	6d Mute Swan	£2250	£900

1861
As No. 1. Perforated

50	1d Mute Swan (red) .	38.00	8.00
76	1d Mute Swan (yellow) .	10.00	40
39	2d Mute Swan (blue)	50.00	29.00
77	2d Mute Swan (yellow). .	12.00	40
56	4d Mute Swan (red) .	38.00	5.00
42	6d Mute Swan (brown). .	£150	35.00
57	6d Mute Swan (violet) .	60.00	9.00
61	1s Mute Swan (green) .	70.00	10.00

1871

As No. 1, *except* 3d

103	1d Mute Swan (pink)	11.00	45
104	2d Mute Swan (grey)	19.00	90
141	3d Black Swan..	3.25	50
105	4d Mute Swan (brown)	90.00	15.00

1874

No. 77 *surcharged* **ONE PENNY**

67	1d on 2d Mute Swan	£110	28.00

1884

Nos. 76 *and* 141 *surcharged in figures*

90	½d on 1d Mute Swan	9.00	2.75
91a	1d on 3d Black Swan	14.00	4.75

1885

138	½d Black Swan..	90	15
95	1d Black Swan	1.75	5
96a	2d Black Swan (grey)..	2.25	25
113	2d Black Swan (yellow)	3.00	25
97	2½d Black Swan	5.50	35
98	4d Black Swan (as 2½d)	5.00	35
99	5d Black Swan (as 2½d)	8.00	1.25
100	6d Black Swan (as 2½d)	10.00	60
102	1s Black Swan (as 2½d)	16.00	90

1893

No. 141 *surcharged in words*

110a	½d on 3d Black Swan	3.50	5.50
107	1d on 3d Black Swan.	8.00	2.75

1901

140	2d Black Swan..	1.40	15
114	2½d Black Swan	4.00	30
142	4d Black Swan..	5.00	70
168	6d Black Swan..	9.00	2.00
144	8d Black Swan (as No. 138)	17.00	5.00
145	9d Black Swan (as 4d)	17.00	3.50
146	10d Black Swan	17.00	7.00
116	1s Black Swan..	18.00	3.50

1906

No. 140 *surcharged* **ONE PENNY**

172	1d on 2d Black Swan	70	30

YEMEN
Arabian peninsula
1965 40 bogaches = 1 rial
1975 100 fils = 1 riyal

Yemen Arab Republic

1965

318	½b Western Reef Heron ('Reef Heron')		
319	½b Arabian Chukar ('Arabian Red Legged Partridge')		
320	¾b Eagle Owl		
321	1b Hammerkop		
322	1½b Yemeni Linnet ('Yemen Linnets')		
323	4b Hoopoe		
324	6b Violet Starling ('Amethyst Starlings') (air)		
325	8b Waldrapp ('Bald Ibis')		
326	12b Arabian Woodpecker		
327	20b Bateleur		
328	1r Yellow-bellied Green Pigeon ('Bruce's Green Pigeon')		
	Set of 11	8.25	5.25

1966

Nos. 318/20 *overprinted* **Prevention of Cruelty to Animals**

368	½b Western Reef Heron		
369	½b Arabian Chukar		
370	¾b Eagle Owl		
	Set of 3	1.25	75

1980

594†	25f Chaffinch	60	25
595†	50f Great Tit	1.10	50
597†	80f Bullfinch (air)..	1.60	90

POSTAGE DUE STAMPS

1966

Nos. 324/8 overprinted **POSTAGE DUE**

D371 6b Violet Starling
D372 8b Waldrapp
D373 12b Arabian Woodpecker
D374 20b Bateleur
D375 1r Yellow-bellied Green Pigeon

Set of 5 15.00 13.00

Appendix

The following stamps have either been issued in excess of postal needs, or have not been made available to the public in reasonable quantities at face value. Miniature sheets, imperforate stamps etc. are excluded from this section.

1969

Paintings from the Uffizi Gallery, Florence. 3b Goldfinch

The Mutawakelite Kingdom of Yemen

1965

R72 ½b Hammerkop
R73 ½b Yemeni Linnet
R74 ½b Hoopoe
R75 4b Arabian Woodpecker

R76 6b Violet Starling (air)

Set of 5 5.50 4.75

1967

Nos. R75/6 surcharged **JORDAN RELIEF FUND** *and premium in English and Arabic and with crown*

R262† 4b + 2b Arabian Woodpecker 1.00 1.00
R263† 6b + 3b Violet Starling 1.75 1.75

Appendix

The following stamps have either been issued in excess of postal needs, or have not been made available to the public in reasonable quantities at face value. Miniature sheets, imperforate stamps etc. are excluded from this section.

1969

World Wildlife Conservation. Postage ½b Common Peafowl, 1b Peregrine Falcon, 2b Four-coloured Bush Shrike, 4b Jay, 6b Violet Starling. Air 8d Northern Goshawk, 10b Rainbow Lory, 18b Blue and White Flycatcher

---

YEMEN PEOPLE'S DEMOCRATIC REPUBLIC

Arabian peninsula
1000 fils = 1 dinar

1971

101 5f Domestic Pigeon ('Pigeon')
102 40f Arabian Chukar ('Partridge')
103 65f Arabian Chukar ('Partridge'), Helmet Guineafowl ('Guinea Fowl')
104 100f Black Kite ('Glede')

Set of 4 2.25 1.60

YUGOSLAVIA

South-east Europe
100 paras = 1 dinar

1934

294 75p + 25p Osprey
295 1d50 + 50p Osprey
296 1d75 + 25p Osprey

Set of 3 22.00 15.00

1954

770† 25d Eastern White Pelican (*Pelecanus onocrotalus*) 2.00 30
771† 30d Lammergeier (*Gypaetus barbatus aureus*) 3.50 35

1958

879 10d Mallard (*Anas platyrhyncha*)
880 15d Capercaillie (*Tetrao urogallus*)

881 20d Ring-necked Pheasant (*Phasianus*
      colchicus)
882 25d Common Coot (*Fulica atra*)
883 30d Water Rail (*Rallus aquaticus*)
884 35d Great Bustard (*Otis tarda*)
885 50d Rock Partridge (*Alectoris graeca*)
886 70d Woodcock (*Scolopax rusticola*)
887 100d Common Crane (*Grus grus*)
                           Set of 9   17.00   5.50

1967

1294† 30p Bobwhite (*Perdix perdix* !).   25   5
1297† 5d Peregrine Falcon (*Falco peregrinus*) .. 1.00   45

1968

1323 50p Bullfinch (*Pyrrhula pyrrhula*)
1324 1d Goldfinch (*Carduelis carduelis*)
1325 1d50 Chaffinch (*Fringilla coelebs*)
1326 2d Greenfinch (*Chloris chloris*)
1327 3d Red Crossbill (*Loxia curvirostra*)
1328 5d Hawfinch (*Coccothraustes
      coccothraustes*)
                           Set of 6   2.50   85

1970

1445† 3d25 Lammergeier (*Gypaetus barbatus*) .. 11.00   7.50
       (1444/5 Set of 2)   12.50   8.50

1971

1516 50p Wallcreeper (*Tichodroma muraria*)
1517 1d25 Little Bustard (*Otis tetrax*)

1518 2d50 Chough (*Pyrrhocorax pyrrhocorax*)
1519 3d25 White Spoonbill (*Platalea
      leucorodia*)
1520 5d Eagle Owl (*Bubo bubo*)
1521 6d50 Rock Ptarmigan (*Lagopus mutus*)
                           Set of 6   3.25   1.10

1974

1605† 80p Great Tit.   40   12

1976

1731† 6d Ferruginous Duck (*Aythya nyroca*). ..   60   20

1977

1776† 10d Red-breasted Flycatcher 1.00   45

1978

1861† 3d40 Rock Partridge   40   12
1863† 4d90 Capercaillie   45   10

1980

1931† 4d90 Little Tern (*Sterna albifrons*).   45   12

1981

2009†	5d60 Rook	35	5
2010†	8d Cattle Egret	45	10

1982

2020	3d50 House Sparrow (*Passer domesticus*) (male)		
2021	5d60 House Sparrow (*Passer domesticus*) (female)		
2022	8d Spanish Sparrow (*Passer montanus* !) (female)		
2023	15d Tree Sparrow (*Passer montanus*)		
	Set of 4	1.00	60

1984

2152	4d Great Black-backed Gull (*Larus marinus*)		
2153	5d Black-headed Gull (*Larus ridibundus*)		
2154	16d50 Herring Gull (*Larus argentatus*)		
2155	40d Common Tern (*Sterna hirundo*)		
	Set of 4	1.40	70

1985

2197	500d Lammergeier		
2198	1000d Swallow sp		
	Set of 2	13.50	6.50

2202	42d Osprey (*Pandion haliaetus*)		
2203	60d Hoopoe (*Upupa epops*)		
	Set of 2	1.75	1.10

1986

2262†	100d Osprey..	80	30
	(2262/3 Set of 2)	1.10	60

ZAIRE
Central Africa
100 sengi· 1 kuta,
100 kuta = 1 zaire

1979

953†	3k Regal Sunbird..	30	10

1980

EXPOSITION PHILATELIQUE BELGO-ZAIROISE 1980

1028†	2k Abdim's Stork (on Congo (Kinshasa) stamp No. 471)	80	40

No. 1028 exists with the exhibition logo either at right or left of the design (same price, either version).

1046† 145k Crowned Crane 90 50

1984

1173† 15k Tawny Eagle ('Aigles Ravisseurs') .. 15 5
1178† 40z Kori Bustard ('Outardes Koris') 2.00 1.75
1179† 40z South African Crowned Crane ('Grues
   Couronnees').. .. .. 2.00 1.75

1981

REPUBLIQUE DU
ZAIRE **125K**

1184† 15z South African Crowned Crane 85 55

1058† 125k Green-winged Macaw. 50 25

1985

1982

1238 5z Great Egret ('Grande aigrette')
1239 10z Common Scoter ('Macreuse a bec
   jaune')
1240 15z Black-crowned Night Heron ('Heron
   bihoreau')
1133 25k Red-billed Quelea ('Travailleur a Bec
   Rouge')
1241 25z Surf Scoter ('Macreuse a front blanc')
                          Set of 4   2.00   1.40
1134 50k African Pygmy Kingfisher ('Martin
   Pecheur Pygmee')
1135 90k Knysna Turaco ('Touraco Vert')
1136 1z50 Three-banded Plover ('Gravelot a
   Triple Collier')
1137 1z70 Temminck's Courser ('Courvite de
   Temminck')
1138 2z Bennett's Woodpecker ('Pic de
   Bennet')   **ZAMBIA**
1139 3z Little Grebe ('Grebe Castagneux')   Central Africa
1140 3z50 Lizard Buzzard ('Buse Unibande')   100 ngwee = 1 kwacha
1141 5z Black Crake ('Marouette Noire a Bec
   Jaune')
1142 8z White-headed Vulture ('Vautour a Tete   **1968**
   Blanche')
                          Set of 10   6.00   5.50

COLLECT MAMMALS ON STAMPS
The second Stanley Gibbons thematic catalogue —
copies are available at £7.50 (p. + p. £1.50) from:
Stanley Gibbons Publications Ltd, 5 Parkside,
Christchurch Road, Ringwood, Hants BH24 3SH.

136† 20n South African Crowned Crane
   ('Crowned Cranes') 55 5

1969

150† 25n Carmine Bee Eater 1.00 80

1975

227† 2n Helmet Guineafowl ('Guinea-Fowl') . .. 10 5
229† 4n African Fish Eagle ('Fish Eagle') 15 5
238† 1k Lady Ross's Turaco 1.75 1.50

1977

262 4n Grimwood's Longclaw
263 9n Shelley's Sunbird
264 10n Black-cheeked Lovebird
265 15n Locust Finch
266 20n Black-chinned Tinkerbird ('White-chested Tinkerbird')
267 25n Chaplin's Barbet
Set of 6 6.00 6.75

1979

289† 42n African Fish Eagle 50 75

1982

368† 1k African Fish Eagle 1.50 2.00

1983

382† 1k Violet-crested Turaco ('Purple Crested Loerie') 1.40 1.75

1987

487 25n Chestnut-headed Crake ('Long-toed Fluff Tail')
488 35n Black and Rufous Swallow
489 1k Bradfield's Hornbill
490 1k25 Boulton's Puff-back Flycatcher ('Margaret's Batis')
491 1k60 Anchieta's Sunbird ('Red-and-Blue Sunbird')
492 1k70 Boehm's Bee Eater
493 1k95 Perrin's Bush Shrike ('Gorgeous Bush Shrike')
494 5k Taita Falcon
Set of 8 2.00 2.10

ZIL ELWANNYEN SESEL
Indian Ocean
100 cents = 1 rupee

A. Inscribed 'ZIL ELOIGNE SESEL'

1980

9† 1r Madagascar Red Fody ('Madagascar Fody') 25 20
11† 1r25 White Tern ('Fairy Tern') 35 35

B. Inscribed 'ZIL ELWAGNE SESEL'

C. Inscribed 'ZIL ELWANNYEN SESEL'

1983

5c

53 5c Aldabra Warbler ('Aldabra Brush
    Warbler')
54 10c Zebra Dove ('Barred Ground Dove')
55 15c Madagascar Nightjar ('Aldabra
    Nightjar')
56 20c Madagascar Cisticola ('Malagasy Grass
    Warbler')
57 25c Madagascar White Eye ('Aldabra White-
    Eye')
58 40c Mascarene Fody ('Aldabra Fody')
59 50c White-throated Rail ('Aldabra Rail')
60 75c Black Bulbul ('Aldabra Bulbul')
61 2r Western Reef Heron ('Dimorphic Little
    Egret')
62 2r10 Souimanga Sunbird ('Aldabra Sunbird')
63 2r50 Madagascar Turtle Dove ('Aldabra
    Turtle Dove')
64 2r75 Sacred Ibis ('Aldabra Sacred Ibis')
65 3r50 Black Coucal ('Aldabra Coucal')
66 7r Seychelles Kestrel ('Aldabra Kestrel')
67 15r Comoro Blue Pigeon ('Aldabra Blue
    Pigeon')
68 20r Greater Flamingo
                          Set of 16   11.00   11.50

1984

R2·75

80† 2r75 White-throated Rail ('Aldabra Rail') .. 60   75
82† 10r Red-footed Booby.. .. .. 2.25 2.75

COLLECT RAILWAYS ON STAMPS

A Stanley Gibbons thematic catalogue on this
popular subject. Copies available at £7.50 (p. + p.
£1.50) from: Stanley Gibbons Publications Ltd, 5
Parkside, Christchurch Road, Ringwood, Hants
BH24 3SH.

1985

As Nos. 54, 57 *and* 61

100 10c Zebra Dove
103 25c Madagascar White Eye
107 2r Western Reef Heron
                          Set of 3   45   50

ZIMBABWE

Central Africa

100 cents = 1 dollar

1984

9c

647 9c African Fish Eagle ('Fish Eagle')
648 11c Long-crested Eagle
649 13c Bateleur
650 17c Verreaux's Eagle ('Black Eagle')
651 21c Martial Eagle
652 30c Bonelli's Eagle ('African Hawk Eagle')
                          Set of 6   1.60   1.25

1987

12c

Zimbabwe

710 12c Barred Owlet ('Barred Owl')
711 18c Pearl-spotted Owlet
712 26c White-faced Scops Owl ('White Faced
     Owl')
713 35c African Scops Owl ('Scops Owl')
                          Set of 4   75   85

Bird Species Section

This section contains two parts.

The **Index** contains two alphabetic lists, by English name or by systematic (zoological) name, of every bird family or species which has appeared on stamps. Against each entry is the numerical code for identification in the Systematic Listing.

In the **Systematic Listing** the birds are grouped in the families recognised by zoologists. To aid identification each family is given a number, as is each species within that family. Penguins, for example, are family No. 7 with the Emperor Penguin as species No. 2 within that family. The numerical code for the Emperor Penguin would therefore be 7-2, the first figure identifying the family and the second the species.

Index

I. By English Name

Winter Wren, see 127-48 WRENS
Wire-tailed Manakin, see 107-40 MANAKINS
Wood Duck, see 27-58 DUCKS, GEESE, SWANS
Wood Hoopoes, see 92 WOOD HOOPOES
Wood Lark, see 116-76 LARKS
Wood Pigeon, see 66-9 DOVES, PIGEONS
Wood Sandpiper, see 58-23 SANDPIPERS, SNIPE
Wood Swallows, see 171 WOOD SWALLOWS
Woodchat Shrike, see 122-79 SHRIKES
Woodcock, see 58-36 SANDPIPERS, SNIPE
Woodcreepers, see 101 WOODCREEPERS
Woodland Kingfisher, see 84-50 KINGFISHERS
Woodpecker Finch, see 154-222 BUNTINGS
Woodpeckers, see 99 WOODPECKERS
Woodstars, see 81 HUMMINGBIRDS
Worm-eating Warbler, see 159-48 NEW WORLD WARBLERS
Wreathed Hornbill, see 93-26 HORNBILLS
Wrens, see 127 WRENS
Wrens, Australian, see 137 AUSTRALIAN WRENS
Wrinkled Hornbill, see 93-23 HORNBILLS
Wryneck, see 99-1 WOODPECKERS

Y

Yellow Canary, see 163-21 FINCHES
Yellow Cardinal, see 156-1 CARDINALS, GROSBEAKS
Yellow Oriole, see 162-25 NEW WORLD BLACKBIRDS
Yellow Wagtail, see 118-2 WAGTAILS, PIPITS
Yellow Warbler, see 159-15 NEW WORLD WARBLERS
Yellow-backed Sunbird, see 151-105 SUNBIRDS
Yellow-backed Tanager, see 157-47 TANAGERS
Yellow-bellied Elaenia, see 108-314 TYRANT FLYCATCHERS
Yellow-bellied Green Pigeon, see 66-192 DOVES, PIGEONS
Yellow-bellied Grosbeak, see 156-10 CARDINALS, GROSBEAKS
Yellow-bellied Sapsucker, see 99-55 WOODPECKERS
Yellow-bellied Seedeater, see 154-173 BUNTINGS
Yellow-bellied Sunbird, see 151-47 SUNBIRDS
Yellow-bellied Waxbill, see 164-46 WAXBILLS
Yellow-billed Amazon, see 69-231 PARROTS
Yellow-billed Hornbill, see 93-13 HORNBILLS
Yellow-billed Oxpecker, see 166-107 STARLINGS
Yellow-billed Stork, see 23-3 STORKS
Yellow-breasted Barbet, see 96-81 BARBETS
Yellow-breasted Chat, see 159-113 NEW WORLD WARBLERS
Yellow-casqued Hornbill, see 93-40 HORNBILLS
Yellow-collared Macaw, see 69-133 PARROTS
Yellow-crested Helmet Shrike, see 122-6 SHRIKES
Yellow-crowned Amazon, see 69-249 PARROTS
Yellow-crowned Night Heron, see 20-25 HERONS, BITTERNS
Yellow-faced Grassquit, see 154-204 BUNTINGS
Yellow-faced Honeyeater, see 153-84 HONEYEATERS
Yellow-fronted Barbet, see 96-26 BARBETS
Yellow-fronted White Eye, see 152-40 WHITE EYES
Yellowhammer, see 154-4 BUNTINGS
Yellow-headed Barbet, see 96-45 BARBETS
Yellow-headed Caracara, see 32-9 FALCONS, CARACARAS
Yellow-headed Warbler, see 159-66 NEW WORLD WARBLERS
Yellow-mantled Whydah, see 165-149 WEAVERS, SPARROWS
Yellow-nosed Albatross, see 10-10 ALBATROSSES
Yellow-rumped Bishop, see 165-147 WEAVERS, SPARROWS
Yellow-tailed Oriole, see 162-28 NEW WORLD BLACKBIRDS
Yellow-tailed Thornbill, see 137-60 AUSTRALIAN WRENS
Yellowthroat, see 159-50 NEW WORLD WARBLERS
Yellow-throated Caracara, see 32-1 FALCONS, CARACARAS
Yellow-throated Warbler, see 159-26 NEW WORLD WARBLERS
Yellow-tufted Bulbul, see 120-30 BULBULS
Yellow-tufted Honeyeater, see 153-74 HONEYEATERS
Yellow-tufted Malachite Sunbird, see 151-87 SUNBIRDS
Yemeni Linnet, see 163-67 FINCHES
Yersin's Laughing Thrush, see 132-186 BABBLERS
Yucatan Vireo, see 161-28 VIREOS
Yuhinas, see 132 BABBLERS

Z

Zapata Rail, see 43-40 RAILS, COOTS
Zapata Sparrow, see 154-95 BUNTINGS
Zapata Wren, see 127-26 WRENS
Zebra Dove, see 66-103 DOVES, PIGEONS
Zenaida Dove, see 66-108 DOVES, PIGEONS

II.By Zoological Name

Both elements of the zoological name are covered in this section.

A

aalge, Uria, see 64-4 Common Guillemot
abbotti, Sula, see 16-6 Abbott's Booby
abdimii, Ciconia, see 23-8 Abdim's Stork
Aburria jacutinga, see 34-25 Black-fronted Piping Guan
abyssinica, Coracias, see 88-2 Abyssinian Roller
abyssinica, Hirundo, see 117-51 Lesser Striped Swallow
abyssinicus, Asio, see 73-125 Abyssinian Long-eared Owl
abyssinicus, Bucorvus, see 93-45 Abyssinian Ground Hornbill
acadicus, Aegolius, see 73-132 Saw-whet Owl
Acanthis cannabina, see 163-66 Linnet
Acanthis flammea, see 163-63 Redpoll
Acanthis yemensis, see 163-67 Yemeni Linnet
Acanthiza chrysorrhoa, see 137-60 Yellow-tailed Thornbill
Accipiter badius, see 30-126 Shikra
Accipiter brachyurus, see 30-101 New Britain Sparrow Hawk
Accipiter fasciatus, see 30-113 Australian Goshawk
Accipiter gentilis, see 30-88 Northern Goshawk
Accipiter gundlachii, see 30-131 Gundlach's Hawk
Accipiter nisus, see 30-102 European Sparrow Hawk
Accipiter rufiventris, see 30-103 Rufous-breasted Sparrow Hawk
Accipiter striatus, see 30-104 Sharp-shinned Hawk
accipitrinus, Deroptyus, see 69-258 Hawk-headed Parrot
Aceros corrugatus, see 93-23 Wrinkled Hornbill
Aceros nipalensis, see 93-22 Rufous-necked Hornbill
Aceros plicatus, see 93-27 Blyth's Hornbill
Aceros undulatus, see 93-26 Wreathed Hornbill
Acridotheres cristatellus, see 166-92 Chinese Jungle Mynah
Acridotheres tristis, see 166-87 Common Mynah
Acrocephalus aequinoctialis, see 136-62 Polynesian Reed
  Warbler
Acrocephalus arundinaceus, see 136-55 Great Reed Warbler
Acrocephalus caffra, see 136-63 Long-billed Reed Warbler
Acrocephalus orientalis, see 136-56 Oriental Great Reed
  Warbler
Acrocephalus rehsei, see 136-60 Finsch's Reed Warbler
Acrocephalus schoenobaenus, see 136-45 Sedge Warbler
Acrocephalus scirpaceus, see 136-52 Reed Warbler
Acrocephalus vaughanii, see 136-66 Pitcairn Warbler
Acryllium vulturinum, see 35-211 Vulturine Guineafowl
Actophilornis africana, see 49-2 African Jacana
acunhae, Nesospiza, see 154-116 Nightingale Finch
acuta, Anas, see 27-87 Pintail
acuticaudus, Lamprotornis, see 166-46 Sharp-tailed Glossy
  Starling
acutirostris, Heteralocha, see 0-62 Huia
adamsii, Gavia, see 8-5 White-billed Diver
adansonii, Excalfactoria, see 35-122 Blue Quail
adelaidae, Dendroica, see 159-24 Adelaide's Warbler
adeliae, Pygoscelis, see 7-4 Adelie Penguin
aedon, Troglodytes, see 127-49 House Wren
Aegithalos caudatus, see 143-1 Long-tailed Tit
Aegolius acadicus, see 73-132 Saw-whet Owl
Aegypius monachus, see 30-55 European Black Vulture
Aegypius occipitalis, see 30-56 White-headed Vulture
aegyptiacus, Alopochen, see 27-39 Egyptian Goose
aenea, Ducula, see 66-261 Green Imperial Pigeon
aequinoctialis, Acrocephalus, see 136-62 Polynesian Reed
  Warbler

Systematic Listing

Haiti 580 584
Japan 1661
Reunion 479
South Georgia 4 16 22 36 37 72
South Georgia and South Sandwich Islands 175
Vietnam 836

7-2   Emperor Penguin (*Aptenodytes forsteri*)
Argentine Republic 1006
Australian Antarctic Territory 5 9 77
Belgium **MS**1994
British Antarctic Territory 42 43 88 92
Chile 381h 382h 383h 1068
French Southern and Antarctic Territories 16 17 46 92 196
Japan 766
Mongolia 1319
Russia 2373 2894 4786
Uganda 526

7-3   Gentoo Penguin (*Pygoscelis papua*)
Argentine Republic **MS**1687
British Antarctic Territory 90
Chile 870
Falkland Islands 116 117 118 119 120 121 122 123 124 125
   126 160 180 192 195 317
French Southern and Antarctic Territories 103 167

7-4   Adelie Penguin (*Pygoscelis adeliae*)
Argentine Republic **MS**1687 2031
Australian Antarctic Territory 25 43
Belgium 2230
Brazil 2003 2269
British Antarctic Territory 20 41 91 100 108
Cuba 1984
French Southern and Antarctic Territories 34 37 149 150 151
Hungary 2062
Japan 1260 1721
Mongolia 1315 1322
New Zealand 1328
Poland 2267 3092
Ross Dependency 15
Russia 3251

7-5   Chinstrap Penguin (*Pygoscelis antarctica*)
Argentine Republic 1127 **MS**1687
British Antarctic Territory 113
Chile 971 988
Falkland Islands Dependencies 84 85 122
South Georgia 4 22
South Georgia and South Sandwich Islands 170

7-7   Snares Island Penguin (*Eudyptes robustus*)
Russia 4784

7-9   Rockhopper Penguin (*Eudyptes crestatus*)
Argentine Republic **MS**1858
Falkland Islands 199 298 532 533 534 535
French Southern and Antarctic Territories 4 5 167 185 186
Tristan Da Cunha 16 168 188 189 190 191 **MS**192 **MS**267 271
   430 431 432 433

7-10   Royal Penguin (*Eudyptes schlegeli*)
Australian Antarctic Territory 58
French Southern and Antarctic Territories 138

7-11   Macaroni Penguin (*Eudyptes chrysolophus*)
Argentine Republic **MS**1858
British Antarctic Territory 89
French Southern and Antarctic Territories 226
South Georgia and South Sandwich Islands 171

7-13   Little Penguin (*Eudyptula minor*)
New Zealand 823

7-16   Humboldt Penguin (*Spheniscus humboldti*)
Hong Kong 465
Peru 1622

7-17   Magellanic Penguin (*Spheniscus magellanicus*)
Argentine Republic 1967 1988

7-18   Galapagos Penguin (*Spheniscus mendiculus*)
Comoro Islands 219

8   DIVERS
8-1   Red-throated Diver (*Gavia stellata*)
Bhutan 627

8-2   Black-throated Diver (*Gavia arctica*)
Dominica 1013
Mongolia 765 1140
Poland 1491
Russia 4546
Sweden 1274

8-4   Great Northern Diver (*Gavia immer*)
Gambia **MS**585
Greenland 65
Iceland 430
United States of America 1952

8-5   White-billed Diver (*Gavia adamsii*)
Canada 495
Mongolia 1140

9   GREBES
9-1   Little Grebe (*Tachybaptus ruficollis*)
Maldive Islands 1084
Zaire 1139

9-2   Australian Dabchick (*Tachybaptus novaehollandiae*)
Australia 673

9-5   Pied-billed Grebe (*Podilymbus podiceps*)
Turks and Caicos Islands 592

9-6   Atitlan Grebe (*Podilymbus gigas*)
Guatemala 889 890

9-7   White-tufted Grebe (*Rollandia rolland*)
Falkland Islands 491

9-9   Great Grebe (*Podiceps major*)
Falkland Islands 489

9-13   Red-necked Grebe (*Podiceps grisegene*)
Rumania 4940

9-14   Great Crested Grebe (*Podiceps cristatus*)
Afghanistan 752
Albania 748
Bulgaria 1834
Czechoslovakia 1186
Fujeira 1 10 39 85 94 123 O48 O158
Hungary 3344
Ireland 443
Lesotho 647
Mongolia 767
Poland 1492
Switzerland J232

9-15   Slavonian Grebe (*Podiceps auritus*)
Antigua 924
Barbuda 794

9-16   Black-necked Grebe (*Podiceps nigricollis*)
Maldive Islands 1196

9-17   Silvery Grebe (*Podiceps occipitalis*)
Falkland Islands 201 490

9-19   Hooded Grebe (*Podiceps gallardoi*)
Argentine Republic 1885

10   ALBATROSSES
10-1   Wandering Albatross (*Diomedea exulans*)
Argentine Republic **MS**1858
Australian Antarctic Territory 29
Falkland Islands Dependencies 127
French Southern and Antarctic Territories 18
Martinique 250
Monaco 510
Mongolia 1317
Oceanic Settlements 207 209
South Georgia 12 64
South Georgia and South Sandwich Islands 174
Tristan Da Cunha 113 174 175 **MS**192 224 335 417

10-2   Royal Albatross (*Diomedea epomophora*)
Aitutaki 345 457

10-4   Short-tailed Albatross (*Diomedea albatrus*)
Japan 1377
Ryukyu Islands 263

10-7   Black-browed Albatross (*Diomedea melanophrys*)
Aitutaki 334
Argentine Republic **MS**1858 1984
Christmas Island 87
Falkland Islands 200 319 492
Falkland Islands Dependencies 126
French Southern and Antarctic Territories 31
Pitcairn Islands 217

10-9   Shy Albatross (*Diomedea cauta*)
New Zealand 947

10-10   Yellow-nosed Albatross (*Diomedea chlororhynchos*)
Ghana 195
Tristan Da Cunha 18 165 231

10-11   Grey-headed Albatross (*Diomedea chrysostoma*)
Falkland Islands Dependencies 125

10-12   Amsterdam Albatross (*Diomedea amsterdamensis*)
French Southern and Antarctic Territories 199

10-13   Sooty Albatross (*Phoebetria fusca*)
Tristan Da Cunha 164

10-14   Light-mantled Sooty Albatross (*Phoebetria palpebrata*)
Argentine Republic **MS**1858
Australian Antarctic Territory 55
Falkland Islands Dependencies 128
French Southern and Antarctic Territories 2 124
South Georgia 8 25
South Georgia and South Sandwich Islands 172

11   PETRELS, SHEARWATERS
11-1   Giant Petrel (*Macronectes giganteus*)
Argentine Republic **MS**1687 1986
French Southern and Antarctic Territories 209
South Georgia and South Sandwich Islands 173

11-2   Hall's Giant Petrel (*Macronectes halli*)
Tristan Da Cunha 222

11-3   Fulmar (*Fulmarus glacialis*)
Germany (East Germany) E1072
Greenland **MS**164
Isle of Man 146
Maldive Islands **MS**1200a

11-4   Southern Fulmar (*Fulmarus glacialoides*)
French Southern and Antarctic Territories 208
Poland 3091

11-5   Antarctic Petrel (*Thalassoica antarctica*)
French Southern and Antarctic Territories 99

11-6   Pintado Petrel (*Daption capense*)
Argentine Republic 1983
French Southern and Antarctic Territories 28
South Georgia and South Sandwich Islands 165

11-7   Snow Petrel (*Pagodroma nivea*)
Argentine Republic **MS**1687
British Antarctic Territory 39
French Southern and Antarctic Territories 16 17 197
Russia 4785

11-8   Great-winged Petrel (*Pterodroma macroptera*)
Tristan Da Cunha 220

11-11   Black-capped Petrel (*Pterodroma hasitata*)
Dominica 1049

11-12   Cahow (*Pterodroma cahow*)
Bermuda 403

11-17   Solander's Petrel (*Pterodroma solandri*)
Norfolk Island 32 67

11-18   Kerguelen Petrel (*Pterodroma brevirostris*)
Tristan Da Cunha 225

11-19   Murphy's Petrel (*Pterodroma ultima*)
Pitcairn Islands 46 79

11-23   Soft-plumaged Petrel (*Pterodroma mollis*)
French Southern and Antarctic Territories 139
Madeira 233
Tristan Da Cunha 223

11-28   White-winged Petrel (*Pterodroma leucoptera*)
Kiribati 165

11-29   Collared Petrel (*Pterodroma brevipes*)
Fiji 710

11-37   Broad-billed Prion (*Pachyptila vittata*)
Tristan Da Cunha 228 336

11-39   Dove Prion (*Pachyptila desolata*)
Australian Antarctic Territory 59
Falkland Islands Dependencies 137

11-41   Fairy Prion (*Pachyptila turtur*)
South Georgia and South Sandwich Islands 169

11-46   White-chinned Petrel (*Procellaria aequinoctialis*)
Tristan Da Cunha 421

11-50   Cory's Shearwater (*Calonectris diomedea*)
Madeira 224
Malta 799
Mauritius 714

11-52   Pale-footed Shearwater (*Puffinus carneipes*)
Maldive Islands 1083

11-53   Greater Shearwater (*Puffinus gravis*)
Greenland 135
Maldive Islands 1194
Tristan Da Cunha 116 227

11-54   Wedge-tailed Shearwater (*Puffinus pacificus*)
Maldive Islands 705
Marshall Islands 103

11-60   Manx Shearwater (*Puffinus puffinus*)
Isle of Man 32

11-66   Audubon's Shearwater (*Puffinus lherminieri*)
Anguilla 671 717
Barbados 838
British Virgin Islands 575 O31
Grenadines of Grenada 294
Kiribati 173 O27
Palau 68 69 70 71 72
St. Lucia 823

12   STORM-PETRELS
12-1   Wilson's Petrel (*Oceanites oceanicus*)
Falkland Islands 492
Grenada 923
Maldive Islands 877

12-4   White-faced Storm Petrel (*Pelagodroma marina*)
Maldive Islands 1086
Tristan Da Cunha 221

12-7   White-throated Storm Petrel (*Nesofregatta fuliginosa*)
Kiribati 174

12-8   British Storm Petrel (*Hydrobates pelagicus*)
Antigua 925
Barbuda 795
Jersey 130
Malta 658

12-11   Madeiran Storm Petrel (*Oceanodroma castro*)
Ascension 80 205 214

12-12   Leach's Storm Petrel (*Oceanodroma leucorhoa*)
Marshall Islands 37

13   DIVING PETRELS
13-3   Georgian Diving Petrel (*Pelecanoides georgicus*)
South Georgia and South Sandwich Islands 166

13-4   Common Diving Petrel (*Pelecanoides urinatrix*)
Falkland Islands 516
Tristan Da Cunha 230

14   TROPIC BIRDS
14-1   Red-billed Tropic Bird (*Phaethon aethereus*)
Anguilla 289 441
Ascension 73 79 211
Brazil 2170
British Virgin Islands 560 O16
Colombia 1175
Grenadines of St. Vincent 121
Montserrat 249
St. Lucia 422
Senegal 732 **MS**733

14-2   Red-tailed Tropic Bird (*Phaethon rubricauda*)
Christmas Island 158
Cocos (Keeling) Islands 16
Cook Islands 151
Marshall Islands 105
Mauritius 345
Norfolk Island 36 71 254 284
Pitcairn Islands 43 76 124 125
Samoa 263

14-3   White-tailed Tropic Bird (*Phaethon lepturus*)
Anguilla 663

Antigua **MS**928
Ascension 62 78 212 214
Bahamas 431
Barbuda **MS798**
Bermuda 114b 143 143a 151 154 387
British Indian Ocean Territory 74
British Virgin Islands 441
Christmas Island 20 163 175
Cuba 2961
Dominica 662 1044
Grenadines of Grenada 299
Maldive Islands 704 873
Palau 52
St. Helena 466
Turks and Caicos Islands 783B
Tuvalu 311

15   PELICANS
15-1   Eastern White Pelican (*Pelecanus onocrotalus*)
Afghanistan 1068
Angola 830
Bahawalpur O4
Congo (Kinshasa) 468
Germany (East Germany) E1533 E1547
Greece 1479
Mauritania 713 D179
Rumania 2557 3312 4352 4386 **MS**4572
Russia 3004
Rwanda 660 1280
Senegal 729 **MS**733
South West Africa 333
Togo 1098
Trieste B124
Vietnam 780
Yugoslavia 770

15-3   Pink-backed Pelican (*Pelecanus rufescens*)
French Somali Coast 446
Gabon 850
Senegal 659
Somalia 337

15-5   Dalmatian Pelican (*Pelecanus crispus*)
Albania 676 1098 1099 1100 1101 1102
Bulgaria 1237 1832 3183 3184 3185 3186
Germany (West Berlin) **MS**B332
Greece 1734
Korea (North Korea) N1904
Mongolia 128 129 878
Rumania 4899 4900 4901 4902

15-7   American White Pelican (*Pelecanus erythrorhynchos*)
Cuba 776 788 1561a
Guinea-Bissau 921
Ivory Coast 840

15-8   Brown Pelican (*Pelecanus occidentalis*)
Anguilla 144 239 416 498 533 576 609 627 659 679 715
Barbuda 786
British Virgin Islands 160 172 180 293 442
Cuba 2955
Dominica 663 1043
Ecuador 1046c 1048 1531
Grenada 319 515 605
Grenadines of Grenada 13
Guinea-Bissau 920
Jamaica 620 621 622 623
Montserrat 246 368 O1
Peru 504 1196
Rumania 4937
St. Kitts 66 124 O18
St. Kitts-Nevis 256 257 391
St. Vincent 397 854

Togo 1819
Turks and Caicos Islands 253 390
United States of America 1471 1947

16 GANNETS, BOOBIES
16-1 Northern Gannet (*Morus bassanus*)
Canada 474
China (Taiwan) 467
Faroe Islands 33 34 35
Guernsey 169 366
Isle of Man 233
Mongolia 1144
St. Pierre et Miquelon 525 526

16-2 Cape Gannet (*Morus capensis*)
South Africa 352 372

16-3 Australian Gannet (*Morus serrator*)
New Zealand 769

16-4 Blue-footed Booby (*Sula nebouxii*)
Ecuador 1524 1530 1688

16-5 Peruvian Booby (*Sula variegata*)
Peru 1196

16-6 Abbott's Booby (*Sula abbotti*)
Christmas Island 98 167

16-7 Blue-faced Booby (*Sula dactylatra*)
Ascension 77 207
Brazil 2169 2170
British Indian Ocean Territory 70
British Virgin Islands 576 O32
Ecuador 1525 1686
French Polynesia 457
Grenada 926
Kiribati 166
New Caledonia 562
Norfolk Island 282

16-8 Red-footed Booby (*Sula sula*)
Ascension 81 83 208 214
British Honduras 209 221 234
Cayman Islands 102 109
Christmas Island 161
Cocos (Keeling) Islands 132
Ecuador 1687
Grenadines of Grenada 352
Grenadines of St. Vincent 120
Kiribati 258
Maldive Islands MS879
Marshall Islands 104
Montserrat 242
New Caledonia 563
Pitcairn Islands 42 75
Seychelles 468
Wallis and Futuna Islands 295
Zil Elwannyen Sesel 82

16-9 Brown Booby (*Sula leucogaster*)
Aitutaki 338 450
Anguilla 669
Antigua **MS**1085b
Ascension 70 210 214
Bahamas 591
British Indian Ocean Territory 67
British Virgin Islands 439
Cayman Islands 595
Christmas Island 160
Cocos (Keeling) Islands 20
Dominica 665
Fiji 712

Grenada 1014
Kiribati 172 O26
Maldive Islands **MS**879
Marshall Islands 39
Montserrat 603 725 O65
New Caledonia 561
Wallis and Futuna Islands 296

17 CORMORANTS
17-1 Double-crested Cormorant (*Phalacrocorax auritus*)
Antigua 927
Barbuda 797
St. Pierre et Miquelon 539

17-4 Common Cormorant (*Phalacrocorax carbo*)
Austria 1218
Germany (East Germany) E432
Hungary 1574
Isle of Man 235
Maldive Islands 1085
Monaco 511a
Poland 1203
Qatar 349 609

17-5 White-breasted Cormorant (*Phalacrocorax lucidus*)
Senegal 732 **MS**733
South West Africa 331 396

17-10 Japanese Cormorant (*Phalacrocorax capillatus*)
Japan 669 808

17-12 Shag (*Phalacrocorax aristotelis*)
Ifni 81 82 83
Isle of Man 237
Jersey 132

17-14 Red-faced Cormorant (*Phalacrocorax urile*)
Russia 4025

17-16 Guanay Cormorant (*Phalacrocorax bougainvillei*)
Peru 504 586 616 785 785a 834 873 1196

17-22 Kerguelen Cormorant (*Phalacrocorax verrucosus*)
French Southern and Antarctic Territories 11 102 130

17-25 Blue-eyed Cormorant (*Phalacrocorax atriceps*)
Argentine Republic 1005 **MS**1687
Chile 1067
Libya 857
South Georgia and South Sandwich Islands 162

17-27 King Cormorant (*Phalacrocorax albiventer*)
Australian Antarctic Territory 56
Falkland Islands 205

17-28 Little Pied Cormorant (*Halietor melanoleucos*)
Solomon Islands 533

17-29 Reed Cormorant (*Halietor africanus*)
Mauritania 186
Rwanda 106

18 ANHINGAS
18-1 African Darter (*Anhinga rufa*)
Burundi 132 138 143 223 228 233 1319 1328
Central African Republic 18
Chad 65
Congo (Brazzaville) 3
French Equatorial Africa 276
Gabon 165
Rwanda 106 665
Senegal 378

18-4   American Anhinga (*Anhinga anhinga*)
Gambia 582
Guinea 1180
Mauritania **MS**826
Panama 944
United States of America 2083

19   FRIGATE BIRDS
19-1   Ascension Frigate Bird (*Fregata aquila*)
Ascension 76 82 213 214

19-2   Christmas Island Frigate Bird (*Fregata andrewsi*)
Christmas Island 19 78 162

19-3   Magnificent Frigate Bird (*Fregata magnificens*)
Anguilla 142 237 661
Antigua 950
Barbados 625
Barbuda 197 227 228 832
Brazil 2169
British Honduras 211
British Virgin Islands 161 173 294 440
Cayman Islands 387 576 627
Dominica 1047
Grenada 320 516 606 1015
Grenadines of Grenada 14
Maldive Islands 1195
Montserrat 244 370 O4
St. Kitts 53
St. Lucia 820
St. Vincent 398
Turks and Caicos Islands 382

19-4   Great Frigate Bird (*Fregata minor*)
Aitutaki 339 451
British Indian Ocean Territory 29
Cocos (Keeling) Islands 19
French Polynesia 333
Gilbert and Ellice Islands 43 64 76
Gilbert Islands 70
Kiribati 178 237
Nauru 51 73 87 108 111 184 187
New Caledonia 586 587
Pitcairn Islands 39 72
Solomon Islands 97 98 99 233a 263 264 300 320

19-5   Lesser Frigate Bird (*Fregata ariel*)
British Indian Ocean Territory 73
Fiji 711
Maldive Islands 702
Marshall Islands 106
Solomon Islands 119 142
Tuvalu 84

20   HERONS, BITTERNS
20-1   Eurasian Bittern (*Botaurus stellaris*)
Bulgaria 2931
Germany (East Germany) E423

20-3   American Bittern (*Botaurus lentiginosus*)
Grenadines of Grenada 738

20-5   Least Bittern (*Ixobrychus exilis*)
British Virgin Islands 566 O22

20-6   Little Bittern (*Ixobrychus minutus*)
Libya 690

20-7   Chinese Little Bittern (*Ixobrychus sinensis*)
Seychelles 523 524 525 526 527

20-12   Black Bittern (*Ixobrychus flavicollis*)
Singapore 468

20-15   Rufescent Tiger Heron (*Tigrisoma lineatum*)
Surinam 1249

20-22   White-backed Night Heron (*Gorsachius leuconotus*)
Kenya 303

20-23   Black-crowned Night Heron (*Nycticorax nycticorax*)
Cayman Islands 523
Cuba 1292d
Czechoslovakia 1185
Grenadines of Grenada 737
Hungary 3341
Montserrat 613
Vietnam 655
Zaire 1240

20-24   Rufous Night Heron (*Nycticorax caledonicus*)
Cocos (Keeling) Islands 133
Solomon Islands 535

20-25   Yellow-crowned Night Heron (*Nycticorax violaceus*)
Anguilla 274 350 421 436 666
Barbuda 509 785
Bermuda 491
British Virgin Islands 561 O17
Dominica 1015
Rumania 4938
St. Kitts 58

20-26   Boat-billed Heron (*Cochlearius cochlearius*)
Belize 488

20-28   Squacco Heron (*Ardeola ralloides*)
Bulgaria 2930
Hungary 1580

20-34   Cattle Egret (*Bubulcus ibis*)
Barbados 626
Biafra 16
Botswana 521
British Virgin Islands 577 O33
Bulgaria 2932
Cameroun 859
Cape Juby 130 137
Central African Republic 972
Czechoslovakia 2308
Gambia 195 217
Grenadines of St. Vincent 119
Kampuchea 508
Liberia 1242
Malagasy Republic **MS**607
Maldive Islands 708
Montserrat 507 600 O62
Niger 297 377 715
Nigeria 185
Russia 4545
Rwanda 101
St. Kitts 65 O17
Southern Rhodesia 72
Spanish Morocco 269 276
Uganda 481
Upper Volta 499
Vietnam N708
Yugoslavia 2010

20-36   Green Heron (*Butorides striatus*)
Anguilla 675 719 760
Barbados 627
Botswana 422 497
British Indian Ocean Territory 72
British Virgin Islands 572 O28
Comoro Islands 96
Dominica 525 1040
Gambia 583

Grenadines of St. Vincent 3
Maldive Islands **MS**711
Montserrat 608 727 O70
St. Vincent 286a 855
Seychelles 442

20-40   Little Blue Heron (*Egretta caerulea*)
British Virgin Islands 574 O30
Maldive Islands 1192
Montserrat 253
Nevis 267
St. Lucia 416
Turks and Caicos Islands 385

20-41   Louisiana Heron (*Egretta tricolor*)
Cayman Islands 519
Colombia 1485
Grenadines of Grenada 736
United States of America 2083

20-42   Reddish Egret (*Egretta rufescens*)
Bahamas 590
Dominica **MS**943

20-43   Eastern Reef Heron (*Egretta sacra*)
Aitutaki 331 490
Christmas Island 152
Cocos (Keeling) Islands 18
Fiji 374 393
French Polynesia 379
Gilbert and Ellice Islands 83
Gilbert Islands 27
Kiribati 127 171
Nauru 178
Tuvalu 82
Vietnam N281 **MS**N282a
Wallis and Futuna Islands 294

20-45   Snowy Egret (*Egretta thula*)
Cayman Islands 592
Grenada 1480
Grenadines of Grenada **MS**301
Uruguay 1369
Venezuela 1695

20-46   Western Reef Heron (*Egretta gularis*)
British Indian Ocean Territory 39
Liberia 563 636
Yemen 318 368
Zil Elwannyen Sesel 61 107

20-47   Little Egret (*Egretta garzetta*)
Albania 678
Bulgaria 1833
Cape Verde Islands 512
France 2065
Hungary 1575
Liberia 568 569 597 598 607 608 644 646
Ryukyu Islands 103
Senegal 548

20-48   Intermediate Egret (*Egretta intermedia*)
Upper Volta 540

20-49   Great Egret (*Egretta alba*)
Barbuda 520
Bermuda 492
Brazil 2083 2091
Bulgaria 2933
Chad 336
Comoro Islands 94 276
Dubai 315
Ecuador 1197
Equatorial Guinea 68

French West Africa 55
Fujeira 5 14 43 89 98 127 O52 O162
Gabon 432
Hungary 1234 1577 **MS**3346
Liberia 229 O242
Mauritania 266
Montserrat 245
New Zealand 806
Niue 628
Rumania 2553 3601 4567
Russia 3610
Somalia 339 491
Togo 213 235
Zaire 1238

20-50   Purple Heron (*Ardea purpurea*)
Cameroun 969
Congo (Brazzaville) 617
Czechoslovakia 1634
Greece 1475
Hungary 1576 3085
Iraq 1257 O1262
Israel 252
Kuwait 603
Malawi 322
Upper Volta 327
Vietnam 652

20-53   Grey Heron (*Ardea cinerea*)
Albania 677
Austria 1220
British Indian Ocean Territory 69
Cambodia 164
Chad 535
Czechoslovakia 1188 2677 2815
France 2421
Germany (East Germany) E422
Hungary 1579
Iraq 1257 O1262
Isle of Man 238
Khmer Republic 347 355
Korea (North Korea) N651
Lebanon 320 321 322 323 324
Malawi 370 371 372 373
Maldive Islands 706
Mauritania D187
Poland 1488
Senegal 660 662
Spanish Sahara 157 160 163
Swaziland 245
Vietnam 649

20-54   Great Blue Heron (*Ardea herodias*)
Anguilla 417
Antigua 926
Barbados 786
Barbuda 796
Canada 1189
Cuba 779
Dominica 1014
Grenadines of Grenada 350
Guinea-Bissau 922
Nevis 268
United States of America 949 1895
Venezuela 2054

20-55   Cocoi Heron (*Ardea cocoi*)
Bolivia 354 355
Surinam 689
Uruguay 1364

20-56   Black-headed Heron (*Ardea melanocephala*)
Botswana 423
Swaziland 240

20-58   Goliath Heron (*Ardea goliath*)
Angola 829
French Territory of the Afars and the Issas 651
Mali 96
Rwanda 662

21   WHALE-HEADED STORK
21-1   Whale-headed Stork (*Balaeniceps rex*)
Burundi 1183 1207
Congo (Kinshasa) 472
Germany (East Germany) E1339
Rwanda 1274
Sudan 124 262 O68
Uganda 119

22   HAMMERKOP
22-1   Hammerkop (*Scopus umbretta*)
Botswana 526
French Territory of the Afars and the Issas 652
Ivory Coast 264
Yemen 321 R72

23   STORKS
23-1   American Wood Stork (*Mycteria americana*)
Anguilla 651
Brazil 2091 2092
Ivory Coast 841

23-3   Yellow-billed Stork (*Mycteria ibis*)
Botswana 523
Burundi 130 136 146 226 236 1325 1334
Ivory Coast 268
Mauritania 525

23-4   Painted Stork (*Mycteria leucocephala*)
India 800
Vietnam 650

23-5   Asian Open-bill Stork (*Anastomus oscitans*)
Thailand 569
Vietnam 656

23-6   African Open-bill Stork (*Anastomus lamelligerus*)
Angola 464
Congo (Kinshasa) 470

23-7   Black Stork (*Ciconia nigra*)
Bulgaria 2934
Czechoslovakia 1637
Germany (East Germany) E433
Korea (South Korea) 1258
Mauritania D186
Poland 1204
Russia 3729
Spain 2193
Vietnam 651

23-8   Abdim's Stork (*Ciconia abdimii*)
Congo (Kinshasa) 471
Venda 74
Zaire 1028

23-11   White Stork (*Ciconia ciconia*)
Afghanistan 886
Ajman 7 16 61 105 114 123 O70 O132
Albania 933
Algeria 290 292 374 755
Belgium 2295
Cape Juby 96 102
Cuba 1559b
Denmark 607
France 2003 2281

French Morocco 157
French Post Offices in Tangier 38
Gabon 675
Germany (West Berlin) B684
Hungary 1225 2346 3084
Ifni 161 164 167
Iraq 798 1520 1522 O1178
Japan 932
Mauritania 520 D188
Monaco 739
Poland 2023 2252
Rumania 4352
Russia 5240
Somalia 334 352
Spanish Morocco 204 210 355 420
Spanish Sahara 143 144 145
Umm Al Qiwain 7 8 9 16 17 18 40 41 42 86 87 88 95 96 97
       104 105 106 O55 O56 O57 O113 O114 O115
Venda 91
Vietnam **MS**687

23-13   Saddle-bill Stork (*Ephippiorhynchus senegalensis*)
Biafra 9
Botswana 427
Burundi 139 147 229 237 1326 1335
Chad 794
Congo (Brazzaville) 534
Congo (Kinshasa) 481
Ivory Coast 665d
Malawi 321
Mozambique 862
Niger 102 103
Nigeria 178 225
Rwanda 663
Senegal 754
Somalia 335
Tanzania 345
Uganda 381

23-14   Jabiru (*Jabiru mycteria*)
Belize 560 **MS**566 577
Brazil 2085
Venezuela 2054

23-16   Greater Adjutant Stork (*Leptoptilos dubius*)
Vietnam N711

23-17   Marabou Stork (*Leptoptilos crumeniferus*)
Belgian Congo 226
Botswana 412
Burundi 1179 1203
Chad 796
Congo (Kinshasa) 473
Mauritania 526
Mozambique 861
Niger 673
Rwanda 98
Somalia 338
Upper Volta 728

24   IBISES, SPOONBILLS
24-1   Sacred Ibis (*Threskiornis aethiopicus*)
British Indian Ocean Territory 31 45 46 78
Cameroun 263
Congo (Kinshasa) 479
Ethiopia 811
French Somali Coast 444
Mauritania 525
Rwanda 666
Seychelles 264
Singapore 193
Somalia 336
Uganda 117
Zil Elwannyen Sesel 64

24-4   Straw-necked Ibis (*Carphibis spinicollis*)
Australia 369 397

24-8   Waldrapp (*Geronticus eremita*)
Algeria 829
Jersey 219
Morocco 426
Turkey 2572
Yemen 325 D372

24-9   Bald Ibis (*Geronticus calvus*)
Lesotho 205
Swaziland 448 449 450 451 452

24-10   Japanese Crested Ibis (*Nipponia nippon*)
China (People's Republic) 3311 3312 3313
Japan 827 1634

24-13   Hadada Ibis (*Hagedashia hagedash*)
Ciskei 12

24-14   Wattled Ibis (*Bostrychia carunculata*)
Ethiopia 675

24-22   White Ibis (*Eudocimus albus*)
Grenadines of Grenada 646

24-23   Scarlet Ibis (*Eudocimus ruber*)
Brazil 1478
Colombia 1485
Congo (Brazzaville) 986
Grenada MS929
Surinam 1250
Tanzania 466
Trinidad and Tobago 292 304 350 551 563 564 565 566 567
   587
Venezuela 1696 2054

24-24   Glossy Ibis (*Plegadis falcinellus*)
Bulgaria 1837
Grenadines of Grenada 739
Hungary 1233 1581
Lesotho 651
Montserrat 607 724 O69
Rumania 3310
Russia 3613
Turks and Caicos Islands MS597

24-27   Crested Wood Ibis (*Lophotibis cristata*)
Malagasy Republic 66

24-28   White Spoonbill (*Platalea leucorodia*)
Bulgaria 1836
Djibouti Republic 920
Guinea 352 357 362
Hungary 1578 3083
Mauritania 875
Rumania 2554
Russia 3613
Senegal 546
Turkey 2569
Yugoslavia 1519

24-29   Black-faced Spoonbill (*Platalea minor*)
Korea (North Korea) N396
Korea (South Korea) 1257
Vietnam 654

24-30   African Spoonbill (*Platalea alba*)
Angola 831
Djibouti Republic 701 747
French Territory of the Afars and the Issas 654
Mauritania 147

24-33   Roseate Spoonbill (*Ajaia ajaja*)
Bahamas 429
Brazil 2084 2092
Tanzania 467

25   FLAMINGOS
25-1   Greater Flamingo (*Phoenicopterus ruber*)
Afghanistan 631
Argentine Republic 1899
Bahamas 145 160 170 251 276 298 352 368 617 618 619 620
   621 686 687 688 689 705
Burundi 1186 1210
Colombia 1509
Congo (Kinshasa) 474
Cuba 1558
Cyprus 679
Czechoslovakia 2356
Djibouti Republic 847
Dominica MS874
Dominican Republic 1309 1579
France 1871
French Somali Coast 440
French Territory of the Afars and the Issas 608 609 610
Germany (East Germany) E288
Grenada 548 1481
Guinea-Bissau 923
Haiti 539 545
Hong Kong 391
Iran 1653
Japan 1660
Laos 903
Libya 1193
Malawi 653
Mauritania 146 714
Mexico 1549
Netherlands Antilles 372 384 386 388 396 467 553 873 874
   875 876
Niger 1022
Portugal 1889
Qatar 351 611
Russia 2787
Rwanda MS668
Senegal 549 550 661
Sierra Leone 800
Singapore 130 193
Somalia 433
South West Africa 176 178 330
Spanish Sahara 260
Surinam 690
Tunisia 605 638
Turkey 2553 2571
Turks and Caicos Islands 236 245 457
Upper Volta 701
Zil Elwannyen Sesel 68

25-2   Chilian Flamingo (*Phoenicopterus chilensis*)
Argentine Republic 1294
Peru 1189

25-3   Lesser Flamingo (*Phoeniconaias minor*)
Burundi 150 240 1321 1330
Kenya, Uganda and Tanganyika 225

25-5   James's Flamingo (*Phoenicoparrus jamesi*)
Chile 1019
Ecuador 1884

26   SCREAMERS
26-2   Crested Screamer (*Chauna torquata*)
Argentine Republic 1415
Uruguay 1292

27   DUCKS, GEESE, SWANS

27-7   White-faced Whistling Duck (*Dendrocygna viduata*)
Argentine Republic 1264
Botswana 421
Gambia 234
Liberia 1587
Malawi 484
Uruguay 1366
Venda 152

27-8   Black-billed Whistling Duck (*Dendrocygna arborea*)
Bahamas 592
Cayman Islands 384 628
Cuba 1796

27-9   Red-billed Whistling Duck (*Dendrocygna autumnalis*)
Grenadines of Grenada 297
Mexico 1704
Venezuela 1756 2054

27-10   Mute Swan (*Cygnus olor*)
Australia **MS**945
Austria 2030 2094
Belgium 2762
Bulgaria 2455
China (People's Republic) 3283 3284
Denmark 292 829
Finland 563
Germany (West Germany) 1616
Great Britain 1046
Guernsey 322
Isle of Man 247
Italy 1910
Japan 1227 Lesotho **MS**604
Mali 620
Mongolia 769
Nicaragua 1575 2088
Poland 2864
Rumania 3311 3598 4285
Russia 2063d 2546 **MS**4129 5465
Sweden 257a
Western Australia 1 3 4c 15 18 25 26 28 39 42 50 56 57 61 67
77 90 103 104 105

27-11   Black Swan (*Cygnus atratus*)
Australia 116 277
Christmas Island 90
Cuba 1561d
Rumania 3198
Western Australia 91a 95 96a 97 98 99 100 102 107 110a 113
114 116 138 140 141 142 143 144 145 146 168 172

27-12   Black-necked Swan (*Cygnus melanocoryphus*)
Falkland Islands 147a 150a 207
Falkland Islands Dependencies A3 B3 C3 D3

27-13   Whooper Swan (*Cygnus cygnus*)
Albania 1767
Bhutan 630
China (People's Republic) 3286
Denmark 407 408
Finland 565 566
Iceland 344 345
Norway 462 463
Sweden 376 377

27-14   Whistling Swan (*Cygnus columbianus*)
China 1344 1345 1346 1347
China (People's Republic) ECP383 ECP384 ECP385 ECP386
ECP387ECP388 ECP403 ECP404 ECP405 ECP406 1450
1451 1452 1453 1453a 1454 1455 1455a 1767 1768 3285
China (Taiwan) 100 101 102 103 104 129 130 131 132 148 149
150
Korea (North Korea) N400
Korea (South Korea) 1267

27-15   Coscoroba Swan (*Coscoroba coscoroba*)
Jersey 328

27-17   Bean Goose (*Anser fabalis*)
China 105 106 107 131 132 133 204 205 232
China (Taiwan) 588 589 590 591 592 593 594 595 596
643**MS**644 709 710 711
Japan 61
Korea (North Korea) N1307
Tibet C10 C11
Upper Volta 452

27-18   White-fronted Goose (*Anser albifrons*)
Afghanistan 775
Albania 1763
Ireland 444
Japan 429 446
Maldive Islands **MS**1200b
Rumania 3308

27-19   Lesser White-fronted Goose (*Anser erythropus*)
Norway 869

27-20   Greylag Goose (*Anser anser*)
Afghanistan 775
Belgium 2293
Czechoslovakia 1189
Germany (East Germany) E1080
Hungary 2353 3340
Tunisia 1118

27-21   Bar-headed Goose (*Anser indicus*)
Mongolia 766
Russia 5238

27-22   Snow Goose (*Anser caerulescens*)
Canada 1190
Japan 429 446
Russia 2785

27-25   Hawaiian Goose (*Branta sandvicensis*)
United States of America 1940

27-26   Canada Goose (*Branta canadensis*)
Canada 407 443 539 O10 O29 O32
Dominica **MS**1017
Grenada 1482
Japan 1725
United States of America **MS**1726 2083

27-27   Barnacle Goose (*Branta leucopsis*)
Netherlands 1404
Norway 914
Poland 2757
Russia 4027

27-28   Brent Goose (*Branta bernicla*)
Grenada **MS**1484
Japan 556
Jersey 131

27-29   Red-breasted Goose (*Branta ruficollis*)
Egypt 913
Germany (East Germany) E2663
Rumania 3980 4568
Russia 2784

27-30   Cereopsis Goose (*Cereopsis novaehollandiae*)
Christmas Island 89

27-32   Blue-winged Goose (*Cyanochen cyanopterus*)
Ethiopia 673

27-34   Magellan Goose (*Chloephaga picta*)
Falkland Islands 152 154 174 189 197 318
Falkland Islands Dependencies A5 B5 C5 D5

27-35   Kelp Goose (*Chloephaga hybrida*)
Falkland Islands 181 204

27-39   Egyptian Goose (*Alopochen aegyptiacus*)
Cuba 1561b
Lesotho 512
Liberia 1587
Venda 154

27-40   Ruddy Shelduck (*Tadorna ferruginea*)
Afghanistan 775
Bulgaria 2456
Iran 1652
Korea (North Korea) N655
Mongolia 1237
Morocco 292
Spanish Sahara 259

27-44   Common Shelduck (*Tadorna tadorna*)
Bulgaria 2457
Iran 1651
Isle of Man 242
Mongolia 764
Rumania 2704 3600

27-48   Falkland Islands Flightless Steamer Duck (*Tachyeres brachypterus*)
Falkland Islands 198

27-49   Spur-winged Goose (*Plectropterus gambensis*)
Gambia 242
Ivory Coast 262
Malawi 478
Mozambique 836
Rwanda 903
Sierra Leone 625 814 815
Togo 1912
Upper Volta 393
Venda 153

27-50   Muscovy Duck (*Cairina moschata*)
Belize 471
Korea (North Korea) N1901
Mexico 1703

27-51   White-winged Wood Duck (*Cairina scutulata*)
Bangladesh 207
India 1154

27-52   Comb Duck (*Sarkidiornis melanotos*)
Botswana 231
Malawi 480
Senegal 380
Venda 151

27-53   Hartlaub's Duck (*Pteronetta hartlaubii*)
Congo (Kinshasa) 476
Rwanda 667
Sierra Leone 633

27-56   African Pygmy Goose (*Nettapus auritus*)
Benin 730
Botswana 520
Dahomey 250 379
Malawi 482 514

27-58   Wood Duck (*Aix sponsa*)
Burkina Faso 789
Central African Republic 1079
Cuba 772 951 1292b

Gambia 584
United States of America 1347

27-59   Mandarin (*Aix galericulata*)
China (Taiwan) 1524
Cuba 1561c
Japan 657 1366 1478
Korea (North Korea) N268a N1906
Korea (South Korea) 621 1365
Mongolia 209
Russia 3850

27-62   Mountain Duck (*Hymenolaimus malacorhynchus*)
New Zealand 1289

27-63   Torrent Duck (*Merganetta armata*)
Chile 381x 382x 383x

27-66   European Wigeon (*Anas penelope*)
Albania 1761

27-67   American Wigeon (*Anas americana*)
Antigua 993
Barbuda 503

27-69   Falcated Teal (*Anas falcata*)
Vietnam N706

27-71   Baikal Teal (*Anas formosa*)
Korea (North Korea) N657

27-72   Green-winged Teal (*Anas crecca*)
China (Taiwan) 361
France 1511
Poland 3011

27-73   Chilean Teal (*Anas flavirostris*)
Falkland Islands 203

27-75   Grey Teal (*Anas gibberifrons*)
New Zealand 776

27-78   New Zealand Teal (*Anas aucklandica*)
New Zealand 1291

27-79   Mallard (*Anas platyrhynchos*)
Albania 945 1179
Andorra F368
Antigua 990
Bhutan 624
Bulgaria 2459 3308
Congo (Brazzaville) 616
Czechoslovakia 1190
Fernando Poo 268 271 274
Germany (East Germany) E1079
Haiti 540 546
Hungary 1452 2018
Ireland 560
Jordan 829
Kiribati 164
Korea (North Korea) N656
Macao 597
Mongolia 768
Norway 857
Poland 1876 1968 2756
Portugal 1631
Rumania 3307 4941
Russia 2060
Rwanda 903
San Marino 566
Switzerland J236
Tanzania 464
United States of America **MS**1726 2089
Yugoslavia 879

27-80   North American Black Duck (*Anas rubripes*)
Antigua 991

27-82   African Yellow-bill (*Anas undulata*)
Ethiopia 674

27-83   Spotbill Duck (*Anas poecilorhyncha*)
Aitutaki 337 449
Korea (North Korea) N654
Solomon Islands 534

27-87   Pintail (*Anas acuta*)
Aitutaki 340 452
Albania 1764
Antigua 992
Barbuda 512
French Southern and Antarctic Territories 172 173
Iceland 674
Portugal 2026
Rumania 2433 2484
St. Pierre et Miquelon 540

27-88   Georgian Teal (*Anas georgica*)
South Georgia and South Sandwich Islands 168

27-89   Bahama Pintail (*Anas bahamensis*)
Bahamas 589

27-90   Red-billed Pintail (*Anas erythrorhyncha*)
Botswana 524
Lesotho 506

27-93   Garganey (*Anas querquedula*)
Bulgaria 2458
Hungary 3089
Malawi 483
Mauritania D180
Poland 3012

27-94   Blue-winged Teal (*Anas discors*)
Barbuda 514
Cuba 1292a
Grenadines of Grenada 645
St. Pierre et Miquelon 425
Turks and Caicos Islands 596

27-99   Common Shoveler (*Anas clypeata*)
Albania 1768
Cuba 1292c
Czechoslovakia 1633
Dominica 1016
Hungary 3342
Kiribati 168
Mauritania D184
Poland 1490

27-101   Marbled Teal (*Marmaronetta angustirostris*)
Iraq 800

27-103   Red-crested Pochard (*Netta rufina*)
Albania 1762
Bulgaria 2460
Poland 3016
Portugal 1888
Spain 2196

27-107   European Pochard (*Aythya ferina*)
Bulgaria 3307

27-109   Ring-necked Duck (*Aythya collaris*)
Dominica 942

27-112   Ferruginous Duck (*Aythya nyroca*)
Yugoslavia 1731

27-115   Tufted Duck (*Aythya fuligula*)
Aland Islands 26
Czechoslovakia 1638
Poland 3013
Uganda 483

27-116   Greater Scaup (*Aythya marila*)
Mongolia 770

27-118   Eider (*Somateria mollissima*)
Aland Islands 25
Albania 1766
Antigua **MS**994
Greenland 16 25
Iceland 369 370
Netherlands 1403
Poland 3015
St. Pierre et Miquelon 422
Sweden 1272
Tanzania 465

27-119   King Eider (*Somateria spectabilis*)
Greenland 130
Grenadines of Grenada **MS**740

27-120   Spectacled Eider (*Somateria fischeri*)
Russia 4028

27-122   Harlequin Duck (*Histrionicus histrionicus*)
Iceland 555
Penrhyn Island 373 **MS**377a

27-123   Long-tailed Duck (*Clangula hyemalis*)
Russia 4418
St. Pierre et Miquelon 507 510

27-124   Common Scoter (*Melanitta nigra*)
Zaire 1239

27-125   Surf Scoter (*Melanitta perspicillata*)
Zaire 1241

27-126   Velvet Scoter (*Melanitta fusca*)
Aland Islands 27
Ivory Coast 842

27-129   Goldeneye (*Bucephala clangula*)
Bhutan 631
Poland 3014

27-130   Hooded Merganser (*Mergus cucullatus*)
Bhutan 629

27-131   Smew (*Mergus albellus*)
Grenada 1483

27-132   Brazilian Merganser (*Mergus octosetaceus*)
Argentine Republic 1883

27-133   Red-breasted Merganser (*Mergus serrator*)
Albania 1765
Benin 729
Ivory Coast 839
Spain 2518

27-135   Goosander (*Mergus merganser*)
Cuba 777
Maldive Islands 1197

27-139   White-headed Duck (*Oxyura leucocephala*)
Rumania 4288

27-144   White-backed Duck (*Thalassornis leuconotos*)
Liberia 1587

Libya **MS**860
Monaco 981
Mongolia 578 1391
Norway 647
Poland 1206 2433
Rumania 2559
Sweden 760

30-40 Steller's Sea Eagle (*Haliaeetus pelagicus*)
Russia 5236

30-41 Lesser Fishing Eagle (*Ichthyophaga nana*)
Vietnam 481

30-43 Palm-nut Vulture (*Gypohierax angolensis*)
Angola 828
Gambia 203 225
Ghana 166 167 168 169 193 196 197 198 199 200
Liberia 356 382 541 552 O369
Togo 261 325

30-44 Egyptian Vulture (*Neophron percnopterus*)
Albania 1089
Libya 1197
Mali 95
Rumania 3445 4286
South West Africa 273

30-45 Lammergeier (*Gypaetus barbatus*)
Algeria 832
Bulgaria 1240
Ethiopia 541
France 2624
Germany (East Germany) E866
Hungary 1856
Lesotho 204 677 680 682 683
Liechtenstein 181 182
Mongolia 992
Rumania 2707 3448
Russia 3006 3223
Swaziland 425 426 427 428 429
Trieste B125
Yugoslavia 771 1445 2197

30-46 Hooded Vulture (*Necrosyrtes monachus*)
Rwanda 836

30-48 African White-backed Vulture (*Gyps africanus*)
Burundi 623 647 678
Upper Volta 728

30-50 Ruppell's Griffon (*Gyps rueppellii*)
Belgian Congo 226
Cameroun 1022
Mali 1076
Mauritania D177
Somalia 438
Upper Volta 539

30-52 Griffon Vulture (*Gyps fulvus*)
Albania 1086
Cyprus (Turkish Cypriot Posts) **MS**187
French Somali Coast 458
Israel 947
Kampuchea 454
Mongolia 991
Rumania 3447

30-53 Cape Vulture (*Gyps coprotheres*)
Botswana 531

30-54 Lappet-faced Vulture (*Torgos tracheliotus*)
Ethiopia 1151
Israel 944
Spanish Sahara 315

30-55 European Black Vulture (*Aegypius monachus*)
Afghanistan 629
Bulgaria 1813
Korea (North Korea) N822
Korea (South Korea) 1266
Mongolia 994
Rumania 3449

30-56 White-headed Vulture (*Aegypius occipitalis*)
Zaire 1142

30-58 Short-toed Eagle (*Circaetus gallicus*)
France 2625
French Indian Settlements 283
Poland 1208
Vietnam 484

30-62 Bateleur (*Terathopius ecaudatus*)
Angola 460
Ethiopia 536
Guinea 353 358 363
Italian East Africa 25 29
Malawi 320
Mali 11 18
Rhodesia 449
Rwanda 840
Senegal 381
Somalia 437
South Africa 363
Uganda 380
Yemen 327 D374
Zimbabwe 649

30-65 Crested Serpent Eagle (*Spilornis cheela*)
Burma 181 202 O190 O202 O213
China (Taiwan) 622
Japan 1730 **MS**1768

30-70 African Harrier Hawk (*Polyboroides typus*)
Gambia 402
Rwanda 834

30-74 Marsh Harrier (*Circus aeruginosus*)
Hungary 1853
Mongolia 993

30-77 Hen Harrier (*Circus cyaneus*)
Isle of Man 318
Turks and Caicos Islands 594
Tuvalu 308

30-79 Pallid Harrier (*Circus macrourus*)
Turkey 2210

30-80 Montagu's Harrier (*Circus pygargus*)
Germany (West Germany) 1651
Togo 545 547 549

30-83 Dark Chanting Goshawk (*Melierax metabates*)
Angola 458
Mauritania 187
Morocco 470

30-85 Gabar Goshawk (*Melierax gabar*)
Botswana 425

30-86 Doria's Goshawk (*Megatriorchis doriae*)
Papua New Guinea 502 503

30-88 Northern Goshawk (*Accipiter gentilis*)
Abu Dhabi 51
Germany (West Berlin) B430
Germany (East Germany) E869
Japan 63

Liechtenstein 180
Mongolia 577
Netherlands 1184

30-101 New Britain Sparrow Hawk (*Accipiter brachyurus*)
Papua New Guinea 500 501

30-102 European Sparrow Hawk (*Accipiter nisus*)
Albania 1087
France 2626
Germany (West Berlin) B432
Spanish Sahara 158 161 164
Turkey 2211

30-103 Rufous-breasted Sparrow Hawk (*Accipiter rufiventris*)
Cameroun 968

30-104 Sharp-shinned Hawk (*Accipiter striatus*)
Bhutan **MS**632

30-113 Australian Goshawk (*Accipiter fasciatus*)
Christmas Island 166

30-126 Shikra (*Accipiter badius*)
Angola 467

30-131 Gundlach's Hawk (*Accipiter gundlachii*)
Cuba 774 1815b 2305

30-139 Grey-faced Buzzard-Eagle (*Butastur indicus*)
China (Taiwan) 1505

30-140 Lizard Buzzard (*Kaupifalco monogrammicus*)
Gambia 401
Ivory Coast 267
Zaire 1140

30-148 White Hawk (*Leucopternis albicollis*)
Belize 457

30-151 Common Black Hawk (*Buteogallus anthracinus*)
Grenadines of St. Vincent 11 496
St. Vincent 294

30-164 Red-shouldered Hawk (*Buteo lineatus*)
Comoro Islands 552
Guinea 1181
St. Vincent 860

30-165 Broad-winged Hawk (*Buteo platypterus*)
Dominica 526 941 1037
Grenada 927
Grenadines of St. Vincent 125
Nevis 265
Tuvalu 307

30-168 Galapagos Hawk (*Buteo galapagoensis*)
Ecuador 1690

30-170 Red-backed Buzzard (*Buteo polyosoma*)
Falkland Islands 385

30-175 Red-tailed Hawk (*Buteo jamaicensis*)
Congo (Brazzaville) 987
Nevis 266

30-176 Common Buzzard (*Buteo buteo*)
Austria 1219
Germany (West Germany) 1649
Germany (East Germany) E867
Hungary 3513
Liechtenstein 179
Mongolia 575

Russia 3217
Turkey 2212

30-179 Rough-legged Buzzard (*Buteo lagopus*)
Burkina Faso 794
Hungary 3512

30-180 Long-legged Buzzard (*Buteo rufinus*)
Libya 335

30-184 Augur Buzzard (*Buteo rufofuscus*)
Botswana 532
Rwanda 837

30-186 Harpy Eagle (*Harpia harpyja*)
Brazil 1215
Costa Rica 1209
Germany (East Germany) E2662
Guyana 491 672 687 791 992 1037 1044 1238 1239 1240a
     1546 O17
Surinam 1291

30-187 New Guinea Harpy Eagle (*Harpyopsis novaeguineae*)
Papua New Guinea 272

30-188 Philippine Eagle (*Pithecophaga jefferyi*)
Philippines 1047 1708

30-190 Lesser Spotted Eagle (*Aquila pomarina*)
Afghanistan 774
Hungary 3507

30-192 Tawny Eagle (*Aquila rapax*)
Algeria 831
French Territory of the Afars and the Issas 509
Liberia 565 573 594 602 604 612 648
Mongolia 996
Russia 3219
Senegal 756
Spanish Sahara 137
Venda 72
Zaire 1173

30-193 Imperial Eagle (*Aquila heliaca*)
Hungary 2348 3508
Mongolia 1527
Spain 2195
Turkey 2209

30-196 Golden Eagle (*Aquila chrysaetos*)
Afghanistan 693
Albania 728 730 749 1084
Andorra F238
Austria 580 581 582 583 584 585 586 1221
Czechoslovakia 1522
Finland 762 935
Germany 526 527 528 529 530 531 532 533 534
Germany (West Berlin) B433
Germany (East Germany) E870
Hungary 1857
Ifni 213 215
Italy 867
Japan 1237
Kampuchea 463
Liechtenstein 145 146 147 149 257
Mexico 454 455 456 519 520 O492 O490 O531 O553
Monaco 1564
Mongolia 120 245 365 926 995 1483
Niger 733
Poland 1207
Portugal 1799
Rumania 2705 3602 4964
Russia 3222
San Marino 1121

Spanish Sahara 136 138 175
Sweden 571
Togo 1820
Trieste 291
Tripolitania 162
Tunisia 963

30-198   Verreaux's Eagle (*Aquila verreauxii*)
Burundi 1193 1217
Lesotho **MS**685
South West Africa 271
Swaziland 247
Zimbabwe 650

30-199   Bonelli's Eagle (*Hieraaetus fasciatus*)
Israel 945
Libya 699
Zimbabwe 652

30-200   Booted Eagle (*Hieraaetus pennatus*)
Hungary 1854
Korea (North Korea) N823

30-205   Long-crested Eagle (*Lophaetus occipitalis*)
Ethiopia 1152
Gambia 403
Mauritania 527
Rwanda 833
Zimbabwe 648

30-206   Cassin's Hawk Eagle (*Spizaetus africanus*)
Upper Volta 543

30-215   Ornate Hawk Eagle (*Spizaetus ornatus*)
Belize 564 581
El Salvador 1666
Jordan 628

30-216   Crowned Eagle (*Stephanoaetus coronatus*)
Gabon 173
Rwanda 963

30-218   Martial Eagle (*Polemaetus bellicosus*)
Botswana 426
Burundi 149 239 1324 1333
Cameroun 967
Mauritania 527
Somaliland Protectorate 143 147
South West Africa 272
Zimbabwe 651

31   SECRETARY BIRD
31-1   Secretary Bird (*Sagittarius serpentarius*)
Angola 480
Botswana 224
Burundi 129 135 142 222 225 232 534 535 1196 1220
Chad 797 **MS**798
Congo (Brazzaville) 118
Congo (Kinshasa) 477
Ethiopia 1153
Ghana 358
Guinea-Bissau 556
Mozambique 1048
South Africa 249
Swaziland 98 151
Tanzania 343

32   FALCONS, CARACARAS
32-1   Yellow-throated Caracara (*Daptrius ater*)
French Guiana 241

32-6   Forster's Caracara (*Phalcoboenus australis*)
Falkland Islands 384

32-7   Common Caracara (*Polyborus plancus*)
Chile 381o 382o 383o
Cuba 780 784 910
Falkland Islands 206 386
St. Vincent 861

32-9   Yellow-headed Caracara (*Milvago chimachima*)
Argentine Republic 560 562 563 569 570 587 625
Paraguay 427 428 428a

32-10   Laughing Falcon (*Herpetotheres cachinnans*)
Belize 492

32-18   Fieldens Falconet (*Polihierax insignis*)
Vietnam 482

32-23   Pied Falconet (*Microhierax melanoleucus*)
Vietnam 478

32-24   Lesser Kestrel (*Falco naumanni*)
Germany (East Germany) E2216
Poland 2341 2342

32-25   Greater Kestrel (*Falco rupicoloides*)
Lesotho 500

32-27   American Kestrel (*Falco sparverius*)
Anguilla 280 349 403 426
British Virgin Islands 569 591 O25
Cuba 1890
Grenadines of St. Vincent 495
Kuwait 601
Montserrat 243 611 728 O73
Netherlands Antilles 368
St. Kitts 69 127 O21
St. Lucia 421
Venezuela 1755

32-28   Common Kestrel (*Falco tinnunculus*)
Albania 1090
Belgium 2296
Germany (East Germany) E868
Hungary 1858
Mongolia 580
Poland 2346 2493
Russia 3218
San Marino 565 1270
Turkey 2208
Vietnam 477

32-30   Mauritius Kestrel (*Falco punctatus*)
Mauritius 324 356 560 678 679 680 681

32-31   Seychelles Kestrel (*Falco araea*)
Seychelles 313 463 464 465 466 467
Zil Elwannyen Sesel 66

32-33   Australian Kestrel (*Falco cenchroides*)
Christmas Island 164

32-37   Red-footed Falcon (*Falco vespertinus*)
Dubai 312
Hungary 1231 2349 3510
Poland 2343 2344

32-39   Merlin (*Falco columbarius*)
Grenada **MS**1382
Iceland 675
Poland 2347

32-41   New Zealand Falcon (*Falco novaezeelandiae*)
New Zealand 807 1290

32-42   European Hobby (*Falco subbuteo*)
Poland 2345

32-46   Eleonora's Falcon (*Falco eleonorae*)
Cyprus 339
Greece 1477
Morocco 378

32-47   Sooty Falcon (*Falco concolor*)
Israel 946

32-52   Lanner Falcon (*Falco biarmicus*)
Abu Dhabi 35
Ajman 9 18 63 107 116 125 O72 O134
Bahrain 148 272 278
Botswana 522
Dubai 257 258 259 260 261 262
Ethiopia 1155
Fujeira 9 18 47 93 102 131 O56 O166
Libya 1190
Manama 4
Spanish Sahara 293

32-55   Saker Falcon (*Falco cherrug*)
Abu Dhabi 12 13 14
Hungary 3511
Kuwait 286 287 288 289 290 291 292 293 606
Qatar 613
Rumania 3444
Saudi Arabia 1022 1023 1024 1025
United Arab Emirates 198 199 200

32-56   Gyrfalcon (*Falco rusticolus*)
Bahrain 271 275 276 277
Greenland 93
Hungary 2586
Iceland 166 173 372 682 O182 O189
Nicaragua 1829
Russia 3224
Sweden 1067

32-58   Taita Falcon (*Falco fasciinucha*)
Zambia 494

32-60   Peregrine Falcon (*Falco peregrinus*)
Afghanistan 1066
Aitutaki 322 480 O21
Bahrain 273 274
Barbados 784
Belgium 2905
Canada 906
Congo (Brazzaville) 643
Czechoslovakia 378 379
Dubai 19 21 23 25
Falkland Islands 387
France 2627
Germany (West Berlin) B431
Germany (East Germany) E437 E993
Grenadines of St. Vincent 497
Iraq 797
Ireland 445
Isle of Man 145 188
Japan 1743 **MS**1768
Libya 1192
Maldive Islands 1198
Malta 797
Mongolia 579
Morocco 544
Niue 632
Norway 870
Pakistan 691
Poland 2348
Qatar 31 32 38 43 145 146 250 318 398
Russia 3221

South West Africa 270
Sweden 756
Switzerland J235
Syria 1372
Vanuatu 402 403 404 405
Yugoslavia 1297

33   MEGAPODES
33-1   Common Scrub Hen (*Megapodius freycinet*)
Solomon Islands 70

33-3   Polynesian Scrub Hen (*Megapodius pritchardii*)
Niuafo'ou 31 35 39 41 45 77 81

34   CURASSOWS, GUANS
34-4   Rufous-vented Chachalaca (*Ortalis ruficauda*)
Trinidad and Tobago 341 382
Venezuela 1758

34-18   Spix's Guan (*Penelope jacquacu*)
Guyana 490 1250

34-18a   White-winged Guan (*Penelope albipennis*)
Peru 1657

34-25   Black-fronted Piping Guan (*Aburria jacutinga*)
Argentine Republic 1884

34-29   Highland Guan (*Penelopina nigra*)
El Salvador 1644

34-37   Great Curassow (*Crax rubra*)
British Honduras 202 217 230
El Salvador 1191

34-40   Black Curassow (*Crax alector*)
Surinam 946

35   PHEASANTS, GROUSE
35-1   Common Turkey (*Meleagris gallopavo*)
Korea (North Korea) N1903
Mexico 1548
Rwanda 908
United States of America 1079

35-2   Ocellated Turkey (*Agriocharis ocellata*)
Belize 456
Guatemala 1124
Nicaragua 2690

35-4   Spruce Grouse (*Dendragapus canadensis*)
Bhutan 628
Canada 1192

35-6   Willow
Red Grouse (*Lagopus lagopus*)
Bhutan 625
Newfoundland 74
United States of America 1931

35-7   Rock Ptarmigan (*Lagopus mutus*)
Andorra F294
Iceland 419 420 445
Japan 930
Monaco 1563
St. Pierre et Miquelon 423
Uganda 494
Yugoslavia 1521

35-9   Georgian Black Grouse (*Tetrao mlokosiewiczi*)
Iran 1856

35-10   Black Grouse (*Tetrao tetrix*)
Austria 1805
Germany (West Germany) 1386
Germany (West Berlin) B263
Germany (East Germany) E435
Liechtenstein 284
Monaco 1560
Poland 1973
Rumania 2706
Russia 2058

35-11   Siberian Capercaillie (*Tetrao parvirostris*)
Mongolia 206

35-12   Capercaillie (*Tetrao urogallus*)
Albania 751 942
Andorra F229
Austria 1338 1944
Bulgaria 1236
Finland 500
Germany (West Germany) 1387
Germany (West Berlin) B264
Liechtenstein 254
Poland 1975 2235
Rumania 2431 2482 4927 **MS**5020a
Russia 4436
Senegal 681
Sweden 848
Switzerland J221
Tuva 53
Yugoslavia 880 1863

35-14   Hazel Grouse (*Bonasa bonasia*)
Bulgaria 1241
Russia 2063c

35-15   Ruffed Grouse (*Bonasa umbellus*)
United States of America 1898 1967

35-16   Sage Grouse (*Centrocercus urophasianus*)
Penrhyn Island 374 **MS**377b
Uganda 495

35-18   Prairie Chicken (*Tympanuchus cupido*)
Canada 977
Maldive Islands 1199

35-24   California Quail (*Lophortyx californica*)
Norfolk Island 175
United States of America 1934

35-28   Bobwhite (*Colinus virginianus*)
Cuba 778 1799
Yugoslavia 1294

35-32   Marbled Wood Quail (*Odontophorus gujanensis*)
Venezuela 2053

35-53   Sand Partridge (*Ammoperdix heyi*)
Jordan 824

35-54   Caucasian Snowcock (*Tetraogallus caucasicus*)
Russia 4184

35-58   Himalayan Snowcock (*Tetraogallus himalayensis*)
Afghanistan 753

35-61   Rock Partridge (*Alectoris graeca*)
Bulgaria 1144 1683
Christmas Island 84
Greece 1153
Monaco 1561
Yugoslavia 885 1861

35-62   Chukar Partridge (*Alectoris chukar*)
Afghanistan 723 1067
Bulgaria 3306
Iran 1705
Jordan 822
St. Helena 395
Syria 1375
United States of America 1448

35-65   Barbary Partridge (*Alectoris barbara*)
Gibraltar 170
Libya 340 1202
Tunisia 606

35-66   Red-legged Partridge (*Alectoris rufa*)
Ifni 159
Lebanon 870
Mauritania D190
San Marino 597
Spain 2097

35-67   Arabian Chukar (*Alectoris melanocephala*)
Oman 267
Yemen 319 369
Yemen People's Democratic Republic 102 103

35-69   Black Partridge (*Francolinus francolinus*)
Cyprus 524
Iraq 799
Pakistan 394 395
Turkey 2679

35-71   Chinese Francolin (*Francolinus pintadeanus*)
Vietnam N277

35-72   Bare-throated Francolin (*Francolinus afer*)
Ascension 209
Malawi 476
Mozambique 834

35-77   Pale-bellied Francolin (*Francolinus ochropectus*)
French Territory of the Afars and the Issas 577

35-81   Cameroun Mountain Francolin (*Francolinus camerunensis*)
Cameroun 941 1071

35-84   Scaly Francolin (*Francolinus squamatus*)
Central African Republic 229

35-86   Double-spurred Francolin (*Francolinus bicalcaratus*)
Gambia 202 224
Morocco 404
Nigeria 487

35-92   Harwood's Francolin (*Francolinus harwoodi*)
Ethiopia 1305

35-96   Ring-necked Francolin (*Francolinus streptophorus*)
Fernando Poo 267 270 273

35-104   White-throated Francolin (*Francolinus albogularis*)
Senegal 755

35-105   Schlegel's Francolin (*Francolinus schlegelii*)
Central African Republic 804

35-106   Latham's Francolin (*Francolinus lathami*)
Ivory Coast 269 560
Liberia 1307

35-110   Grey Partridge (*Perdix perdix*)
Albania 750
Bulgaria 1143 1684

Czechoslovakia 890
Germany (East Germany) E1078
Great Britain 1049
Guernsey 316
Hungary 2036
Laos **MS**937
Poland 1974 3032
Rumania 4922
Russia 2057a

35-116   Common Quail (*Coturnix coturnix*)
Afghanistan 692
Albania 938
Rumania 3303

35-117   Japanese Quail (*Coturnix japonica*)
China (Taiwan) 1118
Korea (North Korea) N1997

35-119   Harlequin Quail (*Coturnix delegorguei*)
Malawi 477

35-122   Blue Quail (*Excalfactoria adansonii*)
Malawi 475
Sierra Leone 766

35-148   Crested Wood Partridge (*Rollulus roulroul*)
Brunei 352
Malaysia 20 48
North Borneo 405
Sabah 422

35-149   Stone Partridge (*Ptilopachus petrosus*)
Ivory Coast 263

35-154   Ceylon Spurfowl (*Galloperdix bicalcarata*)
Sri Lanka 687

35-157   Western Tragopan (*Tragopan melanocephalus*)
India 765
Pakistan 572 573

35-158   Satyr Tragopan (*Tragopan satyra*)
Bhutan 231
Nepal 133

35-160   Temminck's Tragopan (*Tragopan temminckii*)
Korea (North Korea) N1526
Vietnam 281

35-162   Koklass Pheasant (*Pucrasia macrolopha*)
Pakistan 495

35-163   Himalayan Monal Pheasant (*Lophophorus
impeyanus*)
Afghanistan 545 751
Bhutan 258 446
Hungary 3101
India 766
Nepal 131 132 225 386 455
Pakistan 493

35-164   Sclater's Monal Pheasant (*Lophophorus sclateri*)
Bhutan 214

35-166   Red Junglefowl (*Gallus gallus*)
Iran 1655
Korea (North Korea) N1385
Sharjah 102 105

35-167   Ceylon Junglefowl (*Gallus lafayettei*)
Ceylon 494

35-170   Kalij Pheasant (*Lophura leucomelana*)
Bhutan 232
Burma 184 205 O205 O216
Pakistan 494

35-171   Silver Pheasant (*Lophura nycthemera*)
Korea (North Korea) N1524
Laos 909
Vietnam 284

35-173   Edwards's Pheasant (*Lophura edwardsi*)
Vietnam 283

35-174   Swinhoe's Pheasant (*Lophura swinhoii*)
China (Taiwan) 1264

35-177   Crested Fireback Pheasant (*Lophura ignita*)
Malaysia 323

35-178   Siamese Fireback Pheasant (*Lophura diardi*)
Thailand 565
Vietnam N280 280

35-179   Bulwer's Pheasant (*Lophura bulweri*)
Malaysia 325

35-180   White Eared-Pheasant (*Crossoptilon crossoptilon*)
Bhutan 259
Germany (East Germany) E2245
Jersey 57

35-183   Cheer Pheasant (*Catreus wallichii*)
Nepal 350
Pakistan 496 538

35-186   Mikado Pheasant (*Syrmaticus mikado*)
China (Taiwan) 623

35-187   Copper Pheasant (*Syrmaticus soemmerringi*)
Japan 864 1235 1509
Laos 914

35-188   Reeves's Pheasant (*Syrmaticus reevesii*)
Korea (North Korea) N1525
Laos 912

35-189   Ring-necked Pheasant (*Phasianus colchicus*)
Afghanistan 694 1064
Albania 944
Bulgaria 1238 1682
China (Taiwan) 716 717
Cuba 1797
Czechoslovakia 1495 1967
Dubai 310
Germany (West Germany) 1385
Germany (West Berlin) B262
Germany (East Germany) E1077 E1987
Hungary 2034
Iran 1571
Ivory Coast 559
Korea (North Korea) N206 N1527 **MS**N1528
Korea (South Korea) 623
Laos 910
Mongolia 172
Nicaragua 2686
Poland 1969 3034
Rio Muni 66 68
Rumania 2427 2478
St. Helena 395
San Marino 600
United States of America 1970
Vietnam 282
Yugoslavia 881

35-190   Japanese Pheasant (*Phasianus versicolor*)
China (Taiwan) 1527
Japan 575 576 577 578 579

35-191   Golden Pheasant (*Chrysolophus pictus*)
Argentine Republic 1422
China (People's Republic) 2847 2848 2849
Colombia 1372
Cuba 1559a
Korea (North Korea) N1383 N1522
Laos 913
Russia 3611

35-192   Lady Amherst's Pheasant (*Chrysolophus amherstiae*)
Korea (North Korea) N1523
Laos 911

35-195   Germain's Peacock-Pheasant (*Polyplectron
            germaini*)
Vietnam 285

35-196   Burmese Peacock-Pheasant (*Polyplectron
            bicalcaratum*)
Bhutan 189 194 199 220 240
Hungary 3102

35-197   Malay Peacock-Pheasant (*Polyplectron malacense*)
Malaysia 324

35-199   Rheinard's Pheasant (*Rheinartia ocellata*)
Vietnam 286

35-201   Great Argus Pheasant (*Argusianus argus*)
Brunei 352
Hungary 3100
Labuan 65a 86 92 102 114 127 D4
Laos 908
Malaysia 25 326
North Borneo 72 100 112a 131a 146 D4 D19 D39

35-202   Common Peafowl (*Pavo cristatus*)
Bangladesh 236
Ceylon 488
Hungary 3097
India 703
Jaipur 44
Pakistan 411 412
Russia 4231
Tunisia 938

35-203   Green Peafowl (*Pavo muticus*)
Burma 185 206 O206 O217
China (Taiwan) 938
Hungary 2596 3098
Japan 1411
Rwanda 361
Vietnam 287

35-204   Congo Peafowl (*Afropavo congensis*)
Belgium 1821
Burundi 131 137 144 227 234 1322 1331
Congo (Kinshasa) 475
Hungary 3099

35-206   White-breasted Guineafowl (*Agelastes meleagrides*)
Ivory Coast 265

35-207   Helmet Guineafowl (*Numida meleagris*)
Botswana 530
Cape Verde Islands 516
Central African Republic 229
Cuba 1795
Guinea 277 278 279 280 281 282 305 306 307 308 309 310
Korea (North Korea) N531

Malawi 481 536
Nicaragua 2688
Rhodesia 371 386
Rio Muni 58
Rwanda 463
Southern Rhodesia 104
Upper Volta 622
Yemen People's Democratic Republic 103
Zambia 227

35-208   Plumed Guineafowl (*Guttera plumifera*)
Central African Republic 803

35-209   Crested Guineafowl (*Guttera edouardi*)
Congo (Kinshasa) 469

35-211   Vulturine Guineafowl (*Acryllium vulturinum*)
Burundi 1200 1224
Guinea 745 749
Korea (North Korea) N1905
Mauritania D185
Somalia 440

36   HOATZIN
36-1   Hoatzin (*Opisthocomus hoatzin*)
Guyana 492 673

38   BUTTON QUAILS
38-1   Little Button Quail (*Turnix sylvatica*)
Solomon Islands 270 288 308

38-14   Quail Plover (*Ortyxelos meiffrenii*)
Kenya 304

40   CRANES
40-1   Common Crane (*Grus grus*)
Afghanistan 776
Armenia 187 188
Austria 620 622 626 628 631 632 633 634 635
Finland 501
Germany (East Germany) E992
Hungary 3087
Malawi 671
Mauritania D178
Rumania 3309
Sweden 543 966
Vietnam 653
Yugoslavia 887

40-3   Hooded Crane (*Grus monacha*)
Korea (North Korea) N648
Russia 5235

40-5   Manchurian Crane (*Grus japonensis*)
China (Manchuria) 127 128
China (People's Republic) 2029 2030 2031 3301 3302
            MS3303 3342 3347
China (Taiwan) 468 719
Japan 715 811 866 1034 1066 1343 1344 1381 1493 1608
Korea (North Korea) N650
Korea (South Korea) 116 140a 148 622 1065 1269 1367 1453
            1599
Korea (North Korean Occupation of South Korea) 1
Liberia 1095
Monaco 972 974
Russia 3450
Sweden 1266
Upper Volta 303

40-6   Whooping Crane (*Grus americana*)
Canada 479
Uganda **MS**498
United States of America 1100

40-7   Japanese White-necked Crane (*Grus vipio*)
Japan 1608
Korea (North Korea) N649
Korea (South Korea) 1223

40-8   Sarus Crane (*Grus antigone*)
Bangladesh 235
Burma 182 203 O203 O214
Thailand 567

40-10   Great White Crane (*Grus leucogeranus*)
China (People's Republic) 3450 3451 3452 **MS**3453
India 1076
Pakistan 605
Russia 2786

40-11   Wattled Crane (*Bugeranus carunculatus*)
Botswana 541
Malawi 759 760 761 762

40-12   Demoiselle Crane (*Anthropoides virgo*)
India 733
Mongolia 1235
Turkey 1848 2681

40-13   Stanley Crane (*Anthropoides paradisea*)
Ciskei 9
South Africa 362

40-14   Crowned Crane (*Balearica pavonina*)
Biafra 12
Cameroun 600 787
Congo (Brazzaville) 536
Cuba 1559c
Gambia 384
Ghana 227 393 454
Guinea 349 354 359
Niger 100 101 734
Nigeria 181 228
Portuguese Guinea 305
Rumania 3200
Rwanda 101 **MS**668 1130
Senegal 547
Upper Volta 542
Zaire 1046

40-15   South African Crowned Crane (*Balearica regulorum*)
Angola 832
Bulgaria 1814
Burundi 141 231 534 535
Congo (Brazzaville) 117
Congo (Kinshasa) 480
Gabon 909
Ivory Coast 665c
Kenya, Uganda and Tanganyika 110 114 122 131a 139b 143
  149b
Lesotho 502
Mali 75 76 381
Mauritania 265 592
Mozambique 833
Russia 5412
Rwanda 1015
Singapore 260
Togo 272 273 274 275
Transkei 77
Uganda 111 112 126 298 317
Zaire 1179 1184
Zambia 136

43   RAILS, COOTS
43-4   White-throated Rail (*Canirallus cuvieri*)
British Indian Ocean Territory 40 45 46
Zil Elwannyen Sesel 59 80

43-10   Giant Wood Rail (*Eulabeornis ypecaha*)
Kuwait 599

43-13   Grey-necked Wood Rail (*Eulabeornis cajaneus*)
Belize 489

43-25   Banded Rail (*Rallus philippensis*)
Aitutaki 343 455
Cocos (Keeling) Islands 14 134
Niuafo'ou 30 34 36 76 80

43-26   Blue-breasted Banded Rail (*Rallus striatus*)
Singapore 467

43-32   Water Rail (*Rallus aquaticus*)
Mauritania 591
Yugoslavia 883

43-34   Clapper Rail (*Rallus longirostris*)
British Virgin Islands 568 O24
Dominica 939
Grenada 1378

43-36a   Okinawa Rail (*Rallus okinawae*)
Japan 1713

43-37   Inaccessible Island Rail (*Atlantisia rogersi*)
Tristan Da Cunha 26 265 315 316 317 318 424

43-38   Weka Rail (*Gallirallus australis*)
New Zealand 840

43-39   Rouget's Rail (*Rougetius rougetii*)
Ethiopia 1306

43-40   Zapata Rail (*Cyanolimnas cerverai*)
Cuba 2219

43-52   White-spotted Crake (*Coturnicops pulchra*)
Rwanda 958

43-53   Chestnut-headed Crake (*Coturnicops lugens*)
Zambia 487

43-76   Black Crake (*Porzana flavirostra*)
Sierra Leone 632 818
Zaire 1141

43-86   Henderson Island Crake (*Porzana atra*)
Pitcairn Islands 44 77

43-90   Spotted Crake (*Porzana porzana*)
Kuwait 600

43-99   Water Cock (*Gallicrex cinerea*)
Korea (North Korea) N1384
Vietnam N709

43-104   Gough Island Coot (*Gallinula nesiotis comeri*)
Tristan Da Cunha 425

43-106   Moorhen (*Gallinula chloropus*)
Barbados 638
Cape Verde Islands 515
Congo (Brazzaville) 763
Dominica 1041
Great Britain 1111
Grenadines of Grenada 648
Montserrat 602 O64
Penrhyn Island 111
St. Helena 465
St. Lucia 423
Seychelles 568
Singapore 470

43-110   Allen's Gallinule (*Gallinula alleni*)
Comoro Islands 99 271 339

43-111   Purple Gallinule (*Gallinula martinica*)
Barbuda 267
Colombia 1424
Grenadines of St. Vincent 124
Surinam 1248

43-112   Purple Swamphen (*Porphyrio porphyrio*)
Aitutaki 327 486 O27
Burundi 127 133 221 1323 1332
Morocco 471
New Caledonia 777
Niuafo'ou 27 33 40 75
Portugal 2027
Russia 3609
Samoa 285 305
Vietnam N710

43-113   Takahe (*Porphyrio mantelli*)
New Zealand 754

43-114   Red-gartered Coot (*Fulica armillata*)
Chile 381q 382q 383q

43-117   Giant Coot (*Fulica gigantea*)
Chile 1020

43-121   Common Coot (*Fulica atra*)
Afghanistan 776
Germany (West Germany) 1966
Russia 4547
Yugoslavia 882

44   SUNGREBES
44-1   Peters's Finfoot (*Podica senegalensis*)
Senegal 545

44-3   American Finfoot (*Heliornis fulica*)
Belize 470

45   KAGU
45-1   Kagu (*Rhynochetos jubatus*)
New Caledonia 85 86 87 88 112 114 113 90 124 125 107 109
   110 111 267 268 269 270 271 272 273 274 275 276 277 278
   279 280 291 292 293 294 295 296 297 298 306 307 308 358
   408 682 744 745 746 747 748 749 750 751 767
New Hebrides F1 F2 F6 F7
Wallis and Futuna Islands 1 2 3 4 18 5 19 6 29 30 31 32

48   BUSTARDS
48-1   Little Bustard (*Tetrax tetrax*)
Yugoslavia 1517

48-2   Great Bustard (*Otis tarda*)
Austria 1942
Bulgaria 1239
French Somali Coast 448
Hungary 1230 2041 2351 2588 3086
Iran 1854
Korea (South Korea) 1224
Mali 1074
Poland 1201 2492
Rumania 2424 2475 3603 4928
Spain 1465 2094
Turkey 2680
Yugoslavia 884

48-3   Barrow's Bustard (*Neotis cafra*)
Angola 468
Bophuthatswana 115

Malawi 479 535
Sierra Leone 635 819

48-8   Arabian Bustard (*Choriotis arabs*)
Mauritania D192
Niger 842

48-9   Kori Bustard (*Choriotis kori*)
Bophuthatswana 112
Mozambique 863
South West Africa 74 O13 O23
Tanzania 344
Upper Volta 702
Zaire 1178

48-10   Great Indian Bustard (*Choriotis nigriceps*)
India 986

48-12   Houbara Bustard (*Chlamydotis undulata*)
Algeria 830
Israel 250
Jordan 827
Kuwait 597
Libya 338
Morocco 293
Spanish Sahara 177 179 181 183 185
Tunisia 608

48-14   Crested Bustard (*Lophotis ruficrista*)
Bophuthatswana 114

48-15   Little Black Bustard (*Afrotis afra*)
Bophuthatswana 113
Botswana 411

48-20   Blue Bustard (*Eupodotis caerulescens*)
Lesotho 207

49   JACANAS
49-2   African Jacana (*Actophilornis africana*)
Botswana 415
Liberia 739 1587
Rwanda 664
Senegal 377
Uganda 114

49-4   Comb-crested Jacana (*Irediparra gallinacea*)
Australia 680

49-5   Pheasant-tailed Jacana (*Hydrophasianus chirurgus*)
China (Taiwan) 1136

49-7   Northern Jacana (*Jacana spinosa*)
British Honduras 204 218 231
Cuba 781 785 794

49-8   Wattled Jacana (*Jacana jacana*)
British Guiana 319 333
Colombia 1421
Guyana 395 983 985 1288
Uruguay 1368

50   PAINTED SNIPES
50-1   Painted Snipe (*Rostratula benghalensis*)
Lesotho 208

51   CRAB PLOVER
51-1   Crab Plover (*Dromas ardeola*)
Maldive Islands 179 182 187 703

52   OYSTERCATCHERS
52-1   Oystercatcher (*Haematopus ostralegus*)
Australia 677
Benin 996
Ecuador 1526
Faroe Islands 28
French Territory of the Afars and the Issas 505
Guernsey (Alderney) A13
Isle of Man 243
Korea (South Korea) 1252
Netherlands 908
Norway 856
Turks and Caicos Islands 349 **MS**833

52-5   Magellanic Oystercatcher (*Haematopus leucopodus*)
Falkland Islands 202

54   AVOCETS, STILTS
54-1   Black-winged Stilt (*Himantopus himantopus*)
Ghana 471 552
Hungary 1228 3345
Israel 616
Italy 1884
Portugal 1890
Rumania 2552 3599

54-3   Black-tailed Stilt (*Himantopus melanurus*)
Chile 1002
Uruguay 1367

54-4   Black-necked Stilt (*Himantopus mexicanus*)
Anguilla 38
Antigua 669
Bahamas 687 688
Barbuda 539
Niger 1021
Venezuela 1754 1845

54-7   New Zealand Stilt (*Himantopus novaezelandiae*)
New Zealand 777

54-8   South African Stilt (*Himantopus meridionalis*)
Botswana 527

54-10   Avocet (*Recurvirostra avosetta*)
Czechoslovakia 1636
Denmark 615
Hungary 1224
Netherlands 910
Sweden 960

54-12   Red-necked Avocet (*Recurvirostra novaehollandiae*)
Australia 392

55   STONE-CURLEWS
55-1   Stone-Curlew (*Burhinus oedicnemus*)
Kuwait 584

55-4   Cape Dikkop (*Burhinus capensis*)
Ciskei 17

56   COURSERS, PRATINCOLES
56-2   Cream-coloured Courser (*Cursorius cursor*)
Libya 1204
Spanish Sahara 292
Tunisia 603

56-4   Temminck's Courser (*Cursorius temminckii*)
Zaire 1137

56-10   Pratincole (*Glareola pratincola*)
Israel 614

57   PLOVERS
57-1   Lapwing (*Vanellus vanellus*)
Belgium 2294
Czechoslovakia 1187
Denmark 830
France 1510
Hungary 1788 2189
Liechtenstein 633
Mongolia 875
Netherlands 911 1435
Poland 1484
Rumania 2650
San Marino 684

57-3   Spur-winged Plover (*Vanellus spinosus*)
Israel 615
Liberia 1587
Nigeria 485

57-10   Crowned Plover (*Vanellus coronatus*)
Botswana 419

57-11   Senegal Wattled Plover (*Vanellus senegallus*)
Botswana 529
Rhodesia 464

57-14   Sociable Plover (*Vanellus gregarius*)
Russia 5239

57-17   Chilian Lapwing (*Vanellus chilensis*)
Argentine Republic 1165
Uruguay 422 423 429 430 431 432 453 454 456 457 458 459
   460 461 462 463 464 465 466 477 528 529 537 538 539 540
   1639 O439 O440 O441 O442 O443 O444 O445 O446 O499
   O500 O501 O502 O503 O504 O593 O594

57-20   Red-wattled Lapwing (*Vanellus indicus*)
Vietnam N707

57-23   Masked Plover (*Vanellus miles*)
Australia 676

57-24   Blacksmith Plover (*Anitibyx armatus*)
Botswana 528

57-25   Golden Plover (*Pluvialis apricaria*)
Germany (West Germany) 1793
Iceland 599

57-26   American Golden Plover (*Pluvialis dominica*)
Aitutaki 335 447
Barbados 633a
French Polynesia 380
Kiribati 170
Micronesia 41
United States of America 2077

57-27   Grey Plover (*Pluvialis squatarola*)
Brazil 2171
Micronesia 42

57-29   Ringed Plover (*Charadrius hiaticula*)
Guernsey (Alderney) A15
Iceland 444

57-30   Semipalmated Plover (*Charadrius semipalmatus*)
Grenadines of Grenada 295
St. Pierre et Miquelon 424

57-34   Killdeer (*Charadrius vociferus*)
Bahamas 708 711
Barbuda 265
Grenada 924

57-38   St. Helena Sand Plover (*Charadrius sanctaehelenae*)
St. Helena 158 289 290 312 443

57-39   Three-banded Plover (*Charadrius tricollaris*)
Zaire 1136

57-40   Kentish Plover (*Charadrius alexandrinus*)
Hungary 1227
Qatar 608

57-42   Snowy Plover (*Charadrius occidentalis*)
Barbuda 504

57-45   Chestnut-banded Sand Plover (*Charadrius venustus*)
South West Africa 332

57-46   Collared Plover (*Charadrius collaris*)
Grenadines of Grenada **MS**353
Grenadines of St. Vincent 118

57-54   Mountain Plover (*Charadrius montanus*)
Bhutan 626

57-57   Hooded Plover (*Charadrius rubricollis*)
Australia 671

57-62   Dotterel (*Eudromias morinellus*)
Czechoslovakia 1519

58   SANDPIPERS, SNIPE
58-1   Black-tailed Godwit (*Limosa limosa*)
Czechoslovakia 1632
Netherlands 1438
Poland 1486
Senegal 753

58-3   Bar-tailed Godwit (*Limosa lapponica*)
Senegal 585

58-7   Whimbrel (*Numenius phaeopus*)
Aitutaki 333
Faroe Islands 29
Marshall Islands 40
Sweden 1273

58-8   Bristle-thighed Curlew (*Numenius tahitiensis*)
Kiribati 175 O28

58-10   Curlew (*Numenius arquata*)
Guernsey (Alderney) A17
Liechtenstein 583
Maldive Islands 288 291 876
Netherlands 909

58-12   Long-billed Curlew (*Numenius americanus*)
Belize 828
Grenadines of Grenada 300

58-14   Spotted Redshank (*Tringa erythropus*)
Guernsey 172

58-15   Redshank (*Tringa totanus*)
Isle of Man 246
Maldive Islands 288 291
Netherlands 1437

58-17   Greenshank (*Tringa nebularia*)
French Territory of the Afars and the Issas 506
Lesotho 649

58-18   Spotted Greenshank (*Tringa guttifer*)
Japan 1736

58-20   Lesser Yellowlegs (*Tringa flavipes*)
St. Lucia 822
Uganda 496

58-22   Solitary Sandpiper (*Tringa solitaria*)
Penrhyn Island 375 **MS**377c

58-23   Wood Sandpiper (*Tringa glareola*)
Venda 94

58-29   Wandering Tattler (*Heteroscelus incanus*)
Nauru 186

58-31   Turnstone (*Arenaria interpres*)
Guernsey (Alderney) A14
Micronesia 40
St. Kitts 63 123 O15
Tokelau 58

58-34   Red-necked Phalarope (*Phalaropus lobatus*)
Maldive Islands **MS**1087

58-35   Grey Phalarope (*Phalaropus fulicarius*)
Liberia 1602

58-36   Woodcock (*Scolopax rusticola*)
Bulgaria 3309
Germany (West Germany) 1384
Germany (West Berlin) B261
Ireland 429
Poland 1970
Rumania 3304 3339
Russia 2321
San Marino 595
Yugoslavia 886

58-48   African Snipe (*Gallinago nigripennis*)
Malawi 473

58-50   Great Snipe (*Gallinago media*)
French Territory of the Afars and the Issas 576
Mauritania D183

58-51   Common Snipe (*Gallinago gallinago*)
Faroe Islands 27
Guernsey 257
Rumania 3305
Tunisia 479

58-52   Paraguayan Snipe (*Gallinago paraguaiae*)
Argentine Republic 1989

58-69   Little Stint (*Calidris minuta*)
Mauritania D191

58-75   Pectoral Sandpiper (*Calidris melanotos*)
Marshall Islands 38

58-79   Dunlin (*Calidris alpina*)
Guernsey (Alderney) A16
Penrhyn Island 376 **MS**377d
Portugal 1887

58-81   Spoon-billed Sandpiper (*Eurynorhynchus pygmeus*)
Russia 5237

58-83   Stilt Sandpiper (*Micropalama himantopus*)
Lesotho 650

58-85   Ruff (*Philomachus pugnax*)
Mali 677
Netherlands 1436
Poland 1971
Russia 4433

60   SHEATHBILLS
60-1   Snowy Sheathbill (*Chionis alba*)
Argentine Republic **MS**1687
South Georgia and South Sandwich Islands 163

60-2   Black-faced Sheathbill (*Chionis minor*)
French Southern and Antarctic Territories 6 162

61   SKUAS
61-1   Great Skua (*Catharacta skua*)
Chile 1069
French Southern and Antarctic Territories 3
Mongolia 1320
Ross Dependency 9a
South Georgia and South Sandwich Islands 164
Tristan Da Cunha 229

61-2   McCormick's Skua (*Catharacta maccormicki*)
British Antarctic Territory 143

61-3   Pomarine Skua (*Stercorarius pomarinus*)
Aitutaki 342 454
Kiribati 163

61-4   Arctic Skua (*Stercorarius parasiticus*)
Benin 995

62   GULLS, TERNS
62-2   Magellan Gull (*Gabianus scoresbii*)
Argentine Republic 1169

62-4   Dusky Gull (*Larus fuliginosus*)
Ecuador 1689

62-7   White-eyed Gull (*Larus leucophthalmus*)
Djibouti Republic 919

62-10   Japanese Gull (*Larus crassirostris*)
Japan 1006a 1155

62-11   Audouin's Gull (*Larus audouinii*)
Cyprus 335
Gibraltar 385
Greece 1476
Italy 1549
Spain 2521

62-13   Common Gull (*Larus canus*)
Monaco 275 305

62-15   Herring Gull (*Larus argentatus*)
Cuba 775
Finland 854
France 1013
Gibraltar 533
Guernsey (Alderney) A12
Isle of Man 239
Liechtenstein 178
Monaco 509
Mongolia 855 1144
Netherlands 907
Spanish Sahara 159 162 165
United Nations G141
Yugoslavia 2154

62-17   Lesser Black-backed Gull (*Larus fuscus*)
Dubai 317
Isle of Man 234
Liberia 567 572 596 601 606 611 645 647
Sweden 806

62-18   California Gull (*Larus californicus*)
United States of America 1973

62-19   Western Gull (*Larus occidentalis*)
United States of America 1409

62-20   Southern Black-backed Gull (*Larus dominicanus*)
Falkland Islands 194
French Southern and Antarctic Territories 210
South Georgia and South Sandwich Islands 161
South West Africa 396

62-21   Slaty-backed Gull (*Larus schistisagus*)
China (Taiwan) 321

62-22   Great Black-backed Gull (*Larus marinus*)
Isle of Man 241
Kuwait 602
Sweden 569
Yugoslavia 2152

62-24   Glaucous Gull (*Larus hyperboreus*)
St. Pierre et Miquelon 86 87 88 89 90 91 92 112 113 114 115
   116 117 118 119 120 127 128 129 246

62-26   Great Black-headed Gull (*Larus ichthyaetus*)
Albania 1590

62-27   Laughing Gull (*Larus atricilla*)
Anguilla 668
Antigua 1080
Montserrat 606 O68
St. Lucia 415

62-29   Grey-headed Gull (*Larus cirrocephalus*)
Botswana 519
Madagascar and Dependencies 326
Senegal 729 **MS**733

62-32   Silver Gull (*Larus novaehollandiae*)
Cocos (Keeling) Islands 154
New Zealand 822

62-33   Mediterranean Gull (*Larus melanocephalus*)
Ifni 101 104 107
Russia 4029
San Marino 564
Trieste B13 B32

62-36   Brown-hooded Gull (*Larus maculipennis*)
Uruguay 1365

62-37   Black-headed Gull (*Larus ridibundus*)
Ajman 8 17 62 106 115 124 O71 O133
Albania 1589
Austria 1217
Czechoslovakia 848 1434
Great Britain 696
Grenada 922
Hungary 1590
Liechtenstein 177
Rumania 2558
Sweden 928
Yugoslavia 2153

62-38   Slender-billed Gull (*Larus genei*)
Albania 1591
Mauritania 148
Russia 4549
San Marino 1095 1096
Senegal 730 **MS**733

62-39   Bonaparte's Gull (*Larus philadelphia*)
Mauritania 826
Togo 1821
United States of America 1453 1454

62-40   Little Gull (*Larus minutus*)
Poland 1489

62-42   Ross's Gull (*Rhodostethia rosea*)
Russia 4026

62-43   Kittiwake (*Rissa tridactyla*)
Iceland 630
Isle of Man 236
Portugal 2024
St. Pierre et Miquelon 531

62-48   White-winged Black Tern (*Chlidonias leucoptera*)
Albania 1588
Hungary 3343

62-51   Gull-billed Tern (*Gelochelidon nilotica*)
Senegal 730 **MS**733

62-52   Caspian Tern (*Hydroprogne caspia*)
Finland 502
Maldive Islands 878
Qatar 394
St. Pierre et Miquelon 531
Senegal 658 729 **MS**733

62-54   South American Tern (*Sterna hirundinacea*)
Falkland Islands 492

62-55   Common Tern (*Sterna hirundo*)
Albania 1587
Bulgaria 1835
Jersey 129
Yugoslavia 2155

62-56   Arctic Tern (*Sterna paradisaea*)
Iceland 500 501
Isle of Man 244
Niger 1024
Sweden 642 643

62-57   Swallow-tailed Tern (*Sterna vittata*)
Chile 1066
French Southern and Antarctic Territories 98
Norfolk Island 176 177 178
Tristan Da Cunha 226

62-61   Roseate Tern (*Sterna dougallii*)
Anguilla 652 672
Antigua **MS**670
Barbuda **MS**540 783
Cuba E673
Monaco 508a

62-63   White-cheeked Tern (*Sterna repressa*)
Qatar 530

62-64   Black-naped Tern (*Sterna sumatrana*)
Maldive Islands 709 1188
New Caledonia 594
Palau 55
Singapore 70a
Tuvalu 309

62-68   Bridled Tern (*Sterna anaethetus*)
Mauritania 876

62-69   Sooty Tern (*Sterna fuscata*)
Antigua 1084
Ascension 28 67 75 206 214 366
Cocos (Keeling) Islands 17 31 48 131
Grenada **MS**1016
Maldive Islands 874
Micronesia 43

New Caledonia 595
Norfolk Island 277
St. Lucia 425
Turks and Caicos Islands 381
Tuvalu 312

62-75   Little Tern (*Sterna albifrons*)
Dubai 316
Yugoslavia 1931

62-77   Crested Tern (*Thalasseus bergii*)
British Indian Ocean Territory 66
Fiji 713
French Polynesia 350

62-78   Royal Tern (*Thalasseus maximus*)
Anguilla 39
Antigua 1083
Barbuda 264
Grenadines of St. Vincent 122
St. Vincent 396
Senegal 658 662

62-83   Sandwich Tern (*Thalasseus sandvicensis*)
Albania 1592
Netherlands 1403

62-86   Common Noddy (*Anoüs stolidus*)
Antigua 1078
Ascension 74 203
Brazil 2168
British Indian Ocean Territory 68
Christmas Island 153
Grenadines of St. Vincent 128
Kiribati 171a
Maldive Islands 875
Micronesia 39
Nauru 110 328 329 330 331
St. Helena 467
St. Lucia 424
Tokelau 60
Turks and Caicos Islands 453

62-88   White-capped Noddy (*Anous minutus*)
Ascension 71 202
Nauru 176 185
Norfolk Island 256
Palau 54
Tokelau 59
Tuvalu 310

62-89   White Tern (*Gygis alba*)
Aitutaki 75 336 448
Ascension 72 200
British Indian Ocean Territory 65
Cocos (Keeling) Islands 6
Cook Islands 11 15a 18a 28 46 166 210 421 496
French Polynesia 331
Kiribati 175a
Maldive Islands 707
Nauru 62 74 88
Norfolk Island 26 62 255 257
Palau 53 163
Pitcairn Islands 40 73
St. Helena 185 196 289 290
Seychelles 280 413 489 500 501 502 503 504 610 623 **MS**650
Tokelau 57
Tristan Da Cunha 64
Tuvalu 83
Wallis and Futuna Islands 297
Zil Elwannyen Sesel 11

63 SKIMMERS
63-1   Black Skimmer (*Rynchops niger*)
Mauritania 828

63-2   African Skimmer (*Rynchops flavirostris*)
Angola 466

64 AUKS
64-1   Little Auk (*Alle alle*)
Norway 915

64-2   Razorbill (*Alca torda*)
Finland 986
Iceland 676
Isle of Man 240
Monaco 1008
Sweden 878

64-3   Brunnich's Guillemot (*Uria lomvia*)
St. Pierre et Miquelon 539

64-4   Common Guillemot (*Uria aalge*)
Faroe Islands 37
Isle of Man 245
Liberia 1093
Portugal 2024
Russia 3376
Sweden 878

64-5   Black Guillemot (*Cepphus grylle*)
Norway 872

64-20   Atlantic Puffin (*Fratercula arctica*)
Faroe Islands 30 34 36
France 1504
Iceland 584
Isle of Man 232
Mongolia 1396
Niger 1023
Norway 871
Rumania 5059
Russia 4548
St. Pierre et Miquelon 508 511 540

65 SANDGROUSE
65-1   Tibetan Sandgrouse (*Syrrhaptes tibetanus*)
Mongolia 208 1139

65-3   Pin-tailed Sandgrouse (*Pterocles alchata*)
Iran 1706
Iraq 1255 O1260
Kuwait 598

65-5   Chestnut-bellied Sandgrouse (*Pterocles exustus*)
Djibouti Republic 942
Niger 251

65-6   Spotted Sandgrouse (*Pterocles senegallus*)
Libya 339

65-7   Black-bellied Sandgrouse (*Pterocles orientalis*)
Algeria 692
Libya 337 1196
Spain 2192

65-13   Lichtenstein's Sandgrouse (*Pterocles lichtensteinii*)
French Territory of the Afars and the Issas 574
Mauritania 185

65-14   Double-banded Sandgrouse (*Pterocles bicinctus*)
Malawi 474

66 DOVES, PIGEONS
66-1   Rock Dove (*Columba livia*)
Aitutaki 328 485 O25
Bulgaria 3154
Ifni 133 135
Kuwait 583 611
San Marino 567
Sharjah 101 104
Spanish Sahara 178 180 182 184
Syria 1373

66-4   Speckled Pigeon (*Columba guinea*)
French Territory of the Afars and the Issas 655
Lesotho 501

66-5   White-collared Pigeon (*Columba albitorques*)
Ethiopia 637

66-6   Stock Dove (*Columba oenas*)
Bulgaria 3155
Ifni 134

66-8   Somali Stock Dove (*Columba oliviae*)
Somaliland Protectorate 142 146

66-9   Wood Pigeon (*Columba palumbus*)
Bulgaria 3156
Germany (East Germany) E1081
Poland 1972

66-10   Trocaz Pigeon (*Columba trocaz*)
Madeira 231

66-17   Comoro Olive Pigeon (*Columba pollenii*)
Comoro Islands 95

66-22   Sri Lanka Wood Pigeon (*Columba torringtoni*)
Sri Lanka 827

66-26   Black Wood Pigeon (*Columba janthina*)
Japan 1735
Korea (South Korea) 1251

66-27   White-throated Pigeon (*Columba vitiensis*)
Fiji 448
New Caledonia 407

66-31   White-crowned Pigeon (*Columba leucocephala*)
Anguilla 11
Bahamas 430
Burkina Faso **MS**795
Cuba 2528
Ghana 1162
St. Kitts-Nevis 139 146

66-32   Red-necked Pigeon (*Columba squamosa*)
Antigua 473
Barbados 631a 633
Barbuda 309 516
British Virgin Islands 565 O21
Dominica 275 1039
Grenada 928
Grenadines of St. Vincent 7
St. Lucia 429
St. Vincent 364

66-38   Chilean Pigeon (*Columba araucana*)
Chile 381c 382c 383c

66-43   Plain Pigeon (*Columba inornata*)
Antigua 667
Barbuda 537
Cuba 773 783 952 2529

66-51   Pink Pigeon (*Columba mayeri*)
Jersey 217
Mauritius 325 357 708 709 710 711

66-52   Turtle Dove (*Streptopelia turtur*)
Bulgaria 3157
Christmas Island 85
Great Britain 1044
Guernsey 317
Iraq 1254 O1259
Libya 1195
Rumania 3306
Turkey 1850

66-55   Eastern Turtle Dove (*Streptopelia orientalis*)
Japan 931 1642

66-56   Javanese Collared Dove (*Streptopelia bitorquata*)
Kampuchea 465

66-58   African Collared Dove (*Streptopelia roseogrisea*)
Mali 635

66-61   Red-eyed Dove (*Streptopelia semitorquata*)
Cameroun 942
Gambia 201 209 223

66-64   Red Turtle Dove (*Streptopelia tranquebarica*)
Dubai 311
Vietnam 406

66-65   Madagascar Turtle Dove (*Streptopelia picturata*)
British Indian Ocean Territory 76
Zil Elwannyen Sesel 63

66-66   Spotted Dove (*Streptopelia chinensis*)
Thailand 566
Vietnam 185

66-67   Laughing Dove (*Streptopelia senegalensis*)
Grenadines of St. Vincent 127
Uganda MS382

66-69   Bar-tailed Cuckoo Dove (*Macropygia unchall*)
Vietnam 407

66-87   Namaqua Dove (*Oena capensis*)
Djibouti Republic 699 763
French Territory of the Afars and the Issas 653
Ivory Coast 266

66-88   Emerald Dove (*Chalcophaps indica*)
Christmas Island 159
New Caledonia 415
Vanuatu 308
Vietnam 410

66-103   Zebra Dove (*Geopelia striata*)
Aitutaki 330 487 O28
Indonesia 1023
Malaysia 24
Zil Elwannyen Sesel 54 100

66-106   Mourning Dove (*Zenaida macroura*)
Anguilla 660
Bahamas 709 710
Central African Republic 1078
Cuba 1798
Dominica 524
Guinea MS1184
Kuwait 581
Turks and Caicos Islands 831

66-108   Zenaida Dove (*Zenaida aurita*)
Antigua 471
Barbados 632 683
Barbuda 307
British Virgin Islands 290 578 O34
Cook Islands MS1021c
Dominica 497 639
St. Kitts 68 126 O20

66-110   White-winged Dove (*Zenaida asiatica*)
Cayman Islands 337

66-111   Scaly-breasted Ground Dove (*Columbina passerina*)
Barbados 629
British Virgin Islands 573 O29
Grenadines of St. Vincent 126
Netherlands Antilles 370

66-114   Ruddy Ground Dove (*Columbina talpacoti*)
Argentine Republic 1665
Surinam 578

66-120   Purple-breasted Ground Dove (*Claravis mondetoura*)
El Salvador 1861

66-128   White-fronted Dove (*Leptotila verreauxi*)
Netherlands Antilles 734

66-133   Grenada Dove (*Leptotila wellsi*)
Grenadines of Grenada 152

66-134   White-bellied Dove (*Leptotila jamaicensis*)
Cayman Islands 386

66-141   Purple Quail Dove (*Geotrygon saphirina*)
Ecuador 1327

66-142   Grey-faced Quail Dove (*Geotrygon caniceps*)
Cuba 2526 3156

66-145   White-faced Quail Dove (*Geotrygon linearis*)
Venezuela 1762 1879

66-147   Key West Quail Dove (*Geotrygon chrysia*)
Cuba 2525

66-148   Bridled Quail Dove (*Geotrygon mystacea*)
Barbuda 510
British Virgin Islands 571 O27
Montserrat 614 O75

66-150   Ruddy Quail Dove (*Geotrygon montana*)
Cuba 2527
Dominica 1038
Grenada 1063
Grenadines of St. Vincent 17
St. Vincent 300

66-151   Blue-headed Quail Dove (*Starnoenas cyanocephala*)
Cuba 1815c 2217 2524

66-160   White-breasted Ground Pigeon (*Gallicolumba jobiensis*)
Papua New Guinea 333

66-164   Friendly Quail Dove (*Gallicolumba stairi*)
Kiribati 167

66-173   Pheasant Pigeon (*Otidiphaps nobilis*)
Papua New Guinea 335

66-174   Blue Crowned Pigeon (*Goura cristata*)
Netherlands New Guinea 60 61 62
West Irian 34
West New Guinea 23 6 8

66-176   Victoria Crowned Pigeon (*Goura victoria*)
Papua New Guinea 334

66-177   Tooth-billed Pigeon (*Didunculus strigirostris*)
Samoa 223 287

66-192   Yellow-bellied Green Pigeon (*Treron waalia*)
Gambia 239
Ivory Coast 261
Somalia 493
Yemen 328 D375

66-194   African Green Pigeon (*Treron calva*)
Ciskei 18
Malawi 485
Swaziland 237

66-197   Pin-tailed Green Pigeon (*Treron apicauda*)
Vietnam 409

66-199   White-bellied Pin-tailed Green Pigeon (*Treron seimundi*)
Vietnam 411

66-201   White-bellied Wedge-tailed Green Pigeon (*Treron sieboldii*)
China (Taiwan) 620
Vietnam 405

66-208   Merrill's Fruit Dove (*Ptilinopus merrilli*)
Philippines 1504

66-218   Silver-shouldered Fruit Dove (*Ptilinopus tannensis*)
Vanuatu 310

66-219   Orange-fronted Fruit Dove (*Ptilinopus aurantiifrons*)
Papua New Guinea 336

66-223   Purple-capped Fruit Dove (*Ptilinopus porphyraceus*)
Niue 159

66-224   Palau Fruit Dove (*Ptilinopus pelewensis*)
Palau 5

66-225   Rarotongan Fruit Dove (*Ptilinopus rarotongensis*)
Cook Islands 658

66-229   Grey-green Fruit Dove (*Ptilinopus purpuratus*)
French Polynesia 351

66-230   Grey's Fruit Dove (*Ptilinopus greyii*)
New Caledonia 684

66-234   Henderson Island Fruit Dove (*Ptilinopus insularis*)
Pitcairn Islands 47 80

66-240   Red-bibbed Fruit Dove (*Ptilinopus viridis*)
Solomon Islands 269 287 307

66-249   Orange Dove (*Ptilinopus victor*)
Aitutaki 348 460
Fiji 323

66-252   Cloven-feathered Dove (*Drepanoptila holosericea*)
New Caledonia 416

66-253   Madagascar Blue Pigeon (*Alectroenas madagascariensis*)
Malagasy Republic 57

66-254   Comoro Blue Pigeon (*Alectroenas sganzini*)
Comoro Islands 97
Zil Elwannyen Sesel 67

66-255   Seychelles Blue Pigeon (*Alectroenas pulcherrima*)
Seychelles 310 451

66-258   Mindoro Zone-tailed Pigeon (*Ducula mindorensis*)
Philippines 1506

66-261   Green Imperial Pigeon (*Ducula aenea*)
Vietnam 404

66-264   Pacific Pigeon (*Ducula pacifica*)
New Hebrides 184 F199
Samoa 281 510
Tuvalu 81

66-265   Micronesian Pigeon (*Ducula oceanica*)
Nauru 57 78 92

66-276   Christmas Island Imperial Pigeon (*Ducula whartoni*)
Christmas Island 79 155

66-280   Baker's Pigeon (*Ducula bakeri*)
New Hebrides 159 F174 221 F235

66-281   New Caledonian Pigeon (*Ducula goliath*)
New Caledonia 406

66-285   Banded Imperial Pigeon (*Ducula zoeae*)
Papua New Guinea 337

66-286   Mountain Imperial Pigeon (*Ducula badia*)
Vietnam 408

66-293   New Zealand Pigeon (*Hemiphaga novaeseelandiae*)
New Zealand 804
Norfolk Island 111

67   LORIES
67-9   Red Lory (*Eos bornea*)
Belgium 1817

67-11   Dusky Lory (*Pseudeos fuscata*)
Papua New Guinea 123

67-13   Rainbow Lory (*Trichoglossus haematodus*)
Indonesia 1601 **MS**1602
Kampuchea 461
Korea (North Korea) N1419 N1969
New Caledonia 685
Solomon Islands 312
Turks and Caicos Islands 820
Vanuatu 328

67-15   Johnstone's Lorikeet (*Trichoglossus johnstoniae*)
Philippines 1115

67-23   Black-capped Lory (*Lorius lory*)
West Irian 35

67-29   Chattering Lory (*Lorius garrulus*)
Cuba 1560b
Indonesia 1600 **MS**1602

67-30   Collared Lory (*Phigys solitarius*)
Fiji 519

67-31   Blue-crowned Lory (*Vini australis*)
Fiji 652
Niue 160
Tonga O193 O194 O195 O196 O197 O198 O199 O200 O201 O202 O203 O213

67-32   Kuhl's Lory (*Vini kuhlii*)
Kiribati 176

67-33   Stephen's Lory (*Vini stepheni*)
Aitutaki 346 458
Pitcairn Islands 45 78

67-34   Tahitian Lory (*Vini peruviana*)
Aitutaki 325 484 O26
French Polynesia 332

67-39   Palm Lorikeet (*Charmosyna palmarum*)
New Hebrides 167 F182 189 F204 229 F243

67-48   Red-throated Lorikeet (*Charmosyna amabilis*)
Fiji 651

67-49   Duchess Lorikeet (*Charmosyna margarethae*)
Solomon Islands 271 299 319

67-52   Papuan Lory (*Charmosyna papou*)
Papua New Guinea 121

68   COCKATOOS
68-1   Palm Cockatoo (*Probosciger aterrimus*)
Indonesia 1639 **MS**1640
Japanese Occupation of North Borneo J2 J17 J21
Netherlands 1413
North Borneo 285 188 197 224 243 265 304 319 321 336 D64
Singapore 193

68-6   Galah (*Eolophus roseicapillus*)
Australia 365 393 617

68-7   Major Mitchell's Cockatoo (*Cacatua leadbeateri*)
Singapore 193

68-9   Sulphur-crested Cockatoo (*Cacatua galerita*)
Australia 970 971
Benin 868
Cuba 1560d
Indonesia 1638 **MS**1640
Korea (North Korea) N1417
Singapore 263

68-11   Salmon-crested Cockatoo (*Cacatua moluccensis*)
Indonesia 1637

68-13   Red-vented Cockatoo (*Cacatua haematuropygia*)
Philippines 1793

68-17   Ducorp's Cockatoo (*Cacatua ducorps*)
Solomon Islands 125 151

69   PARROTS
69-1   Kea (*Nestor notabilis*)
Aitutaki 7
New Zealand 268a 440 O65
Niue 16
Penrhyn Island 17

69-2   Kaka (*Nestor meridionalis*)
Aitutaki 7
New Zealand 268a 440 831 O65
Niue 16
Penrhyn Island 17

69-12   Edwards's Fig Parrot (*Psittaculirostris edwardsii*)
Papua New Guinea 124

69-14   Guaiabero (*Bolbopsittacus lunulatus*)
Philippines 1794

69-25   Mountain Racket-tailed Parrot (*Prioniturus montanus*)
Philippines 1795

69-29   Great-billed Parrot (*Tanygnathus megalorhynchos*)
Philippines 1048 1796

69-31   Muller's Parrot (*Tanygnathus sumatranus*)
Philippines 1797

69-35   Pesquet's Parrot (*Psittrichas fulgidus*)
Indonesia 1599 **MS**1602
Papua New Guinea 122

69-36   Red Shining Parrot (*Prosopeia tabuensis*)
Fiji 308 654
Tonga 81 69 479 480 481 482 483 484 485 486 487 693 698
891 **MS**892 **MS**955

69-37   Masked Shining Parrot (*Prosopeia personata*)
Fiji 447 653

69-38   Australian King Parrot (*Alisterus scapularis*)
Australia 738
Niue 630

69-50   Crimson Rosella (*Platycercus elegans*)
Norfolk Island 116 160

69-60   Golden-shouldered Parrot (*Psephotus chrysopterygius*)
Australia 734

69-63   Red-fronted Parakeet (*Cyanoramphus novaezelandiae*)
New Zealand 812
Norfolk Island 107

69-66   Horned Parakeet (*Cyanoramphus cornutus*)
New Caledonia 409 413

69-75   Budgerigar (*Melopsittacus undulatus*)
Korea (North Korea) N1420
Netherlands Antilles 476
Niue 634

69-79   Black Parrot (*Coracopsis nigra*)
British Indian Ocean Territory 1
Seychelles 196 255 372

69-80   Grey Parrot (*Psittacus erithacus*)
Biafra 10
Central African Republic 976
Congo (Brazzaville) 886
Cuba 1560a
Gabon 433 676
Ghana 360
Guinea 350 355 360
Ivory Coast 772
Nigeria 179 226
Rio Muni 21 69 70
Sierra Leone 627 811 812
Spanish Guinea 418 419 420
Togo 364

69-81   Cape Parrot (*Poicephalus robustus*)
Ciskei 19

69-85   Senegal Parrot (*Poicephalus senegalus*)
Gambia 196 218
Mali 583

69-87   Meyer's Parrot (*Poicephalus meyeri*)
Bophuthatswana 63

69-88   Ruppell's Parrot (*Poicephalus rueppellii*)
South West Africa 263

69-90   Grey-headed Lovebird (*Agapornis cana*)
Seychelles 445

69-91   Red-faced Lovebird (*Agapornis pullaria*)
Cameroun 664
Central African Republic 15
Togo 363

69-92   Black-winged Lovebird (*Agapornis taranta*)
Ethiopia 677

69-93   Black-collared Lovebird (*Agapornis swinderniana*)
Uganda 125

69-94   Peach-faced Lovebird (*Agapornis roseicollis*)
Angola 481
Cuba 3049
South West Africa 261

69-97   Nyasa Lovebird (*Agapornis lilianae*)
Malawi 314

69-98   Black-cheeked Lovebird (*Agapornis nigrigenis*)
Zambia 264

69-100   Ceylon Hanging Parrot (*Loriculus beryllinus*)
Sri Lanka 685

69-101   Philippine Hanging Parrot (*Loriculus philippensis*)
Philippines 1798

69-110   Rose-ringed Parakeet (*Psittacula krameri*)
Afghanistan **MS**1069
French Territory of the Afars and the Issas 649
Gambia 197 207 219
Ghana 942 **MS**943
Mauritius 347
Niger 295 375
Togo 897

69-111   Mauritius Parakeet (*Psittacula echo*)
Mauritius 322 354 372

69-112   Slaty-headed Parakeet (*Psittacula himalayana*)
Kampuchea 510
Laos 178
Vietnam N282

69-120   Blyth's Parakeet (*Psittacula caniceps*)
Korea (North Korea) N1418

69-122   Hyacinth Macaw (*Anodorhynchus hyacinthinus*)
Bolivia 1058
Cuba 1557

69-123   Glaucous Macaw (*Anodorhynchus glaucus*)
Brazil 2086

69-126   Blue and Yellow Macaw (*Ara ararauna*)
Bolivia 1055
Colombia 1373 1533
Ecuador 1096
French Guiana 239 240
Germany (East Germany) E1745
Grenada 550
Guyana 441 443 442 444
Korea (North Korea) N1416
Russia 5413
Singapore 263
Surinam 414

69-128   Military Macaw (*Ara militaris*)
Bolivia 1059
French Guiana 239 240

69-130   Scarlet Macaw (*Ara macao*)
Belize **MS**810

Bolivia 1053
Brazil 1480 2086 2121
British Honduras 207 220 233
Colombia 1366 1528 1671
Costa Rica 1210
Grenada 550
Guyana 1448
Nicaragua 2307
Panama 916
Surinam 691
Venezuela 2233

69-131   Green-winged Macaw (*Ara chloroptera*)
Bolivia 1054
China (Taiwan) 1663
Zaire 1058

69-132   Red-fronted Macaw (*Ara rubrogenys*)
Bolivia 1056

69-133   Yellow-collared Macaw (*Ara auricollis*)
Argentine Republic 1518
Bolivia 1057

69-134   Chestnut-fronted Macaw (*Ara severa*)
Bolivia 1060
Panama 948 1289

69-142   Finsch's Conure (*Aratinga finschi*)
Nicaragua 2306

69-143   Red-fronted Conure (*Aratinga wagleri*)
Ecuador 1123

69-146   White-eyed Conure (*Aratinga leucophthalmus*)
French Guiana 239 240

69-147   Hispaniolan Conure (*Aratinga chloroptera*)
Dominican Republic 1378

69-148   Cuban Conure (*Aratinga euops*)
Cuba 1815d 2216 2764 2958

69-155   Brown-throated Conure (*Aratinga pertinax*)
Netherlands Antilles 371

69-161   Thick-billed Parrot (*Rhynchopsitta pachyrhyncha*)
Jersey 58

69-162   Patagonian Conure (*Cyanoliseus patagonus*)
Chile 1005

69-208   Brown-backed Parrotlet (*Touit melanonota*)
Brazil 1869

69-211   Black-headed Caique (*Pionites melanocephala*)
Ecuador 1325

69-218   Caica Parrot (*Pionopsitta caica*)
Surinam 867

69-228   White-capped Parrot (*Pionus senilis*)
Belize 467 807

69-231   Yellow-billed Amazon (*Amazona collaria*)
Jamaica 469 606

69-232   Cuban Amazon (*Amazona leucocephala*)
Bahamas 432
Cayman Islands 165 388
Cuba 1722 2953

69-233   Hispaniolan Amazon (*Amazona ventralis*)
Dominican Republic 930

69-234   White-fronted Amazon (*Amazona albifrons*)
Belize 806

69-239   Red-spectacled Amazon (*Amazona pretrei*)
Brazil 1868

69-242   Red-lored Amazon (*Amazona autumnalis*)
Belize 809

69-243   Red-tailed Amazon (*Amazona brasiliensis*)
Brazil 1867

69-249   Yellow-crowned Amazon (*Amazona ochrocephala*)
El Salvador 1187
Venezuela 1694

69-250   Orange-winged Amazon (*Amazona amazonica*)
Surinam 1214

69-252   Mealy Amazon (*Amazona farinosa*)
Belize 808

69-253   Vinaceous Amazon (*Amazona vinacea*)
Brazil 1866

69-254   St. Lucia Amazon (*Amazona versicolor*)
Jersey 329
St. Lucia 257 259 343 344 418 572

69-255   Red-necked Amazon (*Amazona arausica*)
Dominica 253 306 873

69-256   St. Vincent Amazon (*Amazona guildingii*)
Grenadines of St. Vincent 25
St. Vincent 244 288 322 324

69-257   Imperial Amazon (*Amazona imperialis*)
Antigua 470
Barbuda 306
Dominica 173 226 276 306 366 367 529 **MS**746 827 871 954

69-258   Hawk-headed Parrot (*Deroptyus accipitrinus*)
Surinam 870

69-260   Kakapo (*Strigops habroptilus*)
New Zealand 1288

70   TURACOS
70-1   Great Blue Turaco (*Corythaeola cristata*)
Cameroun 663
Central African Republic 12
Fernando Poo 269 272 275
Ghana 223 388 450
Liberia 227 261 O240
Sierra Leone 768
Uganda 123

70-4   Go-away Bird (*Corythaixoides concolor*)
Botswana 229

70-7   Violet Turaco (*Musophaga violacea*)
Gambia 244
Ivory Coast 773
Senegal 236 682

70-8   Lady Ross's Turaco (*Musophaga rossae*)
Zambia 238

70-9   Knysna Turaco (*Tauraco corythaix*)
Belgium 1818
Central African Republic 14
Ciskei 5
Congo (Brazzaville) 119

Gabon 436
Liberia **MS**1313
Malawi 323
Mali 93
Sierra Leone 622
Zaire 1135

70-13   Hartlaub's Turaco (*Tauraco hartlaubi*)
Kenya 18

70-14   White-cheeked Turaco (*Tauraco leucotis*)
Ethiopia 542

70-17   Violet-crested Turaco (*Tauraco porphyreolophus*)
Guinea 741 747
Mozambique 705
Zambia 382

70-18   Ruwenzori Turaco (*Tauraco johnstoni*)
Uganda 121

71   CUCKOOS
71-2   Red-winged Crested Cuckoo (*Clamator coromandus*)
Kampuchea 512

71-11   Red-chested Cuckoo (*Cuculus solitarius*)
Rwanda 244
Transkei 75

71-12   Black Cuckoo (*Cuculus cafer*)
Ciskei 13

71-14   European Cuckoo (*Cuculus canorus*)
Albania 934
Bulgaria 1145
Czechoslovakia 2072 2073
Finland 614
Great Britain 1284

71-16   Little Cuckoo (*Cuculus poliocephalus*)
China (People's Republic) **MS**3207
Japan 655 1226

71-26   Fan-tailed Cuckoo (*Cacomantis pyrrhophanus*)
New Hebrides 286 F299

71-29   African Emerald Cuckoo (*Chrysococcyx cupreus*)
Benin 1009
Dahomey 272
Gambia 205 227
Rwanda 961

71-32   Didric Cuckoo (*Chrysococcyx caprius*)
Botswana 233
Ethiopia 538
Sierra Leone 626

71-46   Long-tailed Koel (*Urodynamis taitensis*)
Kiribati 177 O29
Norfolk Island 106

71-50   Black-billed Cuckoo (*Coccyzus erythrophthalmus*)
Guinea 1178

71-53   Mangrove Cuckoo (*Coccyzus minor*)
Barbuda 506 784
British Virgin Islands 292 562 O18
Central African Republic 1077 1103
Grenadines of Grenada **MS**649
Grenadines of St. Vincent 10 111
Nevis 272
St. Lucia 821
St. Vincent 293

71-57   Chestnut-bellied Cuckoo (*Piaya pluvialis*)
Jamaica 642

71-61   Great Lizard Cuckoo (*Saurothera merlini*)
Cuba 1893 2963

71-62   Jamaican Lizard Cuckoo (*Saurothera vetula*)
Jamaica 565 566 567 568 569

71-66   Greater Green-billed Malcoha (*Rhopodytes tristis*)
Thailand 892

71-77   Smooth-billed Ani (*Crotophaga ani*)
British Virgin Islands 567 O23
Grenadines of St. Vincent 113
Montserrat 248

71-84   Roadrunner (*Geococcyx california*)
United States of America 1960

71-93   Giant Madagascar Coucal (*Coua gigas*)
Malagasy Republic 602

71-99   Crested Madagascar Coucal (*Coua cristata*)
Malagasy Republic 603

71-101   Blue Madagascar Coucal (*Coua caerulea*)
Malagasy Republic 58

71-108   Pheasant Coucal (*Centropus phasianius*)
Maldive Islands 710

71-111   Ceylon Coucal (*Centropus chlororhynchus*)
Sri Lanka 830

71-117   Black Coucal (*Centropus toulou*)
British Indian Ocean Territory 63
Zil Elwannyen Sesel 65

71-123   Blue-headed Coucal (*Centropus monachus*)
Guinea 743

71-124   Senegal Coucal (*Centropus senegalensis*)
Central African Republic 232
Niger 294 374

71-125   White-browed Coucal (*Centropus superciliosus*)
Ciskei 7

72   BARN OWLS
72-2   Barn Owl (*Tyto alba*)
Aitutaki 324 481 O22
Botswana 525
Cape Verde Islands 513
Czechoslovakia 2847
Dominica 1050
Germany (East Germany) E991
Great Britain 1320
Grenadines of Grenada **MS**386
Grenadines of St. Vincent 15
Hungary 3600
Israel 1017
Libya 1203
Madeira 232
Malta 655
Monaco 736
New Caledonia 718
Portugal 1796
Rumania 3442
Russia 4925
Rwanda 1237
St. Vincent 298 382
Samoa 286

73   OWLS
73-8   Striated Scops Owl (*Otus brucei*)
Israel 1016

73-9   Scops Owl (*Otus scops*)
Hungary 2350
Israel 251
Japan 1330
Korea (North Korea) N269

73-11   African Scops Owl (*Otus senegalensis*)
Zimbabwe 713

73-19   Bare-legged Scops Owl (*Otus insularis*)
Seychelles 309 605 606 607 608

73-21   Screech Owl (*Otus asio*)
Cayman Islands 470
Central African Republic 1076
Guinea 1182

73-35   White-faced Scops Owl (*Otus leucotis*)
Rwanda 1238
Zimbabwe 712

73-41   Great Horned Owl (*Bubo virginianus*)
Canada 1191
Guatemala 1127
Honduras 374
Nicaragua 2729
United States of America 1734
Uruguay 1363

73-42   Eagle Owl (*Bubo bubo*)
Afghanistan 630
Benin 867
Czechoslovakia 2844
Finland 562
France 1963
Germany (East Germany) E434 E2413
Hungary 1851 3606
Israel 1015
Poland 1205
Rumania 3443
Spanish Sahara 314
Sweden 581 582
Yemen 320 370
Yugoslavia 1520

73-43   Cape Eagle Owl (*Bubo capensis*)
Ciskei 21

73-44   Spotted Eagle Owl (*Bubo africanus*)
Botswana 424
Guinea-Bissau 555

73-49   Verreaux's Eagle Owl (*Bubo lacteus*)
Gambia 400

73-53   Blakiston's Fish Owl (*Ketupa blakistoni*)
Japan 1714 **MS**1768

73-57   Pel's Fishing Owl (*Scotopelia peli*)
Gabon 743
Swaziland 399 400 401 402 403

73-63   Snowy Owl (*Nyctea scandiaca*)
Czechoslovakia 1621
Hungary 3604
Mongolia 1395
Rumania 4923
St. Pierre et Miquelon 509 512

73-67   Cuban Pygmy Owl (*Glaucidium siju*)
Cuba 1813a 1891 2302

73-70 Ferruginous Pygmy Owl (*Glaucidium brasilianum*)
Chile 1011

73-71 Pearl-spotted Owlet (*Glaucidium perlatum*)
Zimbabwe 711

73-73 Barred Owlet (*Glaucidium capense*)
Rwanda 960
Zimbabwe 710

73-84 Boobook Owl (*Ninox novaeseelandiae*)
Norfolk Island 110 338 339 340 341 342

73-85 Brown Hawk Owl (*Ninox scutulata*)
Korea (North Korea) N397

73-92 Indonesian Hawk Owl (*Ninox squamipila*)
Christmas Island 165 236

73-99 Bare-legged Owl (*Gymnoglaux lawrencii*)
Cuba 2215

73-101 Little Owl (*Athene noctua*)
Germany (East Germany) E2412
Hungary 3601
Luxembourg 1161

73-104 Burrowing Owl (*Speotyto cunicularia*)
Aruba 9
Nevis 275
St. Kitts 56

73-107 Black-banded Owl (*Ciccaba huhula*)
Surinam 873

73-109 African Wood Owl (*Ciccaba woodfordii*)
Sierra Leone 767

73-110 Hume's Tawny Owl (*Strix butleri*)
Israel 1018

73-114 Tawny Owl (*Strix aluco*)
Czechoslovakia 2846
Hungary 3602
Mongolia 576
Poland 2432
Sweden 913
Uganda MS484

73-116 Barred Owl (*Strix varia*)
El Salvador 1646
Ghana 1160
United States of America 1733

73-119 Ural Owl (*Strix uralensis*)
Hungary 3605
Japan 1546

73-121 Great Grey Owl (*Strix nebulosa*)
United States of America 1731

73-123 Long-eared Owl (*Asio otus*)
Czechoslovakia 2845
Hungary 3603
Nevis 276

73-124 Stygian Owl (*Asio stygius*)
Dominican Republic 1578

73-125 Abyssinian Long-eared Owl (*Asio abyssinicus*)
Ethiopia 1154

73-127 Short-eared Owl (*Asio flammeus*)
Czechoslovakia 2848
Turks and Caicos Islands 830

73-129 Jamaican Owl (*Pseudoscops grammicus*)
Jamaica 497

73-132 Saw-whet Owl (*Aegolius acadicus*)
United States of America 1732

74 OILBIRD
74-1 Oilbird (*Steatornis caripensis*)
Venezuela 2474

78 NIGHTJARS
78-14 Great Eared Nightjar (*Eurostopodus macrotis*)
Philippines 1509

78-16 Pauraque (*Nyctidromus albicollis*)
Venezuela 1760 1877

78-22 Chuck Will's Widow (*Caprimulgus carolinensis*)
Central African Republic 1100

78-34 Spot-tailed Nightjar (*Caprimulgus maculicaudus*)
Surinam 863

78-42 European Nightjar (*Caprimulgus europaeus*)
Albania 937
Russia 4926

78-48 Madagascar Nightjar (*Caprimulgus madagascariensis*)
Zil Elwannyen Sesel 55

78-69 Pennant-winged Nightjar (*Semeiophorus vexillarius*)
Ghana 226 392 453

79 SWIFTS
79-15 Grey-rumped Swiftlet (*Collocalia francica*)
Mauritius 348

79-16 Seychelles Cave Swiftlet (*Collocalia elaphra*)
Seychelles 444

79-24 Cook Islands Swiftlet (*Collocalia sawtelli*)
Cook Islands 583

79-32 White-bellied Swiftlet (*Collocalia esculenta*)
Christmas Island 154

79-78 Common Swift (*Apus apus*)
Finland 515
Gibraltar 482
Libya 1191

81 HUMMINGBIRDS
81-7 Rufous-breasted Hermit (*Glaucis hirsuta*)
Grenada 1061

81-14 Green Hermit (*Phaethornis guy*)
Trinidad and Tobago 344

81-16 Long-tailed Hermit (*Phaethornis superciliosus*)
Belize 493

81-24 Straight-billed Hermit (*Phaethornis bourcieri*)
Surinam 580

81-28 Planalto Hermit (*Phaethornis pretrei*)
Brazil 1898

81-42 Grey-breasted Sabrewing (*Campylopterus largipennis*)
Surinam 866

81-46   Violet Sabrewing (*Campylopterus hemileucurus*)
Nicaragua 2309
Panama 1290

81-52   White-necked Jacobin (*Florisuga mellivora*)
Grenada 925

81-55   Green Violetear (*Colibri thalassinus*)
Costa Rica 1336

81-60   Black-throated Mango (*Anthracothorax nigricollis*)
Ghana 1161

81-64   Jamaican Mango (*Anthracothorax mango*)
Jamaica 468

81-66   Purple-throated Carib (*Eulampis jugularis*)
Anguilla 36
Dominica 273 1046
Grenadines of Grenada 296
Grenadines of St. Vincent 9
Montserrat 254 574 O5
St. Kitts 55 118
St. Lucia 256 258 573
St. Vincent 292 381 489

81-67   Green-throated Carib (*Sericotes holosericeus*)
Antigua 668
Barbados 631
Barbuda 515 538
British Virgin Islands 289 479 480
Montserrat 251 572
St. Kitts 62 122 O14
St. Vincent 491

81-68   Ruby-Topaz Hummingbird (*Chrysolampis mosquitus*)
Brazil 1895

81-69   Antillean Crested Hummingbird (*Orthorhyncus
         cristatus*)
Anguilla 662
Antigua 469 Barbados 628
Barbuda 305
British Virgin Islands 289 481 482
Montserrat 252 335 338 573
St. Kitts 70 128 O22
St. Vincent 488

81-75   Frilled Coquette (*Lophornis magnifica*)
Brazil 1897

81-89   Blue-tailed Emerald (*Chlorostilbon mellisugus*)
Netherlands Antilles 865

81-93   Cuban Emerald (*Chlorostilbon ricordii*)
Cuba 1897 2763

81-94   Hispaniolan Emerald (*Chlorostilbon swainsonii*)
Dominican Republic 928

81-103   Blue-headed Hummingbird (*Cyanophaia bicolor*)
Dominica 527 872
Montserrat 571
St. Vincent 487 490

81-125   Streamertail (*Trochilus polytmus*)
Jamaica 166 186 224 434 435 436 437 470

81-127   White-tailed Goldenthroat (*Polytmus guainumbi*)
Surinam 865

81-155   Copper-rumped Hummingbird (*Amazilia tobaci*)
Trinidad and Tobago 296

81-157   Snowy-breasted Hummingbird (*Amazilia edward*)
Gabon 910

81-187   Brazilian Ruby (*Clytolaema rubricauda*)
Brazil 1436

81-200   Crimson Topaz (*Topaza pella*)
Nicaragua 2724

81-225   Sword-billed Hummingbird (*Ensifera ensifera*)
Ecuador 1099

81-243   Coppery-bellied Puffleg (*Eriocnemis cupreoventris*)
Colombia 1728

81-254   Black-tailed Trainbearer (*Lesbia victoriae*)
Ecuador 1099

81-278   Long-tailed Sylph (*Aglaiocercus kingi*)
Venezuela 1753

81-279   Violet-tailed Sylph (*Aglaiocercus coelestis*)
Ecuador 1328 1335

81-286   Horned Sungem (*Heliactin cornuta*)
Brazil 1896

81-294   Bahama Woodstar (*Philodice evelynae*)
Bahamas 685

81-300   Slender-tailed Woodstar (*Microstilbon burmeisteri*)
Argentine Republic 1293

81-303   Ruby-throated Hummingbird (*Archilochus colubris*)
Anguilla 419 425
Barbados 762
Cuba 1897
Rwanda 1239
Turks and Caicos Islands 461

81-309   Bee Hummingbird (*Calypte helenae*)
Cuba 1003c 2357 2950 3046

81-322   Broad-tailed Hummingbird (*Selasphorus playcercus*)
Nicaragua 2202

82   MOUSEBIRDS
82-6   Blue-naped Mousebird (*Colius macrourus*)
Ghana 361

83   TROGONS
83-1   Resplendent Quetzal (*Pharomachrus mocinno*)
Colombia 1522
Costa Rica 1332
El Salvador 1643
Guatemala 15 16 17 19 21 22 23 24 25 157 198 295 296 326
         327 333 402 403 447 448 449 450 **MS**518 546 554 555 556
         557 558 559 560 561 562 563 564 565 606 637 641 653 708
         712 716 720 736 817 909 910a 911 912 **MS**926 1002 1007
         1008 1029 1032 1036 1039 **MS**1129 1165 1166 1224 1225
         1226 1227
Nicaragua **MS**2267
Panama 945

83-4   Golden-headed Trogon (*Pharomachrus auriceps*)
Ecuador 1320

83-7   Cuban Trogon (*Priotelus temnurus*)
Cuba 1003b 1892 2306 **MS**2965b

83-8   Hispaniolan Trogon (*Temnotrogon roseigaster*)
Dominican Republic 931 1379
Haiti 1128 1132

Singapore 75 262
Thailand 568
Vietnam N279

84-47   Black-capped Kingfisher (*Halcyon pileata*)
Hong Kong 337
Korea (North Korea) N640
Korea (South Korea) 1765

84-49   Grey-headed Kingfisher (*Halcyon leucocephala*)
Cape Verde Islands 514
Equatorial Guinea 93
French Territory of the Afars and the Issas 504
Jordan 629

84-50   Woodland Kingfisher (*Halcyon senegalensis*)
Benin 864
Gabon 434
Niger 293 373
Rwanda 240

84-52   Blue-breasted Kingfisher (*Halcyon malimbica*)
Biafra 11
Nigeria 180 227
Sierra Leone 631
Uganda 118

84-53   Brown-hooded Kingfisher (*Halcyon albiventris*)
Bechuanaland 175
Botswana 213

84-59   Forest Kingfisher (*Halcyon macleayii*)
Australia 672
Ghana 461 542
Papua New Guinea 402

84-62   Chestnut-bellied Kingfisher (*Halcyon farquhari*)
New Hebrides 164 F179 188 F203 226 F240

84-67   Sacred Kingfisher (*Halcyon sancta*)
New Caledonia 412
New Zealand 803
Norfolk Island 117 160
Papua New Guinea 403

84-70   White-collared Kingfisher (*Halcyon chloris*)
Ethiopia 633
New Hebrides 109 F125
Niuafo'ou 28 38 79
Singapore 262

84-71   White-headed Kingfisher (*Halcyon saurophaga*)
Papua New Guinea 401

84-72   Flat-billed Kingfisher (*Halcyon recurvirostris*)
Aitutaki 352 461 494 O33

84-75   Mangaia Kingfisher (*Halcyon ruficollaris*)
Cook Islands 563

84-91   White-tailed Kingfisher (*Tanysiptera sylvia*)
Australia 675
Papua New Guinea 404

85   TODIES
85-1   Cuban Tody (*Todus multicolor*)
Cuba 1813b 2304 2952 3048

85-2   Narrow-billed Tody (*Todus angustirostris*)
Dominican Republic 927

85-3   Jamaican Tody (*Todus todus*)
Jamaica 467

86   MOTMOTS
86-1   Tody-Motmot (*Hylomanes momotula*)
El Salvador 1862

86-5   Turquoise-browed Motmot (*Eumomota superciliosa*)
El Salvador 1189
Nicaragua 1782
Panama 946

86-9   Blue-crowned Motmot (*Momotus momota*)
Belize 454
Colombia 1729
Costa Rica 1335
Ecuador 1321
Nicaragua 2310
Peru 1135

87   BEE EATERS
87-4   Black Bee Eater (*Merops gularis*)
Sierra Leone 634 813
Uganda 113

87-5   Blue-headed Bee Eater (*Merops muelleri*)
Gabon 172

87-6   Red-throated Bee Eater (*Merops bulocki*)
Botswana 517
Chad 166 307
Gambia 235

87-7   White-fronted Bee Eater (*Merops bullockoides*)
Gabon 741

87-8   Little Bee Eater (*Merops pusillus*)
Burundi 128 134 145 224 235 1320 1329
Ethiopia 1307
French Somali Coast 441

87-9   Blue-breasted Bee Eater (*Merops variegatus*)
Ethiopia 634

87-10   Cinnamon-chested Bee Eater (*Merops oreobates*)
Rwanda 246

87-11   Swallow-tailed Bee Eater (*Merops hirundineus*)
Bechuanaland 172
Botswana 210
Ghana 941 MS943

87-14   White-throated Bee Eater (*Merops albicollis*)
Chad 164 305
Djibouti Republic 941

87-15   Little Green Bee Eater (*Merops orientalis*)
Chad 167

87-16   Boehm's Bee Eater (*Merops boehmi*)
Malawi 736
Zambia 492

87-18   Blue-cheeked Bee Eater (*Merops superciliosus*)
Comoro Islands 65 272 338 341 434

87-20   Australian Bee Eater (*Merops ornatus*)
Australia 735

87-21   European Bee Eater (*Merops apiaster*)
Albania 936
Angola 461
Brazil 2257
Congo (Brazzaville) 114
Cyprus (Turkish Cypriot Posts) 140
Dubai 313

France 1505
Hungary 1232 2352
Israel 247
Italy 1835
Kuwait 605
Lebanon 872 1119
Libya 336 693 1199
Mozambique 710
Portugal 1483
Qatar 396
Rumania 3979 4798
Venda 71

87-24   Carmine Bee Eater (*Merops nubicus*)
Bophuthatswana 61
Botswana 414
Chad 86 536
Ghana 494
Malawi 316 356
Mali 582
Niger 113
Rhodesia 462
Senegal 234
Somalia 492
Zambia 150

88   ROLLERS
88-1   Common Roller (*Coracias garrulus*)
Bulgaria 1521
Cyprus 334
Czechoslovakia 1451
Djibouti Republic 944
Germany (East Germany) E996
Libya 1201
Poland 1212
Qatar 391
Rumania 4797
Somalia 439
Tunisia 607
Turkey 2570

88-2   Abyssinian Roller (*Coracias abyssinica*)
Central African Republic 13
Ethiopia 535
French Territory of the Afars and the Issas 507
Niger 296 567
Senegal 235 697
Upper Volta 157

88-3   Lilac-breasted Roller (*Coracias caudata*)
Congo (Brazzaville) 115
Lesotho 513
Mozambique 706
Swaziland 250a
Uganda 124

88-4   Racquet-tailed Roller (*Coracias spatulata*)
Angola 459

88-5   Rufous-crowned Roller (*Coracias naevia*)
Gambia 200 208 222
Ghana 465 546
Liberia 1309

88-6   Indian Roller (*Coracias benghalensis*)
Burma 177 178 179 198 199 200 O188 O189 O195 O199 O200
O210 O211
Laos 181

88-8   Blue-bellied Roller (*Coracias cyanogaster*)
Gambia 240

88-9   Broad-billed Roller (*Eurystomus glaucurus*)
Benin 1008
Dahomey 271

88-10   Blue-throated Roller (*Eurystomus gularis*)
Liberia 736

88-11   Eastern Broad-billed Roller (*Eurystomus orientalis*)
Korea (North Korea) N398
Korea (South Korea) 1762
Mongolia 207
Solomon Islands 536

89   GROUND ROLLERS
89-3   Pitta-like Ground Roller (*Atelornis pittoides*)
Malagasy Republic 65

89-5   Long-tailed Ground Roller (*Uratelornis chimaera*)
French Southern and Antarctic Territories 1
Madagascar and Dependencies 323 324

90   COUROL
90-1   Courol (*Leptosomus discolor*)
Comoro Islands 63 337
Malagasy Republic 451

91   HOOPOE
91-1   Hoopoe (*Upupa epops*)
Afghanistan 1065
Albania 935
Algeria 725
Bechuanaland 169
Botswana 207 221 451
Bulgaria 1141
Burundi 552 576
China (People's Republic) 3202
Ciskei 14c
Congo (Brazzaville) 619 644
Cyprus 338
Dubai 314
French Territory of the Afars and the Issas 575
Fujeira 3 12 41 87 96 125 O50 O160
Germany (West Germany) 1315
Germany (East Germany) E436
Gibraltar 389
Hungary 2188
Iran 1657
Iraq 795
Italy 1836
Korea (North Korea) N741
Korea (South Korea) 1766
Kuwait 582
Laos 540
Lebanon 869
Lesotho 510
Libya 694 1205
Macao 595
Malta 798
Mongolia 204
Oman 268
Poland 1697 1701 2865
Qatar 395 530
Rhodesia 459
San Marino 596 1124
Sharjah 103 106
Switzerland J230
Syria 1374
Upper Volta 538
Vietnam N457
Yemen 423 R74
Yugoslavia 2203

92   WOOD HOOPOES
92-1   Green Wood Hoopoe (*Phoeniculus purpureus*)
Botswana 413
Rhodesia 542
Rwanda 245

92-8   Scimitar-bill (*Rhinopomastus cyanomelas*)
Botswana 230

93   HORNBILLS
93-3   Crowned Hornbill (*Tockus alboterminatus*)
Rwanda 959

93-4   Bradfield's Hornbill (*Tockus bradfieldi*)
Zambia 489

93-6   African Grey Hornbill (*Tockus nasutus*)
Bechuanaland 173
Botswana 211
Niger 292 372

93-11   Red-billed Dwarf Hornbill (*Tockus camurus*)
Ivory Coast 665b

93-12   Red-billed Hornbill (*Tockus erythrorhynchus*)
Niger 247

93-13   Yellow-billed Hornbill (*Tockus flavirostris*)
Angola 477
Botswana 225
South Africa 359
Uganda 378

93-16   Long-crested Hornbill (*Berenicornis comatus*)
Malaysia 274
Vietnam 137

93-18   Tickell's Hornbill (*Ptilolaemus tickelli*)
Vietnam 136

93-22   Rufous-necked Hornbill (*Aceros nipalensis*)
Bhutan 190 195 200 221 241
Vietnam 142

93-23   Wrinkled Hornbill (*Aceros corrugatus*)
Malaysia 273

93-26   Wreathed Hornbill (*Aceros undulatus*)
Vietnam 138

93-27   Blyth's Hornbill (*Aceros plicatus*)
Papua New Guinea 270
Solomon Islands 115 138 149

93-30   Black Hornbill (*Anthracoceros malayanus*)
Vietnam 140

93-31   Indian Pied Hornbill (*Anthracoceros malabaricus*)
Burma 183 204 O204 O215
Vietnam 139

93-32   Malabar Pied Hornbill (*Anthracoceros coronatus*)
Sarawak 191

93-36   Brown-cheeked Hornbill (*Bycanistes cylindricus*)
Liberia 1310
Spanish Guinea 371 372 373

93-37   Black and White Casqued Hornbill (*Bycanistes subcylindricus*)
Liberia 559 637

93-39   Black-casqued Hornbill (*Ceratogymna atrata*)
Congo (Kinshasa) 478

93-40   Yellow-casqued Hornbill (*Ceratogymna elata*)
Cameroun 1061
Liberia 737
Nigeria 96

93-41   Rhinoceros Hornbill (*Buceros rhinoceros*)
Malaysia 23 275
North Borneo 174 198 225 244 267 404 D56b
Sabah 421

93-42   Great Indian Hornbill (*Buceros bicornis*)
India 1094
Kampuchea 467
Liberia 412 426 O440 O454
Nepal 349
Singapore 261
Thailand 562
Vietnam S355 135 141 785

93-43   Rufous Hornbill (*Buceros hydrocorax*)
Philippines 1046

93-44   Helmeted Hornbill (*Rhinoplax vigil*)
Brunei 352
Malaysia 272
Singapore 130

93-45   Abyssinian Ground Hornbill (*Bucorvus abyssinicus*)
Burundi 140 148 230 238 1318 1327
Ethiopia 534
Guinea 351 356 361
Mali 94 678
Senegal 663

93-46   Southern Ground Hornbill (*Bucorvus leadbeateri*)
Angola 465 827
Guinea 746
Swaziland 103 156 481 482 483 484 485
Upper Volta 704

94   JACAMARS
94-11   Rufous-tailed Jacamar (*Galbula ruficauda*)
British Honduras 212

95   PUFFBIRDS
95-1   White-necked Puffbird (*Notharchus macrorhynchos*)
Belize 563 580

95-8   Collared Puffbird (*Bucco capensis*)
Ecuador 1331 1357 1358 1359

96   BARBETS
96-8   Lemon-throated Barbet (*Eubucco richardsoni*)
Ecuador 1329

96-13   Toucan Barbet (*Semnornis ramphastinus*)
Ecuador 1538

96-26   Yellow-fronted Barbet (*Megalaima flavifrons*)
Sri Lanka 688

96-28   Muller's Barbet (*Megalaima oorti*)
China (Taiwan) 618

96-45   Yellow-headed Barbet (*Stactolaema anchietae*)
Angola 463

96-55   Black-chinned Tinkerbird (*Pogoniulus makawai*)
Zambia 266

96-66   Black-collared Barbet (*Lybius torquatus*)
Ciskei 14
Swaziland 244
Venda 104

96-69   Chaplin's Barbet (*Lybius chaplini*)
Zambia 267

96-73   Double-toothed Barbet (*Lybius bidentatus*)
Ethiopia 537
Rwanda 242

96-77   Levaillant's Barbet (*Trachyphonus vaillantii*)
Botswana 232

96-81   Yellow-breasted Barbet (*Trachyphonus margaritatus*)
Djibouti Republic 943
Mali 580
Togo 365

97   HONEYGUIDES
97-14   Lyre-tailed Honeyguide (*Melichneutes robustus*)
Gabon 170

98   TOUCANS
98-1   Emerald Toucanet (*Aulacorhynchus prasinus*)
Belize 967
El Salvador 1645

98-4   Crimson-rumped Toucanet (*Aulacorhynchus haematopygus*)
Belize 968

98-9   Red-necked Aracari (*Pteroglossus bitorquatus*)
Panama 947

98-11   Black-necked Aracari (*Pteroglossus aracari*)
French Guiana 243

98-14   Collared Aracari (*Pteroglossus torquatus*)
Belize 965

98-27   Red-breasted Toucan (*Ramphastos dicolorus*)
Brazil 2017
Ecuador 1097

98-28   Channel-billed Toucan (*Ramphastos vitellinus*)
Brazil 2018
British Guiana 343
French Guiana 243
Guyana 405

98-30   Keel-billed Toucan (*Ramphastos sulfuratus*)
Belgium 1819
Belize 662 678 743 963
British Honduras 210
Colombia 1364 1438
Cuba 1560c
Gabon 911
Nicaragua 2305
Panama 1291

98-31   Toco Toucan (*Ramphastos toco*)
Argentine Republic 1215
Bolivia 358 359
Brazil 2015
Kampuchea 653
Poland 2149
Singapore 193
Vietnam **MS**599

98-32   Cuvier's Toucan (*Ramphastos tucanus*)
Brazil 2016

French Guiana 236 237 238 243
Panama 915
Peru 1134
Surinam 868

99   WOODPECKERS
99-1   Wryneck (*Jynx torquilla*)
Kuwait 604

99-38   Red-headed Woodpecker (*Melanerpes*)
Togo 1823

99-43   Black-cheeked Woodpecker (*Melanerpes pucherani*)
Panama 917

99-46   Hispaniolan Woodpecker (*Melanerpes striatus*)
Dominican Republic 932
Haiti 1135

99-48   Jamaican Woodpecker (*Melanerpes radiolatus*)
Jamaica 472 662

99-49   Red-crowned Woodpecker (*Melanerpes rubricapillus*)
Venezuela 1761 1878

99-52   Golden-fronted Woodpecker (*Melanerpes aurifrons*)
El Salvador 1193

99-54   West Indian Red-bellied Woodpecker (*Melanerpes superciliaris*)
Cayman Islands 340
Cuba 2956

99-55   Yellow-bellied Sapsucker (*Sphyrapicus varius*)
Barbuda 518
Turks and Caicos Islands 595

99-57   Red-breasted Sapsucker (*Sphyrapicus ruber*)
Comoro Islands 553

99-59   Cuban Green Woodpecker (*Xiphidiopicus percussus*)
Cuba 1813c 2353

99-61   Bennett's Woodpecker (*Campethera bennettii*)
Botswana 417 498
Zaire 1138

99-70   Ground Woodpecker (*Geocolaptes olivaceus*)
Lesotho 210

99-74   Cardinal Woodpecker (*Dendropicos fuscescens*)
Gambia 243

99-76   Stierling's Woodpecker (*Dendropicos stierlingi*)
Malawi 733

99-81   Grey Woodpecker (*Dendropicos goertae*)
Upper Volta 150 499

99-89   Lesser Spotted Woodpecker (*Picoides minor*)
Andorra F252
Bulgaria 2684
Russia 4923

99-92   Brown-fronted Pied Woodpecker (*Picoides auriceps*)
India 579

99-94   Arabian Woodpecker (*Picoides dorae*)
Yemen 326 D373 R75 R262

99-98   White-backed Woodpecker (*Picoides leucotos*)
Japan 1742
Korea (North Korea) N268

99-99   Middle Spotted Woodpecker (*Picoides medius*)
Bulgaria 2683
Hungary 2187
Rumania 4817

99-102   Syrian Woodpecker (*Picoides syriacus*)
Bulgaria 2681

99-104   Great Spotted Woodpecker (*Picoides major*)
Bulgaria 1142
China (People's Republic) 3206
Czechoslovakia 1120
Great Britain 638
Luxembourg 691
Monaco 734
Rumania 2652
Rwanda 898
Sweden 1210
Switzerland J231

99-109   Downy Woodpecker (*Picoides pubescens*)
Cook Islands 1015
Ghana **MS**1163

99-110   Red-cockaded Woodpecker (*Picoides borealis*)
Cook Islands **MS**1021a

99-114   Three-toed Woodpecker (*Picoides tridactylus*)
Bulgaria 2682
Liechtenstein 599

99-134   Crimson-mantled Woodpecker (*Piculus rivolii*)
Colombia 1423

99-138   Common Flicker (*Colaptes auratus*)
Antigua 873
Barbuda 752
Burkina Faso 793
Cayman Islands 383
Cuba 3157
Grenada 1380
Hungary 3635 3639
Nevis 287
St. Vincent 857
Tuvalu 301
United States of America 1362 1930

99-139   Fernandina's Flicker (*Colaptes fernandinae*)
Cuba 1894 2303

99-156   Lineated Woodpecker (*Dryocopus lineatus*)
Argentine Republic 1265
Belize 490
Colombia 1721
Nicaragua 2304

99-157   Pileated Woodpecker (*Dryocopus pileatus*)
Central African Republic **MS**1105
Hungary 3637
St. Vincent 856

99-158   White-bellied Black Woodpecker (*Dryocopus javensis*)
Korea (North Korea) N744 N1777 N1778 N1779 N1780 N1781

Korea (South Korea) 414 1244

99-159   Black Woodpecker (*Dryocopus martius*)
Bulgaria 2680
Czechoslovakia 1449
Liberia 1091

99-168   Magellanic Woodpecker (*Campephilus magellanicus*)
Argentine Republic 966

99-169   Ivory-billed Woodpecker (*Campephilus principalis*)
Central African Republic 1101
Cuba 782 786 1003d 2441

99-178   Scaly-bellied Green Woodpecker (*Picus squamatus*)
Afghanistan 543

99-183   Green Woodpecker (*Picus viridis*)
Afghanistan 1063
Albania 834
Bulgaria 2685
Czechoslovakia 1447
Poland 1697 1698 2256
San Marino 601

99-187   Golden-backed Three-toed Woodpecker (*Dinopium javanense*)
Philippines 1113
Thailand 891

99-188   Lesser Golden-backed Woodpecker (*Donopium benghalense*)
Bangladesh 206

99-193   Pryer's Woodpecker (*Sapheopipo noguchii*)
Japan 1724
Malagasy Republic 320
Ryukyu Islands 175

100   BROADBILLS
100-11   Long-tailed Broadbill (*Psarisomus dalhousiae*)
Thailand 831
Vietnam N456

101   WOODCREEPERS
101-27   Straight-billed Woodcreeper (*Xiphorhynchus picus*)
Colombia 1727

101-44   Spot-crowned Woodcreeper (*Lepidocolaptes affinis*)
El Salvador 1859

102   OVENBIRDS
102-30   Blackish Cinclodes (*Cinclodes antarcticus*)
Falkland Islands 433

102-36   Rufous Hornero (*Furnarius rufus*)
Argentine Republic 1166
Uruguay 1206

103   ANTBIRDS
103-16   Barred Antshrike (*Thamnophilus doliatus*)
Belize 561 578

106   COTINGAS
106-48   Jamaican Becard (*Pachyramphus niger*)
Jamaica 643

106-56   Plum-throated Cotinga (*Cotinga maynana*)
Colombia 1422

106-58   Banded Cotinga (*Cotinga maculata*)
Brazil 1711

106-59   Spangled Cotinga (*Cotinga cayana*)
Surinam 871

106-60   Pompadour Cotinga (*Xipholena punicea*)
Colombia 1425

106-72   Amazonian Umbrellabird (*Cephalopterus ornatus*)
Peru 1132

106-79   Guianan Cock of the Rock (*Rupicola rupicola*)
Belgium 1816
Guyana 493
Surinam 1268
Venezuela 1698

106-80   Andean Cock of the Rock (*Rupicola peruviana*)
Colombia 1365
Ecuador 1121
Peru 1133

107   MANAKINS
107-36   Swallow-tailed Manakin (*Chiroxiphia caudata*)
Brazil 1434

107-40   Wire-tailed Manakin (*Pipra filicauda*)
Ecuador 1323

107-51   Red-capped Manakin (*Pipra mentalis*)
Belize 452
Pakistan 710

107-55   Crimson-hooded Manakin (*Pipra aureola*)
Surinam 869

108   TYRANT FLYCATCHERS
108-23   Dark-faced Ground-Tyrant (*Muscisaxicola
macloviana*)
Falkland Islands 438

108-45   Say's Phoebe (*Sayornis saya*)
Tuvalu 302

108-66   Vermilion Flycatcher (*Pyrocephalus rubinus*)
Argentine Republic 1101 1594
Uruguay 1211

108-72   Scissor-tailed Flycatcher (*Muscivora forficata*)
Nicaragua 1784
United States of America 1965

108-73   Fork-tailed Flycatcher (*Muscivora tyrannus*)
Argentine Republic 965
Ghana 1159
Grenadines of Grenada **MS**605
Uruguay 1214

108-74   Eastern Kingbird (*Tyrannus tyrannus*)
Grenadines of Grenada 599

108-76   Tropical Kingbird (*Tyrannus melancholicus*)
Grenada 1060

108-78   Grey Kingbird (*Tyrannus dominicensis*)
Aitutaki 518
Anguilla 670 759
Barbados 623
British Virgin Islands 564 O20
Grenadines of St. Vincent 129
St. Kitts 61 121 O13

108-79   Loggerhead Kingbird (*Tyrannus caudifasciatus*)
Antigua 472
Barbuda 308

108-100   Rusty-margined Flycatcher (*Myiozetetes cayanensis*)
Guyana 886

108-104   Great Kiskadee (*Pitangus sulphuratus*)
Argentine Republic 1102 1595
British Honduras 205 219 232
Guyana 457 792 1243

Nicaragua 1787 2730
Surinam 576
Uruguay 1213
Venezuela 1749

108-107   Rufous-tailed Flycatcher (*Myiarchus validus*)
Jamaica 645

108-116   Wied's Crested Flycatcher (*Myiarchus oberi*)
Barbuda 517
Dominica 743
St. Kitts 54

108-117   Grenada Flycatcher (*Myiarchus nugator*)
Grenadines of St. Vincent 123 241

108-121   La Sagra's Flycatcher (*Myiarchus sagrae*)
Cayman Islands 629
Cuba 3154

108-153   Lesser Antillean Pewee (*Contopus latirostris*)
Dominica 745

108-174   Belted Flycatcher (*Xenotriccus callizonus*)
El Salvador 1863

108-195   Amazonian Royal Flycatcher (*Onychorhynchus
coronatus*)
Brazil 1220

108-196   Northern Royal Flycatcher (*Onychorhynchus
mexicanus*)
Belize 562 579
Colombia 1426

108-314   Yellow-bellied Elaenia (*Elaenia flavogaster*)
Grenadines of St. Vincent 16 117
St. Vincent 299

108-315   Caribbean Elaenia (*Elaenia martinica*)
Anguilla 664
Barbados 635
Barbuda 519
St. Lucia 430

111   PITTAS
111-7   Koch's Pitta (*Pitta kochi*)
Philippines 1508

111-8   Red-breasted Pitta (*Pitta erythrogaster*)
Papua New Guinea 527
Philippines 1508

111-13   Blue-tailed Pitta (*Pitta guajana*)
Malaysia 27

111-17   Blue-winged Pitta (*Pitta brachyura*)
India 763
Korea (South Korea) 1243

111-18   African Pitta (*Pitta angolensis*)
Gabon 742

111-22   Steere's Pitta (*Pitta steerei*)
Philippines 1507

111-23   Moluccan Pitta (*Pitta moluccensis*)
Vietnam N453

111-25   Rainbow Pitta (*Pitta iris*)
Australia 739

114   LYREBIRDS
114-1   Superb Lyrebird (*Menura superba*)
Australia 140 191 O18
British Occupation of Japan B5
New South Wales 257 345a O43

116   LARKS
116-46   Hoopoe Lark (*Alaemon alaudipes*)
Spanish Sahara 150 151

116-55   Raza Island Lark (*Calandrella razae*)
Cape Verde Islands **MS**517

116-70   Crested Lark (*Galerida cristata*)
Burundi 543 567
Korea (North Korea) N743
Uganda 482

116-76   Wood Lark (*Lullula arborea*)
Great Britain 638

116-77   Sky Lark (*Alauda arvensis*)
Burundi 542 566
Denmark 831
Ifni 163 166 169

116-80   Temminck's Horned Lark (*Eremophila bilopha*)
Algeria 724

117   SWALLOWS, MARTINS
117-1   African River Martin (*Pseudochelidon eurystomina*)
Gabon 740

117-2   White-eyed River Martin (*Pseudochelidon sirintarae*)
Thailand 829

117-7   Chilean Swallow (*Tachycineta leucopyga*)
Argentine Republic 1125

117-13   Caribbean Martin (*Progne dominicensis*)
Grenadines of Grenada 298
St. Kitts 57
Turks and Caicos Islands 832

117-17   Blue and White Swallow (*Notiochelidon cyanoleuca*)
Costa Rica 1337

117-28   Sand Martin (*Riparia riparia*)
Burundi 539 563

117-29   Banded Sand Martin (*Riparia cincta*)
Ciskei 60

117-37   Barn Swallow (*Hirundo rustica*)
Anguilla 418 424 650
Antigua **MS**959
Austria 1216
Barbados 836
Barbuda **MS**850
Benin 863
Bulgaria 1520
Cameroun 943
Central African Republic 1104
China (People's Republic) 3203
China (Taiwan) 466
Ciskei 63
Comoro Islands 550
Czechoslovakia 857 2357
Finland 883 1085
France 1076
Grenadines of Grenada 600
Hungary 2184
Ifni 140 141 142

Iran 1493 1656
Italy 671 952 675 676
Japan 439
Kampuchea 462
Korea (North Korea) N495
Korea (South Korea) 371
Kuwait 592
Laos 539
Liechtenstein 176 889
Rumania 2651
San Marino 568
Switzerland 919
Trieste 19 20 22 81 116
Turkey 1843
Vatican City 133 135 136
Venezia Giulia and Istria 49 50 52 53

117-40   Pacific Swallow (*Hirundo tahitica*)
Ryukyu Islands 178

117-48   Black and Rufous Swallow (*Hirundo nigrorufa*)
Zambia 488

117-50   Greater Striped Swallow (*Hirundo cucullata*)
Ciskei 62

117-51   Lesser Striped Swallow (*Hirundo abyssinica*)
Ethiopia 676

117-61   American Cliff Swallow (*Petrochelidon pyrrhonota*)
Lesotho 646

117-66   House Martin (*Delichon urbica*)
Burundi 556 580
Ciskei 61
Lebanon 418 419
Turkey 1847

118   WAGTAILS, PIPITS
118-1   Forest Wagtail (*Dendronanthus indicus*)
Kampuchea 514

118-2   Yellow Wagtail (*Motacilla flava*)
Burundi 538 562
Great Britain 1112
Monaco 730
Rumania 3375

118-4   Grey Wagtail (*Motacilla cinerea*)
Burundi 550 574
Germany (East Germany) E1574
Hungary 2798
Kampuchea 513
Kuwait 607
Laos 543

118-5   Pied Wagtail (*Motacilla alba*)
Great Britain 1235
Hungary 3088
Iceland 673
Japan 62
Korea (North Korea) N642
Kuwait 608

118-8   African Pied Wagtail (*Motacilla aguimp*)
Congo (Brazzaville) 764

118-10   Cape Wagtail (*Motacilla capensis*)
Ciskei 6

118-13   Cape Longclaw (*Macronyx capensis*)
Ciskei 16
Lesotho 509
Rhodesia 539

122-71   Great Grey Shrike (*Lanius excubitor*)
Burundi 536 560
Guinea 744
Kuwait 585 610 612
Libya 691
Nepal 384
Sierra Leone MS857
Tunisia 602

122-79   Woodchat Shrike (*Lanius senator*)
Burundi 544 568
Malta 657
Switzerland J223

122-80   Masked Shrike (*Lanius nubicus*)
Jordan 930

123   VANGA SHRIKES
123-1   Red-tailed Vanga (*Calicalicus madagascariensis*)
Malagasy Republic 605

123-2   Rufous Vanga (*Schetba rufa*)
Malagasy Republic 604

123-3   Hook-billed Vanga (*Vanga curvirostris*)
Malagasy Republic 450

123-7   Sicklebill (*Falculea palliata*)
Malagasy Republic 606

123-12   Helmet Bird (*Euryceros prevostii*)
Malagasy Republic 64

124   WAXWINGS
124-1   Bohemian Waxwing (*Bombycilla garrulus*)
Aitutaki 519
Albania 1283
Finland 561
Germany (East Germany) E1570
Grenada 1381
Hungary 3636
Liberia 1599
Sweden 1209
Tuvalu 304

124-2   Japanese Waxwing (*Bombycilla japonica*)
Korea (South Korea) 1763

124-3   Cedar Waxwing (*Bombycilla cedrorum*)
Turks and Caicos Islands 463

125   PALM CHAT
125-1   Palm Chat (*Dulus dominicus*)
Dominican Republic 929
Haiti 1129

126   DIPPERS
126-1   Dipper (*Cinclus cinclus*)
Great Britain 1110
Luxembourg 1199
Norway 858

127   WRENS
127-4   Cactus Wren (*Campylorhynchus brunneicapillus*)
United States of America 1932

127-7   Rufous-naped Wren (*Campylorhynchus rufinucha*)
Nicaragua 1786

127-20   Short-billed Marsh Wren (*Cistothorus platensis*)
Falkland Islands 435

127-26   Zapata Wren (*Ferminia cerverai*)
Cuba 1813d 2356 2954

127-38   Carolina Wren (*Thryothorus ludovicianus*)
United States of America 1969

127-48   Winter Wren (*Troglodytes troglodytes*)
Albania 832
Burundi 540 564
Hungary 2791
Iceland 598
Ireland 442
Isle of Man 181

127-49   House Wren (*Troglodytes aedon*)
Antigua 871
Barbuda 750
Grenadines of St. Vincent 114
Niue 581 **MS**586a
St. Vincent 285

127-60   Quadrille Wren (*Cyphorhinus aradus*)
Brazil 1219

128   MOCKINGBIRDS, THRASHERS
128-1   Catbird (*Dumetella carolinensis*)
Grenadines of Grenada 604
Turks and Caicos Islands 386

128-5   Northern Mockingbird (*Mimus polyglottos*)
British Virgin Islands 563 O19
Burkina Faso 790
Cuba 2951
Mexico 1591
Turks and Caicos Islands 460
United States of America 1933 1938 1953 1971 1972

128-6   Tropical Mockingbird (*Mimus gilvus*)
Grenadines of Grenada 385
Grenadines of St. Vincent 110
Netherlands Antilles 735
Venezuela 1699

128-10   Chalk-browed Mockingbird (*Mimus saturninus*)
Argentine Republic 1076
Uruguay 1207

128-17   Brown Thrasher (*Toxostoma rufum*)
Guinea 1183
United States of America 1939

128-27   Brown Trembler (*Cinclocerthia ruficauda*)
Dominica 1048
St. Lucia 420

128-28   White-breasted Trembler (*Ramphocinclus brachyurus*)
St. Lucia 427

128-30   Scaly-breasted Thrasher (*Allenia fusca*)
Barbuda 508
Montserrat 605 O67
St. Kitts 60 120 O12

128-31   Pearly-eyed Thrasher (*Margarops fuscatus*)
Anguilla 667 716 758
British Virgin Islands 570 O26
Caicos Islands 70

129   ACCENTORS
129-10   Dunnock (*Prunella modularis*)
Burundi 549 573

130 THRUSHES, CHATS

130-11 Rufous Bushchat (*Erythropygia galactotes*)
Spanish Sahara 261

130-20 Rufous Rockjumper (*Chaetops frenatus*)
Lesotho 206

130-30 East Coast Akelat (*Erithacus gunningi*)
Malawi 735

130-31 European Robin (*Erithacus rubecula*)
Albania 1684
Belgium 2846
Cameroun 1063
Cyprus (Turkish Cypriot Posts) 142
Czechoslovakia 1450
Germany (West Germany) 1194
Germany (East Germany) E2100
Great Britain 698 1235
Hungary 2793
Isle of Man 182 226 331
Jersey 403
Liechtenstein 890
Malta 796
Monaco 731
Norway 895 979
Rumania 3373

130-33 Riukiu Robin (*Erithacus komadori*)
Japan 1419

130-36 Nightingale (*Erithacus megarhynchos*)
Albania 1689
Bulgaria 1524
Cameroun 1021
Hungary 1781
Monaco 735
San Marino 594

130-38 Bluethroat (*Erithacus svecicus*)
Afghanistan 1065
Benin 862
Germany (East Germany) E1571
Hungary 2797
Kuwait 596
Norway 894
Poland 1485
Rumania 3374 4795
San Marino 942
Switzerland J234

130-45 Red-flanked Bluetail (*Erithacus cyanurus*)
China (People's Republic) **MS**3207

130-52 Chorister Robin Chat (*Cossypha dichroa*)
Swaziland 242

130-54 White-browed Robin Chat (*Cossypha heuglini*)
Malawi 312
Venda 103

130-56 Cape Robin Chat (*Cossypha caffra*)
Lesotho 504

130-62 White-crowned Robin Chat (*Cossypha albicapilla*)
Ghana 940 **MS**943

130-79 Magpie Robin (*Copsychus saularis*)
Bangladesh 204
China (People's Republic) **MS**3207
China (Taiwan) 718
Vietnam N742 359

130-80 Seychelles Magpie Robin (*Copsychus sechellarum*)
Seychelles 311 434

130-82 White-rumped Shama (*Copsychus malabaricus*)
Singapore 74 324
Thailand 564

130-91 Black Redstart (*Phoenicurus ochruros*)
Burundi 546 570

130-92 Redstart (*Phoenicurus phoenicurus*)
Burundi 548 572
Czechoslovakia 1446
Kuwait 594
Poland 1697 1702
Rumania 3372
Switzerland J233

130-98 Daurian Redstart (*Phoenicurus auroreus*)
China (People's Republic) **MS**3207

130-99 Moussier's Redstart (*Phoenicurus moussieri*)
Algeria 723
Morocco 533

130-107 Eastern Bluebird (*Sialia sialis*)
Bermuda 389 493
Liberia 1603
Nevis 269
United States of America 1954 1961

130-109 Mountain Bluebird (*Sialia currucoides*)
United States of America 1941 1957

130-122 Cuban Solitaire (*Myadestes elisabeth*)
Cuba 1814a 2437 2962

130-123 Rufous-throated Solitaire (*Myadestes genibarbis*)
Antigua 474
Barbuda 310
Grenadines of St. Vincent 6
St. Vincent 289

130-125 Slate-coloured Solitaire (*Myadestes unicolor*)
El Salvador 1647

130-144 Hodgson's Bushchat (*Saxicola insignis*)
Russia 5162

130-146 Stonechat (*Saxicola torquata*)
Swaziland 241

130-166 Common Wheatear (*Oenanthe oenanthe*)
Kuwait 595

130-168 Black-eared Wheatear (*Oenanthe hispanica*)
San Marino 945

130-171 Mourning Wheatear (*Oenanthe lugens*)
Israel 246

130-175 White-crowned Black Wheatear (*Oenanthe leucopyga*)
Jordan 929

130-188 Rock Thrush (*Monticola saxatilis*)
Albania 1461
Bulgaria 1519
Burundi 545 569
Hungary 2792
Kuwait 593
Poland 1209
Qatar 393 612
Rumania 2648
Spain 2850

130-192 Blue Rock Thrush (*Monticola solitarius*)
Gibraltar 171
Iraq 1256 O1261
Malta 457 458

130-193 Ceylon Whistling Thrush (*Myiophoneus blighi*)
Sri Lanka 686

130-211 Varied Thrush (*Zoothera naevia*)
Nevis 289

130-233 Tristan Thrush (*Nesocichla eremita*)
Tristan Da Cunha 115 174 175 257

130-234 Forest Thrush (*Cichlherminia lherminieri*)
Dominica 742
Montserrat 254a 612 O6 O74

130-238 Orange-billed Nightingale Thrush (*Catharus aurantiirostris*)
Nicaragua 2725

130-241 Frantzius's Nightingale Thrush (*Catharus frantzii*)
Nicaragua 2728

130-244 Veery (*Catharus fuscescens*)
Niue 582 **MS**586b

130-247 Hermit Thrush (*Catharus guttatus*)
Canada 640
United States of America 1974

130-255 Taita Olive Thrush (*Turdus helleri*)
Kenya 305

130-256 Kurrichane Thrush (*Turdus libonyanus*)
Venda 106

130-260 Groundscraper Thrush (*Turdus litsipsirupa*)
Botswana 222

130-261 Black-breasted Thrush (*Turdus dissimilis*)
Korea (North Korea) N742

130-265 Ring Ousel (*Turdus torquatus*)
Burundi 547 571
Czechoslovakia 1523

130-267 Blackbird (*Turdus merula*)
Czechoslovakia 2149
Great Britain 699 1045 1233 1234
Guernsey 319
Hungary 1786
Sweden 630

130-268 Island Thrush (*Turdus poliocephalus*)
Christmas Island 157
New Caledonia 778
Norfolk Island 109
Samoa 288

130-278 Fieldfare (*Turdus pilaris*)
Burundi 558 582

130-279 Redwing (*Turdus iliacus*)
Albania 1683

130-280 Song Thrush (*Turdus philomelos*)
Czechoslovakia 2077

130-283 White-chinned Thrush (*Turdus aurantius*)
Jamaica 471

130-284 Grand Cayman Thrush (*Turdus ravidus*)
Cayman Islands 222 238 273 319

130-285 Red-legged Thrush (*Turdus plumbeus*)
Cuba 1896 2957
Dominica 1045

130-289 Glossy-black Thrush (*Turdus serranus*)
Venezuela 1750

130-295 Rufous-bellied Thrush (*Turdus rufiventris*)
Argentine Republic 1395
Kampuchea 654
Uruguay 1205

130-296 Austral Thrush (*Turdus falcklandii*)
Falkland Islands 227

130-297 Pale-breasted Thrush (*Turdus leucomelas*)
Surinam 582

130-302 Cocoa Thrush (*Turdus fumigatus*)
Grenadines of Grenada 148

130-306 Clay-coloured Thrush (*Turdus grayi*)
Costa Rica 1334

130-307 Bare-eyed Thrush (*Turdus nudigenis*)
Grenada 321 517 607
Grenadines of Grenada 15
Grenadines of St. Vincent 12
St. Vincent 295

130-308 White-eyed Thrush (*Turdus jamaicensis*)
Jamaica 644

130-313 American Robin (*Turdus migratorius*)
Rumania 4936
United States of America 1936 1951 1978

132 BABBLERS

132-33 Long-billed Scimitar Babbler (*Pomatorhinus hypoleucos*)
Thailand 893

132-36 Slaty-headed Scimitar Babbler (*Pomatorhinus schisticeps*)
India 580

132-104 Brown Tit-Babbler (*Macronous striaticeps*)
Philippines 1505

132-112 Spiny Babbler (*Turdoides nipalensis*)
Nepal 352

132-120 Fulvous Babbler (*Turdoides fulvus*)
Libya 692
Spanish Sahara 152
Tunisia 601

132-136 Pied Babbler (*Turdoides bicolor*)
Bophuthatswana 60

132-146 White-crested Laughing Thrush (*Garrulax leucolophus*)
Laos 179
Singapore 325

132-155 Black-throated Laughing Thrush (*Garrulax chinensis*)
Vietnam 189

132-173 Hwamei (*Garrulax canorus*)
Hong Kong 335
Singapore 325
Vietnam 186

132-186   Yersin's Laughing Thrush (*Garrulax yersini*)
Vietnam 191

132-187   Crimson-winged Laughing Thrush (*Garrulax formosus*)
Vietnam 188

132-189   Red-faced Liocichla (*Liocichla phoenicea*)
Bhutan 187 192 197 242

132-191   Steere's Liocichla (*Liocichla steerii*)
China (Taiwan) 1265

132-193   Pekin Robin (*Leiothrix lutea*)
Macao 596

132-208   Chestnut-tailed Minla (*Minla strigula*)
Thailand 1019

132-248   Formosan Yuhina (*Yuhina brunneiceps*)
China (Taiwan) 1266

132-252   Fire-tailed Myzornis (*Myzornis pyrrhoura*)
Bhutan 191 196 201 218 222 262

133   PARROTBILLS
133-1   Bearded Reedling (*Panurus biarmicus*)
Albania 1288
Spain 2852

133-9   Vinous-throated Parrotbill (*Paradoxornis webbianus*)
Russia 5161

134   ROCKFOWL
134-2   Grey-necked Bald Crow (*Picathartes oreas*)
Gabon 435
Togo 1529

135   GNATWRENS
135-4   Blue-grey Gnatcatcher (*Polioptila caerula*)
Cuba 1814b
Turks and Caicos Islands 454

135-6   Cuban Gnatcatcher (*Polioptila lembeyei*)
Cuba 2438 2964

136   OLD WORLD WARBLERS
136-10   Japanese Bush Warbler (*Cettia diphone*)
Japan 933

136-45   Sedge Warbler (*Acrocephalus schoenobaenus*)
Burundi 557 581
Uganda 480

136-52   Reed Warbler (*Acrocephalus scirpaceus*)
Benin 865

136-55   Great Reed Warbler (*Acrocephalus arundinaceus*)
Burundi 554 578
Congo (Brazzaville) 618
Kuwait 590
Rumania 3371

136-56   Oriental Great Reed Warbler (*Acrocephalus orientalis*)
Korea (North Korea) N1208

136-60   Finsch's Reed Warbler (*Acrocephalus rehsei*)
Nauru 64 77 91 145

136-62   Polynesian Reed Warbler (*Acrocephalus aequinoctialis*)
Kiribati 169 O25

136-63   Long-billed Reed Warbler (*Acrocephalus caffra*)
Aitutaki 341 453

136-66   Pitcairn Warbler (*Acrocephalus vaughanii*)
Cook Islands 617
Pitcairn Islands 41 74

136-71   Rodriguez Brush Warbler (*Bebrornis rodericanus*)
Mauritius 346

136-72   Seychelles Brush Warbler (*Bebrornis sechellensis*)
Seychelles 308

136-75   Aldabra Warbler (*Nesillas aldabranus*)
Zil Elwannyen Sesel 53

136-86   Barred Warbler (*Sylvia nisoria*)
Mongolia 1236

136-89   Garden Warbler (*Sylvia borin*)
Sierra Leone 855

136-90   Blackcap (*Sylvia atricapilla*)
Albania 1688
Kuwait 591
Monaco 733

136-91   Whitethroat (*Sylvia communis*)
Libya 1194

136-95   Sardinian Warbler (*Sylvia melanocephala*)
Gibraltar 377
Malta 656
San Marino 946

136-96   Cyprus Warbler (*Sylvia melanothorax*)
Cyprus 336

136-98   Subalpine Warbler (*Sylvia cantillans*)
Spain 2849

136-100   Tristram's Warbler (*Sylvia deserticola*)
Algeria 722

136-102   Dartford Warbler (*Sylvia undata*)
Guernsey 171

136-104   Willow Warbler (*Phylloscopus trochilus*)
Kuwait 589

136-107   Bonelli's Warbler (*Phylloscopus bonelli*)
Andorra F313

136-156   Ruby-crowned Kinglet (*Regulus calendula*)
Antigua 872
Barbuda 751
Belize 824

136-158   Firecrest (*Regulus ignicapillus*)
Albania 1460
Burundi 541 565
Germany (East Germany) E1568
Great Britain 1235
Guernsey 170
Hungary 2794
Luxembourg 854
Madeira 230
San Marino 939
Switzerland J224

136-160   Golden-crowned Kinglet (*Regulus satrapa*)
Nevis 286

136-161   Severtzov's Tit Warbler (*Leptopoecile sophiae*)
Russia 5158

136-173   Madagascar Cisticola (*Cisticola cherina*)
Zil Elwannyen Sesel 56

136-217   Graceful Prinia (*Prinia gracilis*)
Israel 248

136-235   White-winged Apalis (*Apalis chariessa*)
Kenya 307

136-254   Damaraland Rock Jumper (*Sphenoeacus
              pycnopygius*)
South West Africa 262

136-265   Long-tailed Tailor Bird (*Orthotomus sutorius*)
Laos 544

136-279   Grey-backed Camaroptera (*Camaroptera
              brevicaudata*)
Ghana 1047

136-324   Japanese Marsh Warbler (*Megalurus pryeri*)
Japan 1729

136-327   Striated Canegrass Warbler (*Megalurus palustris*)
Vietnam N740

136-333   New Caledonian Grass Warbler (*Megalurulus
              mariei*)
New Caledonia 404

136-334   Thicket Warbler (*Cichlornis whitneyi*)
New Hebrides 108 F123 F124

136-337   Long-legged Warbler (*Trichocichla rufa*)
Fiji 566

137   AUSTRALIAN WRENS
137-6   Blue Wren (*Malurus cyaneus*)
Australia 367

137-8   Variegated Wren (*Malurus lamberti*)
Australia 206 678
Niue 631

137-41   New Zealand Grey Flyeater (*Gerygone igata*)
Norfolk Island 105

137-60   Yellow-tailed Thornbill (*Acanthiza chrysorrhoa*)
Australia 363 386

138   OLD WORLD FLYCATCHERS
138-24   Pied Flycatcher (*Ficedula hypoleuca*)
Burundi 553 577

138-27   Narcissus Flycatcher (*Ficedula narcissina*)
China (Taiwan) 1011

138-29   Red-breasted Flycatcher (*Ficedula parva*)
Rumania 3369
San Marino 602
Yugoslavia 1776

138-50   Blue and White Flycatcher (*Cyanoptila
              cyanomelaena*)
Japan 1667

138-75   Spotted Flycatcher (*Muscicapa striata*)
Finland 514
Sierra Leone 854

138-98   Sri Lanka Dusky Blue Flycatcher (*Eumyias sordida*)
Sri Lanka 829

138-105   Humblot's Flycatcher (*Humblotia flavirostris*)
Comoro Islands 98

138-123   Scarlet Robin (*Petroica multicolor*)
Aitutaki 320 477 O18
Australia 368 396
New Hebrides 284 F297
Norfolk Island 103

138-125   Flame Robin (*Petroica phoenicea*)
Australia 679

138-134   Chatham Island Robin (*Petroica traversi*)
New Zealand 1293

138-137   Eastern Yellow Robin (*Eopsaltria australis*)
Australia 674

138-147   Olive-yellow Robin (*Poecilodryas placens*)
Papua New Guinea 528

139   PUFFBACK & WATTLED FLYCATCHER
139-4   Cape Puff-back Flycatcher (*Batis capensis*)
Ciskei 15a
Transkei 76

139-6   Boulton's Puff-back Flycatcher (*Batis margaritae*)
Zambia 490

139-7   Ruwenzori Puff-back Flycatcher (*Batis diops*)
Rwanda 473

139-14   Pygmy Puff-back Flycatcher (*Batis perkeo*)
Somalia 658

140   MONARCH FLYCATCHERS
140-11   African Paradise Flycatcher (*Terpsiphone viridis*)
Botswana 416
Chad 84
Ethiopia 635
Malawi 319 369
Venda 92

140-14   Madagascar Paradise Flycatcher (*Terpsiphone
              mutata*)
Comoro Islands 64 274 342

140-15   Seychelles Paradise Flycatcher (*Terpsiphone
              corvina*)
Seychelles 312 369 435

140-16   Mascarene Paradise Flycatcher (*Terpsiphone
              bourbonnensis*)
Mauritius 320 352

140-17   Asiatic Paradise Flycatcher (*Terpsiphone paradisi*)
Malaysia 26
Russia 5159
Thailand 830

140-18   Black Paradise Flycatcher (*Terpsiphone atrocaudata*)
Korea (North Korea) N399

140-26   Black-naped Blue Monarch (*Hypothymis azurea*)
Laos 542

140-39 Slaty Flycatcher (*Mayrornis lessoni*)
Fiji 444

140-40 Buff-bellied Flycatcher (*Neolalage banksiana*)
New Hebrides 107 F122
Vanuatu 329

140-82 Palau Myiagra Flycatcher (*Myiagra erythrops*)
Palau 98

140-87 New Caledonian Myiagra Flycatcher (*Myiagra caledonica*)
Vanuatu 327

140-88 Red-bellied Flycatcher (*Myiagra vanikorensis*)
Aitutaki 350 492 O31

140-89 White-vented Flycatcher (*Myiagra albiventris*)
Samoa 283

140-92 Blue-headed Flycatcher (*Myiagra azureocapilla*)
Aitutaki 349 491 O30
Fiji 511

141 FANTAIL FLYCATCHERS
141-11 Palau Fantail (*Rhipidura lepida*)
Palau 8

141-16 Rufous Fantail (*Rhipidura rufifrons*)
Aitutaki 321 479 O20
Papua New Guinea 525

141-26 Collared Grey Fantail (*Rhipidura fuliginosa*)
New Zealand 577 832 O120
Norfolk Island 114
Vanuatu 330

141-27 Samoan Fantail (*Rhipidura nebulosa*)
Samoa 289

141-35 White-browed Fantail (*Rhipidura aureola*)
Burma 174 175 176 195 196 197 O186 O187 O192 O193 O194 O196 O197 O198 O207 O208 O209
Vietnam N743

141-36 Pied Fantail (*Rhipidura javanica*)
Indonesia 1022

141-40 Willie Wagtail (*Rhipidura leucophrys*)
Solomon Islands 309

142 WHISTLERS
142-24 Golden Whistler (*Pachycephala pectoralis*)
Aitutaki 319 478 506 **MS**507 **MS**549 O19
Australia 366 394
Norfolk Island 104
Solomon Islands 267 285 305
Vanuatu 309

142-28 New Caledonian Whistler (*Pachycephala caledonica*)
New Caledonia 405

142-46 Morning Bird (*Pitohui tenebrosus*)
Palau 6

143 LONG-TAILED TITS
143-1 Long-tailed Tit (*Aegithalos caudatus*)
Albania 1286
Great Britain 638
Hungary 2185
Rumania 2656

144 PENDULINE TITS
144-1 Penduline Tit (*Remiz pendulinus*)
Albania 833
Czechoslovakia 1635
Rumania 3376 3981

145 TITS, CHICKADEES
145-4 Black-capped Chickadee (*Parus atricapillus*)
United States of America 1948 1950

145-21 Crested Tit (*Parus cristatus*)
Albania 1457
Brazil 2257
Russia 4924

145-33 Great Tit (*Parus major*)
Albania 837
Bulgaria 1140
China (People's Republic) 3205
Finland 513 940 1001 1037
Great Britain 1235
Hungary 1782
Japan 1259
Korea (North Korea) N641
Mongolia 1240
Netherlands 1410
Norway 859
Poland 1697 1705
Rumania 2654
Sweden 631
Vietnam N744
Yemen 595
Yugoslavia 1605

145-38 Chinese Yellow Tit (*Parus spilonotus*)
Thailand 1018

145-40 Blue Tit (*Parus caeruleus*)
Albania 1462
Algeria 691
Andorra F251
Czechoslovakia 1121
Germany (East Germany) E2102
Great Britain 697
Hungary 2796
Portugal 1620
San Marino 940
Sweden 634
Switzerland J229

145-42 Varied Tit (*Parus varius*)
Japan 486 **MS**487

145-45 Tufted Titmouse (*Parus bicolor*)
Bhutan **MS**633

145-46 Sultan Tit (*Melanochlora sultanea*)
Thailand 832

146 NUTHATCHES
146-1 European Nuthatch (*Sitta europaea*)
Albania 836
Czechoslovakia 1122
Germany (East Germany) E2099
Great Britain 1235
Sweden 1211

146-12 White-breasted Nuthatch (*Sitta carolinensis*)
Burkina Faso 792

146-14 Kabylie Nuthatch (*Sitta ledanti*)
Algeria 761

146-22   Wallcreeper (*Tichodroma muraria*)
Albania 1287
Andorra F314
Czechoslovakia 1520
Germany (East Germany) E1575
Monaco 1562
Poland 1211
Rumania 2657 4819
Switzerland J227
Yugoslavia 1516

147 TREECREEPERS
147-1   Treecreeper (*Certhia familiaris*)
Albania 835

150 FLOWERPECKERS
150-5   Streaked Berrypecker (*Melanocharis striativentris*)
Papua New Guinea 526

150-43   Mistletoe Flowerpecker (*Dicaeum hirundinaceum*)
Pakistan 707

150-52   Spotted Pardalote (*Pardalotus punctatus*)
Pakistan 708

151 SUNBIRDS
151-4   Anchieta's Sunbird (*Anthreptes anchietae*)
Zambia 491

151-8   Ruby-cheeked Sunbird (*Anthreptes singalensis*)
Vietnam 413

151-9   Violet-backed Sunbird (*Anthreptes longuemarei*)
Togo 1533

151-16   Collared Sunbird (*Anthreptes collaris*)
Rwanda 470 1145
Venda 38

151-17   Pygmy Sunbird (*Anthreptes platurus*)
Upper Volta 154

151-18   Blue-naped Sunbird (*Hypogramma hypogrammicum*)
Vietnam 417

151-30   Blue-headed Sunbird (*Nectarinia alinae*)
Rwanda 1146

151-37   Scarlet-chested Sunbird (*Nectarinia senegalensis*)
Bechuanaland 170
Botswana 208
Chad 83
Malawi 310
Rwanda 475
Venda 41

151-42   Van Hasselt's Sunbird (*Nectarinia sperata*)
Vietnam 418

151-44   Macklot's Sunbird (*Nectarinia calcostetha*)
Vietnam 416

151-45   Seychelles Sunbird (*Nectarinia dussumieri*)
Seychelles 370

151-47   Yellow-bellied Sunbird (*Nectarinia jugularis*)
Singapore 76

151-51   Souimanga Sunbird (*Nectarinia souimanga*)
British Indian Ocean Territory 75
Zil Elwannyen Sesel 62

151-53   Anjouan Sunbird (*Nectarinia comorensis*)
Comoro Islands 60 275 343

151-55   Variable Sunbird (*Nectarinia venusta*)
French Territory of the Afars and the Issas 650
Mauritania D182
Rwanda 471

151-56   Southern White-bellied Sunbird (*Nectarinia talatala*)
Venda 40

151-59   Lesser Double-collared Sunbird (*Nectarinia chalybea*)
Botswana 516

151-60   Greater Double-collared Sunbird (*Nectarinia afra*)
Rwanda 472
South Africa 358

151-61   Northern Double-collared Sunbird (*Nectarinia
    preussi*)
Rwanda 1134 1141 1246

151-64   Olive-bellied Sunbird (*Nectarinia chloropygia*)
Congo (Brazzaville) 761
Rwanda 1149
Sierra Leone 623
Upper Volta 155

151-66   Regal Sunbird (*Nectarinia regia*)
Congo (Brazzaville) 116
Rwanda 247 957 1142
Zaire 953

151-73   Palestine Sunbird (*Nectarinia osea*)
Israel 249
Jordan 931

151-74   Coppery Sunbird (*Nectarinia cuprea*)
Rwanda 1148

151-77   Purple-breasted Sunbird (*Nectarinia purpureiventris*)
Rwanda 1147

151-78   Shelley's Sunbird (*Nectarinia shelleyi*)
Zambia 263

151-79   Mariqua Sunbird (*Nectarinia mariquensis*)
Bophuthatswana 166
Venda 39

151-82   Splendid Sunbird (*Nectarinia coccinigastra*)
Biafra 6
Nigeria 174
Togo 1530
Upper Volta 156

151-83   Red-chested Sunbird (*Nectarinia erythrocerca*)
Rwanda 1150

151-85   Beautiful Sunbird (*Nectarinia pulchella*)
Gambia 193 215

151-87   Yellow-tufted Malachite Sunbird (*Nectarinia famosa*)
Ciskei 8
Lesotho 508

151-88   Red-tufted Malachite Sunbird (*Nectarinia johnstoni*)
Rwanda 1143

151-90   Madame Verreaux's Sunbird (*Nectarinia johannae*)
Gabon 171

151-92   Bronze Sunbird (*Nectarinia kilimensis*)
Rwanda 1144

151-100   Mrs Gould's Sunbird (*Aethopyga gouldiae*)
Bhutan 448
Vietnam 415

151-101   Green-tailed Sunbird (*Aethopyga nipalensis*)
Vietnam 419

151-104   Black-throated Sunbird (*Aethopyga saturata*)
Vietnam 414

151-105   Yellow-backed Sunbird (*Aethopyga siparaja*)
India 581
Vietnam 412

151-107   Fire-tailed Sunbird (*Aethopyga ignicauda*)
Nepal 385

152   WHITE EYES
152-2   Japanese White Eye (*Zosterops japonica*)
Macao 594
Vietnam N745

152-4   Oriental White Eye (*Zosterops palpebrosa*)
Singapore 323

152-5   Large Sri Lanka White Eye (*Zosterops ceylonensis*)
Sri Lanka 828 921

152-6   Bridled White Eye (*Zosterops conspicillata*)
Palau 101

152-29   Christmas Island White Eye (*Zosterops natalis*)
Christmas Island 156

152-38   Savaii White Eye (*Zosterops samoensis*)
Samoa 289b

152-40   Yellow-fronted White Eye (*Zosterops flavifrons*)
New Hebrides 285 F298

152-44   Grey-backed White Eye (*Zosterops lateralis*)
Fiji 509

152-46   White-chested White Eye (*Zosterops albogularis*)
Norfolk Island 112 269 270 271 272 273

152-48   Grey-brown White Eye (*Zosterops cinerea*)
Palau 101

152-53   Bourbon White Eye (*Zosterops borbonica*)
Mauritius 317 349 370

152-57   Madagascar White Eye (*Zosterops maderaspatana*)
British Indian Ocean Territory 71
Zil Elwannyen Sesel 57 103

152-59   Seychelles Brown White Eye (*Zosterops modesta*)
Seychelles 371

152-62   Mauritius Olive White Eye (*Zosterops chloronothos*)
Mauritius 319 351

152-66   Palau White Eye (*Rukia palauensis*)
Palau 7

153   HONEYEATERS
153-32   Scarlet Honeyeater (*Myzomela sanguinolenta*)
New Caledonia 414

153-33   Cardinal Honeyeater (*Myzomela cardinalis*)
Fiji 436
New Hebrides 106 F121
Palau 99

153-40   Orange-breasted Honeyeater (*Myzomela jugularis*)
Fiji 380 400 476

153-74   Yellow-tufted Honeyeater (*Meliphaga melanops*)
Australia 959

153-83   Carunculated Honeyeater (*Foulehaio carunculata*)
Samoa 280

153-84   Yellow-faced Honeyeater (*Foulehaio provocator*)
Fiji 445

153-86   Bonin Island Honeyeater (*Apalopteron familiare*)
Japan 1405

153-94   Blue-faced Honeyeater (*Entomyzon cyanotis*)
Australia 387

153-95   Stitchbird (*Notiomystis cincta*)
New Zealand 1294

153-115   New Caledonian Friarbird (*Philemon diemenensis*)
New Caledonia 411

153-137   Green Honeyeater (*Gymnomyza viridis*)
Niuafo'ou 32 74

153-138   Black-breasted Honeyeater (*Gymnomyza samoensis*)
Samoa 289a

153-139   Red-faced Honeyeater (*Gymnomyza aubryana*)
New Caledonia 410

153-147   White-bellied Honeyeater (*Phylidonyris notabilis*)
New Hebrides 283 F296

153-164   New Zealand Bell Bird (*Anthornis melanura*)
New Zealand 839

153-169   Tui (*Prosthemadura novaeseelandiae*)
New Zealand 588 O131

154   BUNTINGS
154-4   Yellowhammer (*Emberiza citrinella*)
Hungary 1787

154-7   Siberian Meadow Bunting (*Emberiza cioides*)
Japan 934

154-8   Jankowski's Bunting (*Emberiza jankowskii*)
Russia 5160

154-12   Ortolan Bunting (*Emberiza hortulana*)
Central African Republic 805
San Marino 941

154-29   Golden-breasted Bunting (*Emberiza flaviventris*)
Lesotho 209
Rhodesia 461

154-34   Black-headed Bunting (*Emberiza melanocephala*)
Central African Republic 805

154-40   Reed Bunting (*Emberiza schoeniclus*)
Rumania 4799

154-47   Lark Bunting (*Calamospiza melanocorys*)
United States of America 1935

154-52   Rufous-collared Sparrow (*Zonotrichia capensis*)
Argentine Republic 1077
Netherlands Antilles 864
Uruguay 1208

154-54   White-crowned Sparrow (*Zonotrichia leucophrys*)
Cook Islands 1020

154-55   White-throated Sparrow (*Zonotrichia albicollis*)
Canada 638

154-61   Savannah Sparrow (*Passerculus sandwichensis*)
Canada 639

154-62   Seaside Sparrow (*Ammodramus maritimus*)·
British Virgin Islands 588
Cook Islands **MS**1021b

154-66   Henslow's Sparrow (*Ammodramus henslowii*)
Niue 584 **MS**586d

154-67   Grasshopper Sparrow (*Ammodramus savannarum*)
Niue 583 **MS**586c

154-72   Chipping Sparrow (*Spizella passerina*)
Montserrat 661

154-77   Vesper Sparrow (*Pooecetes gramineus*)
Lesotho 648
Niue 585 **MS**586e

154-78   Lark Sparrow (*Chondestes grammacus*)
Montserrat 660

154-95   Zapata Sparrow (*Torreornis inexpectata*)
Cuba 1812 2440

154-107   Black-throated Finch (*Melanodera melanodera*)
Falkland Islands 436

154-109   Slaty Finch (*Haplospiza rustica*)
El Salvador 1860

154-116   Nightingale Finch (*Nesospiza acunhae*)
Tristan Da Cunha 258

154-117   Wilkin's Finch (*Nesospiza wilkinsi*)
Tristan Da Cunha 114 420

154-119   Common Diuca Finch (*Diuca diuca*)
Chile 1008

154-150   Saffron Finch (*Sicalis flaveola*)
Argentine Republic 1394
Brazil 1710
Kampuchea 649

154-151   Grassland Yellow Finch (*Sicalis luteola*)
Barbados 622

154-173   Yellow-bellied Seedeater (*Sporophila nigricollis*)
Grenadines of Grenada 382

154-177   Double-collared Seedeater (*Sporophila caerulescens*)
Argentine Republic 1441 1592

154-203   Cuban Grassquit (*Tiaris canora*)
Cuba 1000 2354 2960

154-204   Yellow-faced Grassquit (*Tiaris olivacea*)
Cayman Islands 630

154-205   Black-faced Grassquit (*Tiaris bicolor*)
Caicos Islands 69
Netherlands Antilles 863
St. Kitts 64 O16

154-209   Greater Antillean Bullfinch (*Loxigilla violacea*)
Caicos Islands 71

154-210   Lesser Antillean Bullfinch (*Loxigilla noctis*)
Anguilla 665a 759
Barbados 624
Grenadines of St. Vincent 4
St. Kitts 67 125 O19
St. Vincent 287

154-211   St. Lucia Black Finch (*Melanospiza richardsoni*)
St. Lucia 428

154-212   Large Ground Finch (*Geospiza magnirostris*)
Great Britain 1177

154-216   Cactus Ground Finch (*Geospiza scandens*)
Great Britain 1177

154-219   Large Insectivorous Tree Finch (*Camarhynchus psittacula*)
Ecuador 1691

154-220   Charles Insectivorous Tree Finch (*Camarhynchus pauper*)
Ecuador 1691

154-222   Woodpecker Finch (*Camarhynchus pallidus*)
Ecuador 1691

154-227   Rufous-sided Towhee (*Pipilo erythrophthalmus*)
Antigua 869
Barbuda 748

156   CARDINALS, GROSBEAKS

156-1   Yellow Cardinal (*Gubernatrix cristata*)
Uruguay 1215

156-2   Red-crested Cardinal (*Paroaria coronata*)
Argentine Republic 1124
Brazil 1218
Uruguay 1209

156-3   Red-cowled Cardinal (*Paroaria dominicana*)
Brazil 2085

156-7   Dickcissel (*Spiza americana*)
Cook Islands 1019

156-10   Yellow-bellied Grosbeak (*Pheucticus chrysogaster*)
Ecuador 1324

156-12   Rose-breasted Grosbeak (*Pheucticus ludovicianus*)
Barbuda 505
Cuba 1290d
Grenadines of Grenada 602

156-13   Black-headed Grosbeak (*Pheucticus melanocephalus*)
Congo (Brazzaville) 985

156-14   Common Cardinal (*Cardinalis cardinalis*)
Aitutaki 521
Belize 827
Bermuda 391
Hungary 3640
Liberia 1604
Nevis 270
United States of America 1470 **MS**1726 1942 1943 1946 1962 1964 1975 1977

156-15   Vermilion Cardinal (*Pyrrhuloxia phoeniceus*)
Venezuela 1748

156-40   Blue Grosbeak (*Guiraca caerulea*)
Montserrat 664

156-41   Indigo Bunting (*Passerina cyanea*)
Cuba 1289

156-44   Painted Bunting (*Passerina ciris*)
Belize 825
Cuba 1290a
Nevis 285
Nicaragua 2727
St. Vincent 858
Turks and Caicos Islands 464

157   TANAGERS
157-47   Yellow-backed Tanager (*Hemithraupis flavicollis*)
Surinam 864

157-52   Black-crowned Palm Tanager (*Phaenicophilus palmarum*)
Dominican Republic 1380

157-54   Chat-Tanager (*Calyptophilus frugivorus*)
Dominican Republic 1381

157-86   Summer Tanager (*Piranga rubra*)
Aitutaki 520

157-88   Scarlet Tanager (*Piranga olivacea*)
Barbados 840
Cuba 1288
Ecuador 1326 1337
Mauritania 825

157-89   Western Tanager (*Piranga ludoviciana*)
Anguilla **MS**654a
Mauritania 825
Nevis 288

157-94   Crimson-collared Tanager (*Ramphocelus sanguinolentus*)
Belize 468

157-95   Masked Crimson Tanager (*Ramphocelus nigrogularis*)
Ecuador 1120 1539

157-96   Crimson-backed Tanager (*Ramphocelus dimidiatus*)
Panama 920 1288

157-98   Silver-beaked Tanager (*Ramphocelus carbo*)
Surinam 577

157-100   Scarlet-rumped Tanager (*Ramphocelus passerinii*)
British Honduras 206

157-102   Stripe-headed Tanager (*Spindalis zena*)
Caicos Islands **MS**72
Cayman Islands 341
Cuba 1895
Haiti 1130 1134

157-103   Blue-grey Tanager (*Thraupis episcopus*)
Belize 491
Panama 918
Surinam 579 1134

157-104   Sayaca Tanager (*Thraupis sayaca*)
Uruguay 1217

157-110   Blue & Yellow Tanager (*Thraupis bonariensis*)
Argentine Republic 1192
Kampuchea 650
Uruguay 1218

157-125   Black-chinned Mountain Tanager (*Anisognathus notabilis*)
Ecuador 1536

157-126   Diademed Tanager (*Stephanophorus diadematus*)
Uruguay 1210 1343

157-148   Blue-hooded Euphonia (*Euphonia musica*)
Barbuda 263
Dominica 744
Grenadines of Grenada **MS**154 383
Grenadines of St. Vincent 14
Haiti 1127 1131
St. Vincent 297 380

157-170   Turquoise Tanager (*Tangara mexicana*)
Surinam 581

157-171   Paradise Tanager (*Tangara chilensis*)
Ecuador 1322
Surinam 862 1292

157-172   Seven-coloured Tanager (*Tangara fastuosa*)
Brazil 1712

157-193   Hooded Tanager (*Tangara cucullata*)
Grenadines of Grenada 150
Grenadines of St. Vincent 13
St. Vincent 296

157-201   Blue-necked Tanager (*Tangara cyanicollis*)
Ecuador 1540

157-202   Golden-masked Tanager (*Tangara larvata*)
Belize 565 **MS**566 582

157-223   Green Honeycreeper (*Chlorophanes spiza*)
Surinam 861

157-227   Red-legged Honeycreeper (*Cyanerpes cyaneus*)
British Honduras 203
Costa Rica 1333
Nicaragua 1788

158   SWALLOW TANAGER
158-1   Swallow Tanager (*Tersina viridis*)
Venezuela 1752

159   NEW WORLD WARBLERS
159-1   Black & White Warbler (*Mniotilta varia*)
Dominica 940

159-4   Blue-winged Warbler (*Vermivora pinus*)
Cuba 1291b

159-13   Parula Warbler (*Parula americana*)
Antigua 870
Barbuda 749
Turks and Caicos Islands 459

159-15   Yellow Warbler (*Dendroica petechia*)
Barbados 787 837
Cayman Islands 385
Cuba 3155
Grenadines of Grenada 384 601
Nevis 273
Togo **MS**1824

159-16   Chestnut-sided Warbler (*Dendroica pensylvanica*)
Cook Islands 1018

159-17   Cerulean Warbler (*Dendroica cerulea*)
Nevis 274

159-18   Black-throated Blue Warbler (*Dendroica caerulescens*)
Cook Islands 1016
Montserrat 657
Pakistan 709

159-19   Plumbeous Warbler (*Dendroica plumbea*)
Dominica 870

159-24   Adelaide's Warbler (*Dendroica adelaidae*)
Barbuda 507

159-25   Olive-capped Warbler (*Dendroica pityophila*)
Cuba 3153

159-26   Yellow-throated Warbler (*Dendroica dominica*)
Cook Islands 1017
Cuba 1291a

159-28   Townsend's Warbler (*Dendroica townsendi*)
Tuvalu 303

159-32   Prairie Warbler (*Dendroica discolor*)
Barbados 785
Grenada **MS**1064

159-33   Vitelline Warbler (*Dendroica vitellina*)
Cayman Islands 338

159-35   Blackburnian Warbler (*Dendroica fusca*)
Cuba 1290c
Nevis 291

159-36   Magnolia Warbler (*Dendroica magnolia*)
Turks and Caicos Islands 829

159-38   Palm Warbler (*Dendroica palmarum*)
Montserrat 658

159-41   Bay-breasted Warbler (*Dendroica castanea*)
Liberia 1600

159-43   American Redstart (*Setophaga ruticilla*)
Barbados 636
Cuba 1290b

159-44   Ovenbird (*Seiurus aurocapillus*)
Turks and Caicos Islands 593

159-48   Worm-eating Warbler (*Helmitheros vermivorus*)
Tuvalu 306

159-49   Prothonotary Warbler (*Protonotaria citrea*)
Cuba 1291c
Tuvalu 305
United States of America 2083

159-50   Yellowthroat (*Geothlypis trichas*)
Grenadines of Grenada 603

159-66   Yellow-headed Warbler (*Teretistris fernandinae*)
Cuba 1814d

159-67   Oriente Warbler (*Teretistris fornsi*)
Cuba 1811 2301 2439

159-69   Hooded Warbler (*Wilsonia citrina*)
Cuba 1291d
Grenada 1379

159-72   Red-faced Warbler (*Cardellina rubrifrons*)
El Salvador 1864

159-113   Yellow-breasted Chat (*Icteria virens*)
Antigua **MS**874
Barbuda **MS**753
British Virgin Islands 590

159-124   Bananaquit (*Coereba flaveola*)
Anguilla 37 673 718
Barbados 633b 634 684
Barbuda 262
Cayman Islands 593
Dominica 528
Grenada 318 513 604 761
Grenadines of Grenada 12
Grenadines of St. Vincent 8 115
Montserrat 247 369 610 O2 O3 O72
Netherlands Antilles 736
St. Kitts 59 119 O11
St. Vincent 291
Turks and Caicos Islands 462

160   HAWAIIAN HONEYCREEPERS
160-14   Apapane (*Himatione sanguinea*)
Penrhyn Island 109

160-16   Iiwi (*Vestiaria coccinea*)
Penrhyn Island 107

161   VIREOS
161-9   White-eyed Vireo (*Vireo griseus*)
Bermuda 388

161-13   Cuban Vireo (*Vireo gundlachii*)
Cuba 1814c 2214

161-14   Thick-billed Vireo (*Vireo crassirostris*)
Caicos Islands 68

161-24   Solitary Vireo (*Vireo solitarius*)
Anguilla **MS**654b

161-27   Red-eyed Vireo (*Vireo olivaceus*)
Venezuela 2058

161-28   Yucatan Vireo (*Vireo magister*)
Cayman Islands 342

161-29   Black-whiskered Vireo (*Vireo altiloquus*)
Anguilla 665
Barbados 839
Barbuda 513
Montserrat 604 O66
Turks and Caicos Islands 387

162   NEW WORLD BLACKBIRDS
162-8   Montezuma Oropendola (*Psarocolius montezuma*)
British Honduras 213
Nicaragua 1781

162-20   Solitary Cacique (*Cacicus solitarius*)
Ecuador 1122

162-23   Epaulet Oriole (*Icterus cayanensis*)
Ecuador 1537

162-25   Yellow Oriole (*Icterus nigrogularis*)
Netherlands Antilles 369

162-28   Yellow-tailed Oriole (*Icterus mesomelas*)
Ecuador 1330 1336

162-32   Spotted-breasted Oriole (*Icterus pectoralis*)
El Salvador 1188
Nicaragua 1785

162-35   Hooded Oriole (*Icterus cucullatus*)
Belize 453

162-36   Troupial (*Icterus icterus*)
Brazil 1435
Grenada 1062
Nicaragua 2726
Panama 919
Venezuela 1697

162-37   Northern Oriole (*Icterus galbula*)
Burkina Faso 791
Comoro Islands 551
Cuba 1287
Hungary 3638
Montserrat 662
Nevis 292
Rumania 4939
United States of America 1949

162-39   Black-cowled Oriole (*Icterus dominicensis*)
Dominican Republic 1382
Haiti 1133

162-41   St. Lucia Oriole (*Icterus laudabilis*)
St. Lucia 419

162-43   Montserrat Oriole (*Icterus oberi*)
Montserrat 250 630

162-48   Saffron-cowled Blackbird (*Xanthopsar flavus*)
Argentine Republic 1416 1593
Kampuchea 648

162-49   Oriole Blackbird (*Gymnomystax mexicanus*)
Venezuela 1759

162-53   Red-winged Blackbird (*Agelaius phoeniceus*)
Cuba 1723 3152

162-61   Red-breasted Blackbird (*Sturnella militaris*)
Surinam 575 860

162-64   Long-tailed Meadowlark (*Sturnella loyca*)
Falkland Islands 196 299

162-65   Eastern Meadowlark (*Sturnella magna*)
Cuba 2959
Rwanda 1240

162-66   Western Meadowlark (*Sturnella neglecta*)
United States of America 1945 1955 1956 1963 1966 1979

162-69   Scarlet-headed Blackbird (*Amblyramphus holosericeus*)
Argentine Republic 1191
Kampuchea 651
Uruguay 1219

162-77   Cuban Blackbird (*Dives atroviolacea*)
Cuba 1810 2355

162-79   Great-tailed Grackle (*Quiscalus mexicanus*)
El Salvador 1190
Nicaragua 1789
Togo 1822

162-83   Antillean Grackle (*Quiscalus niger*)
Cayman Islands 339

162-84   Carib Grackle (*Quiscalus lugubris*)
Barbados 627a 630 682
Barbuda 511
Grenadines of St. Vincent 116
Montserrat 601 726 O63

162-89   Common Cowbird (*Molothrus bonariensis*)
Barbuda 266
Uruguay 1212 1604
Venezuela 2058

162-91   Brown-headed Cowbird (*Molothus ater*)
Uganda 497

162-93   Bobolink (*Dolichonyx oryzivorus*)
Grenadines of Grenada 598
Montserrat 659

163   FINCHES

163-1   Chaffinch (*Fringilla coelebs*)
Albania 1463
Equatorial Guinea 93
Germany (East Germany) E2098
Hungary 1783
Poland 1697 1704
Tunisia 604
Yemen 594
Yugoslavia 1325

163-5   Serin (*Serinus serinus*)
Albania 1458

163-8   Citril Finch (*Serinus citrinella*)
Andorra F259

163-21   Yellow Canary (*Serinus flaviventris*)
Ascension 199
Lesotho 505
St. Helena 177 422
Tristan Da Cunha 56

163-38   Golden-winged Grosbeak (*Rhynchostruthus socotranus*)
Somalia 659

163-39   Greenfinch (*Carduelis chloris*)
Albania 1685
San Marino 947
Sweden 633
Yugoslavia 1326

163-43   Siskin (*Carduelis spinus*)
Hungary 2838
Poland 1697 1703

163-50   Hooded Siskin (*Carduelis magellanica*)
Argentine Republic 1442 1591
Uruguay 1216

163-58   Black-chinned Siskin (*Carduelis barbata*)
Falkland Islands 434

163-59   American Goldfinch (*Carduelis tristis*)
Montserrat 663
United States of America 1944 1959 1976

163-62   Goldfinch (*Carduelis carduelis*)
Afghanistan 887 1065
Albania 838
Andorra F369
Belgium 2849
Bulgaria 1522
Cyprus (Turkish Cypriot Posts) 141
Czechoslovakia 1124 2076
Germany (East Germany) E1572
Great Britain 1235
Grenada 414 418
Hungary 1746 1750 2803 2838
Ifni 162 165 168

Iran 1570
Jordan 821
Lebanon 868
Monaco 732
Mongolia 1239
Rumania 2653
San Marino 598
Switzerland J225
Syria 1371
Yugoslavia 1324

163-63 Redpoll (*Acanthis flammea*)
Czechoslovakia 1521

163-66 Linnet (*Acanthis cannabina*)
Albania 1459
Germany (East Germany) E2103
Hungary 2795
San Marino 944

163-67 Yemeni Linnet (*Acanthis yemensis*)
Yemen 322 R73

163-74 Trumpeter Finch (*Rhodopechys githaginea*)
Spanish Sahara 290 291

163-81 Common Rosefinch (*Carpodacus erythrinus*)
Germany (East Germany) E2101
Korea (North Korea) N740

163-82 Purple Finch (*Carpodacus purpureus*)
United States of America 1958

163-90 Sinai Rosefinch (*Carpodacus synoicus*)
Israel 244

163-105 Red Crossbill (*Loxia curvirostra*)
Central African Empire 596
Czechoslovakia 2676
Hungary 2186
Monaco 738
Rumania 3370
Yugoslavia 1327

163-106 White-winged Crossbill (*Loxia leucoptera*)
Aitutaki 522
Germany (East Germany) E1569
Liberia 1601
St. Vincent 859

163-112 Bullfinch (*Pyrrhula pyrrhula*)
Albania 1686
Andorra F260
Azores 468
Bulgaria 1517
Czechoslovakia 1125 2075
Finland 1001
Germany (West Germany) 1317
Germany (East Germany) E994
Lebanon 867
Norway 964
Rumania 2655
San Marino 943
Sweden 632
Switzerland J222
Yemen 597
Yugoslavia 1323

163-113 Hawfinch (*Coccothraustes coccothraustes*)
Albania 1687
Belgium 2845
Czechoslovakia 1448
Sweden 1208
Yugoslavia 1328

163-114 Black-tailed Hawfinch (*Coccothraustes migratorius*)
Korea (North Korea) N644

163-115 Masked Hawfinch (*Coccothraustes personatus*)
China (People's Republic) 3194

163-120 Evening Grosbeak (*Coccothraustes vespertinus*)
Nevis 290

164 WAXBILLS
164-13 Green-winged Pytilia (*Pytilia melba*)
Swaziland 238

164-20 Black-bellied Seedcracker (*Pyrenestes ostrinus*)
Togo 361 964 1315

164-21 Lesser Seedcracker (*Pyrenestes minor*)
Malawi 734

164-27 Peters's Twin-spot (*Hypargos niveoguttatus*)
Mozambique 709

164-33 Red-billed Fire Finch (*Lagonosticta senegala*)
Algeria 689
Malawi 313
Mali 634
Rwanda 474

164-37 Black-faced Fire Finch (*Lagonosticta larvata*)
Mali 633

164-38 Cordon-bleu (*Uraeginthus angolensis*)
Botswana 223

164-39 Red-cheeked Cordon-bleu (*Uraeginthus bengalus*)
Gambia 233
Iran 1707
Mali 632

164-46 Yellow-bellied Waxbill (*Estrilda melanotis*)
Iran 1707

164-49 Orange-cheeked Waxbill (*Estrilda melpoda*)
Gambia 204 226

164-53 Common Waxbill (*Estrilda astrild*)
Ascension 201 214
French Polynesia 352
Rwanda 469
St. Helena 421

164-55 Black-crowned Waxbill (*Estrilda nonnula*)
Rwanda 962

164-59 Red Munia (*Amandava amandava*)
Aitutaki 351 493 O32

164-64 Locust Finch (*Ortygospiza locustella*)
Zambia 265

164-66 Painted Finch (*Emblema picta*)
Niue 629

164-71 Crimson Finch (*Neochmia phaeton*)
Australia 670

164-73 Spotted-sided Finch (*Poephila guttata*)
Australia 669

164-83 Blue-faced Parrot Finch (*Erythrura trichroa*)
Palau 100
Vanuatu 307

164-85   Red-throated Parrot Finch (*Erythrura psittacea*)
New Caledonia 403

164-87   Red-headed Parrot Finch (*Erythrura cyaneovirens*)
Aitutaki 347 459
New Hebrides 161 F176 223 F237
Niuafo'ou 29 37 78
Samoa 284

164-88   Pink-billed Parrot Finch (*Erythrura kleinschmidti*)
Fiji 567

164-89   Gouldian Finch (*Chloebia gouldiae*)
Aitutaki 317 475 O17

164-95   Black & White Mannikin (*Lonchura bicolor*)
Togo 362

164-107   Chestnut Mannikin (*Lonchura malacca*)
Vietnam S354

164-118   Chestnut-breasted Mannikin (*Lonchura castaneothorax*)
Aitutaki 329 488 O29
French Polynesia 381

164-126   Java Sparrow (*Padda oryzivora*)
Aitutaki 323 482 O23
Cocos (Keeling) Islands 15
Indonesia 1026
St. Helena 419

165   WEAVERS, SPARROWS
165-1   Village Indigobird (*Vidua chalybeata*)
Ethiopia 543
Mali 579

165-6   Fischer's Whydah (*Vidua fischeri*)
Sierra Leone 853

165-7   Shaft-tailed Whydah (*Vidua regia*)
Bophuthatswana 62

165-8   Pin-tailed Whydah (*Vidua macroura*)
French Territory of the Afars and the Issas 648
Gambia 245
Nigeria 484
Rwanda 243
Swaziland 249a
Togo 893

165-9   Paradise Whydah (*Vidua paradisaea*)
Malawi 318 357
Mauritania D189
Somalia 494

165-10   Broad-tailed Paradise Whydah (*Vidua orientalis*)
Ethiopia 540
Liberia 740
Malawi 370 371 372 373
Niger 376 714
Togo 894

165-11   White-billed Buffalo Weaver (*Bubalornis albirostris*)
Mali 636

165-20   Sociable Weaver (*Philetairus socius*)
Congo (Brazzaville) 113

165-22   House Sparrow (*Passer domesticus*)
San Marino 938
Yugoslavia 2020 2021

165-23   Spanish Sparrow (*Passer hispaniolensis*)
Yugoslavia 2022

165-38   Tree Sparrow (*Passer montanus*)
China (Taiwan) 1071
Vietnam S356
Yugoslavia 2023

165-39   Sudan Golden Sparrow (*Auripasser luteus*)
Niger 1045

165-64   Little Masked Weaver (*Ploceus luteolus*)
Niger 250 250a

165-65   Spectacled Weaver (*Ploceus ocularis*)
Transkei 78

165-67   Strange Weaver (*Ploceus alienus*)
Rwanda 956

165-73   Orange Weaver (*Ploceus aurantius*)
Uganda 115

165-74   Heuglin's Masked Weaver (*Ploceus heuglini*)
Rwanda 1279

165-83   African Masked Weaver (*Ploceus velatus*)
Botswana 515

165-85   Vitelline Masked Weaver (*Ploceus vitellinus*)
Djibouti Republic 712
Mali 581

165-86   Speke's Weaver (*Ploceus spekei*)
Sierra Leone 856

165-88   Village Weaver (*Ploceus cucullatus*)
Benin 864
Biafra 7
Ethiopia 636
Gambia 199 221
Nigeria 175 222
Senegal 379

165-103   Asian Golden Weaver (*Ploceus hypoxanthus*)
Vietnam S353

165-107   Baya Weaver (*Ploceus philippinus*)
Vietnam S353

165-125   Red-headed Malimbe (*Malimbus rubricollis*)
Biafra 7
Nigeria 175 222

165-128   Red-headed Weaver (*Anaplectes melanotis*)
Bechuanaland 174
Botswana 212
Ethiopia 1308
Mozambique 707

165-130   Red-headed Quelea (*Quelea erythrops*)
Rwanda 476

165-131   Red-billed Quelea (*Quelea quelea*)
Niger 1046
Rwanda 241
Zaire 1133

165-132   Madagascar Red Fody (*Foudia madagascariensis*)
Malagasy Republic 59
St. Helena 181 195 420
Seychelles 412 487 653
Tristan Da Cunha 60
Zil Elwannyen Sesel 9

165-133   Mascarene Fody (*Foudia eminentissima*)
British Indian Ocean Territory 64
Comoro Islands 62 MS277
Zil Elwannyen Sesel 58

165-135   Mauritius Fody (*Foudia rubra*)
Mauritius 321 353

165-136   Seychelles Fody (*Foudia sechellarum*)
Seychelles 441

165-137   Rodriguez Fody (*Foudia flavicans*)
Mauritius 318 350 371

165-140   Golden Bishop (*Euplectes afer*)
Gambia 237

165-144   Red-crowned Bishop (*Euplectes hordeacea*)
Congo (Brazzaville) 762
Ghana 220 385 447
Uganda 120

165-145   Red Bishop (*Euplectes orix*)
Botswana 418
Chad 82
Lesotho 511
Niger 249a
Nigeria 486
Rwanda 239 899
Senegal 237
Swaziland 248a
Togo 1534

165-147   Yellow-rumped Bishop (*Euplectes capensis*)
Bechuanaland 171
Botswana 209
Malawi 315

165-148   Fan-tailed Whydah (*Euplectes axillaris*)
Angola 473
Rwanda 248

165-149   Yellow-mantled Whydah (*Euplectes macrourus*)
Congo (Brazzaville) 765
Gambia 194 206 216
Rhodesia 538
Togo 895

165-152   Red-collared Whydah (*Euplectes ardens*)
Togo 1532

165-153   Long-tailed Whydah (*Euplectes progne*)
Swaziland 96 136 149
Togo 896

166   STARLINGS
166-4   Samoan Starling (*Aplonis atrifusca*)
Samoa 282

166-8   Norfolk Island Starling (*Aplonis fusca*)
Norfolk Island 115

166-29   African Red-winged Starling (*Onychognathus morio*)
Ciskei 10

166-37   Iris Glossy Starling (*Lamprotornis iris*)
Benin 1011
Dahomey 252

166-42   Red-shouldered Glossy Starling (*Lamprotornis nitens*)
Angola 471

166-44   Greater Blue-eared Glossy Starling (*Lamprotornis chalybaeus*)
Chad 163

166-45   Lesser Blue-eared Glossy Starling (*Lamprotornis chloropterus*)
Rhodesia 541

166-46   Sharp-tailed Glossy Starling (*Lamprotornis acuticaudus*)
Angola 472

166-47   Splendid Glossy Starling (*Lamprotornis splendidus*)
Niger 251a

166-55   Violet Starling (*Cinnyricinclus leucogaster*)
Angola 478
Gambia 198 220
Ghana 363
Malawi 311
Mali 10 17
Mozambique 708
Niger 298 568
Swaziland 239
Togo 1531
Venda 73
Yemen 324 D371 R76 R263

166-57   White-winged Starling (*Neocichla gutturalis*)
Angola 476

166-61   Superb Starling (*Spreo superbus*)
Ivory Coast 665a
Uganda 379

166-76   Daurian Starling (*Sturnus sturninus*)
Korea (North Korea) N1210

166-77   Rose-coloured Starling (*Sturnus roseus*)
Albania 1284
Bulgaria 1523
Mongolia 203
Rumania 4796
Russia 2783

166-78   Common Starling (*Sturnus vulgaris*)
Aitutaki 318 476
Burundi 537 561
Denmark 828
Monaco 737

166-79   Spotless Starling (*Sturnus unicolor*)
Spain 2851

166-80   Grey Starling (*Sturnus cineraceus*)
Korea (North Korea) N1209

166-86   Rothschild's Mynah (*Leucopsar rothschildi*)
Indonesia 1682 MS1684
Jersey 74

166-87   Common Mynah (*Acridotheres tristis*)
Aitutaki 332 489
Ascension 204

166-92   Chinese Jungle Mynah (*Acridotheres cristatellus*)
China (Taiwan) 718
Vietnam N278 190

166-104   Hill Myna (*Gracula religiosa*)
Ceylon 485
Thailand 563
Vietnam 184

166-107   Yellow-billed Oxpecker (*Buphagus africanus*)
Central African Republic 974

166-108   Red-billed Oxpecker (*Buphagus erythrorhynchus*)
Upper Volta 703

167   ORIOLES
167-11   Golden Oriole (*Oriolus oriolus*)
Albania 839
Botswana 220
Bulgaria 1518
Burundi 559 583
Cyprus (Turkish Cypriot Posts) 143
Czechoslovakia 1123
Germany (West Germany) 1316
Germany (East Germany) E1573
Guinea 742 748
Hungary 1226 1785 2347
Kuwait 588
Lebanon 871
Libya 1198
Mauritania D181
Mongolia 205 1241
Poland 1697 1700
Qatar 397
Rumania 2649
Russia 4922
San Marino 593
Switzerland J226

167-12   African Golden Oriole (*Oriolus auratus*)
Angola 469
Bechuanaland 168
Botswana 206
Rwanda 478

167-13   Black-naped Oriole (*Oriolus chinensis*)
China (People's Republic) 3015 3204
China (Taiwan) 718 1134
Indonesia 1025
Korea (North Korea) N270 N1561
Korea (South Korea) 1764
Malaysia 22 50
Vietnam N454

167-16   Western Black-headed Oriole (*Oriolus brachyrhynchus*)
Sierra Leone 624

167-17   Dark-headed Oriole (*Oriolus monacha*)
Ethiopia 539

167-18   African Black-headed Oriole (*Oriolus larvatus*)
Ciskei 14a
Swaziland 236
Venda 105

167-20   Asian Black-headed Oriole (*Oriolus xanthornus*)
Ceylon 495
India 764

167-23   Maroon Oriole (*Oriolus traillii*)
Bhutan **MS**449
China (Taiwan) 619
Vietnam N458

168   DRONGOS
168-6   Aldabra Drongo (*Dicrurus aldabranus*)
British Indian Ocean Territory 62

168-9   Black Drongo (*Dicrurus macrocercus*)
Indonesia 1024

169   WATTLEBIRDS
169-1   Kokako (*Callaeas cinerea*)
New Zealand 1292

169-2   Saddleback (*Creadion carunculatus*)
New Zealand 813 1295

171   WOOD SWALLOWS
171-2   White-breasted Wood Swallow (*Artamus leucorhynchus*)
Aitutaki 326 483 O24

171-6   Masked Wood Swallow (*Artamus personatus*)
Australia 737

172   BUTCHER BIRDS
172-7   Black-backed Magpie (*Gymnorhina tibicen*)
Australia 364 740
New Caledonia 791

173   BOWERBIRDS
173-3   Spotted Catbird (*Ailuroedus melanotis*)
Australia 734b

173-8   Striped Gardener Bowerbird (*Amblyornis subularis*)
Papua New Guinea 61

173-11   Flamed Bowerbird (*Sericulus aureus*)
Indonesia 1766

173-12   Adelbert Bowerbird (*Sericulus bakeri*)
Papua New Guinea 62

173-13   Regent Bowerbird (*Sericulus chrysocephalus*)
Australia 736

173-17   Lauterbach's Bowerbird (*Chlamydera lauterbachi*)
Indonesia 1765

174   BIRDS OF PARADISE
174-3   Sickle Crested Bird of Paradise (*Cnemophilus macgregorii*)
Papua New Guinea 176

174-13   Magnificent Riflebird (*Ptiloris magnificus*)
Papua New Guinea 71

174-15   Twelve-wired Bird of Paradise (*Seleucidis melanoleuca*)
Indonesia 1687
Papua New Guinea 70

174-18   Black-billed Sicklebill (*Drepanornis albertisii*)
Indonesia 1723 1724
Papua New Guinea 65

174-20   Black Sicklebill (*Epimachus fastosus*)
Indonesia 1722

174-21   Brown Sicklebill (*Epimachus meyeri*)
Papua New Guinea 67

174-22   Arfak Bird of Paradise (*Astrapia nigra*)
Indonesia 1767

174-24   Ribbon-tailed Bird of Pardise (*Astrapia mayeri*)
Papua New Guinea 239

174-25   Princess Stephanie's Bird of Paradise (*Astrapia stephaniae*)
Papua New Guinea 240

174-27   Superb Bird of Paradise (*Lophorina superba*)
Indonesia 1768

174-28   Arfak Parotia (*Parotia sefilata*)
Indonesia 1686 **MS**1689

174-29   Queen Carola's Parotia (*Parotia carolae*)
Papua New Guinea 237

174-30   Lawes's Parotia (*Parotia lawesii*)
Papua New Guinea 64

174-33   King of Saxony Bird of Paradise (*Pteridophora*
alberti)
Papua New Guinea 173

174-34   King Bird of Paradise (*Cicinnurus regius*)
Indonesia 1683
Papua New Guinea 174

174-35   Magnificent Bird of Paradise (*Diphyllodes*
magnificus)
Papua New Guinea 69

174-36   Wilson's Bird of Paradise (*Diphyllodes respublica*)
Indonesia 1721

174-37   Greater Bird of Paradise (*Paradisaea apoda*)
Belgium 1820
Indonesia 964
Netherlands New Guinea 27 28 29 39 40
Papua New Guinea 4 16 D6
Trinidad and Tobago 303
West Irian 25 26 36
West New Guinea 5 7 9

174-38   Raggiana Bird of Paradise (*Paradisaea raggiana*)
Australia 904
New Guinea 150 151 152 153 154 155 156 157 158 159 160
161 162 163 164 165 166 167 168 169 170 171 172 173 174
175 176 177 178 179 179a 180 180a 181 182 183 184 185
186 187 188 189 190 191 192 193 193a 194 194a 195 196
197 198 199 200 201 202 203 206 207 O10 O11 O12 O13
O14 O15 O16 O17 O18 O19 O20 O21 O22 O23 O24 O25
O26 O27 O28 O29 O30 O31 O32 O33
Papua 133 151
Papua New Guinea 42 175 452

174-39   Lesser Bird of Paradise (*Paradisaea minor*)
Netherlands New Guinea 25 26 38
Papua New Guinea 68
West New Guinea 20 3

174-40   Goldie's Bird of Paradise (*Paradisaea decora*)
Papua New Guinea 238

174-41   Red Bird of Paradise (*Paradisaea rubra*)
Indonesia 1688 **MS**1689

174-42   Emperor of Germany Bird of Paradise (*Paradisaea*
guilielmi)
Papua New Guinea 66

174-43   Blue Bird of Paradise (*Paradisaea rudolphi*)
Papua New Guinea 63

175   CROWS, JAYS
175-4   Blue Jay (*Cyanocitta cristata*)
Central African Republic 1099
Mauritania 827
United States of America **MS**1726

175-29   Plush-crested Jay (*Cyanocorax chrysops*)
Argentine Republic 1517

175-35   White-throated Magpie-Jay (*Calocitta formosa*)
El Salvador 1192
Nicaragua 1783

175-36   Collie's Magpie-Jay (*Calocitta colliei*)
Central African Republic 1102
United States of America 1223 A1304

175-37   Jay (*Garrulus glandarius*)
Cyprus 337
Djibouti Republic 746
Hungary 1784
Iraq 796
Macao 593
Poland 1697 1699
Rumania 4850
Switzerland J228
Togo 1314

175-38   Lanceolated Jay (*Garrulus lanceolatus*)
Afghanistan 544

175-39   Purple Jay (*Garrulus lidthi*)
Japan 929
Malagasy Republic **MS**325

175-40   Grey Jay (*Perisoreus canadensis*)
Canada 620
Mongolia 1139

175-43   Ceylon Blue Magpie (*Urocissa ornata*)
Sri Lanka 684

175-44   Formosan Blue Magpie (*Urocissa caerulea*)
China (Taiwan) 621

175-46   Red-billed Blue Magpie (*Urocissa erythrorhyncha*)
China (Taiwan) 360
India 578

175-48   Green Magpie (*Cissa chinensis*)
Nepal 351
Thailand 894

175-51   Azure-winged Magpie (*Cyanopica cyana*)
Korea (North Korea) N643 N1558
Mongolia 1238
Portugal 1618
Spain 2194

175-61   Magpie (*Pica pica*)
Aden Protectorate States 112
Afghanistan 1062
Ascension 133
Cambodia 162
China (Taiwan) 580
Czechoslovakia 2074
Great Britain 1231
Kampuchea 466
Korea (South Korea) 121 154 1063a 1424 1546

175-70   Nutcracker (*Nicifraga caryocatactes*)
Czechoslovakia 1524
Monaco 1559

175-71   Chough (*Pyrrhocorax pyrrhocorax*)
Isle of Man 126
Yugoslavia 1518

175-87   Rook (*Corvus frugilegus*)
Austria 1215
Japan 1435
Yugoslavia 2009

175-97   Carrion Crow (*Corvus corone*)
Netherlands 486 790a
Sweden 571

175-109   Raven (*Corvus corax*)
Denmark 827
Greenland 65
Iceland 600
Niger 453
Poland 1202

How often do you get an offer you can't refuse?

Members of the Stanley Gibbons Collectors Club regularly receive offers similar to those above at attractive prices and on top quality material. Stanley Gibbons Collectors Club stocks Thematics, Great Britain, Commonwealth and Foreign from 1840 to date, from unmounted mint to used, from First Day Covers to Presentation Packs.

What Club membership means to you: Attractive prices on top quality material. • A range which eclipses most dealers' stocks. • Advice and help with your collection. • Regular Club price lists with special "members only" offers. • Albums/Catalogues/Accessories. • Official Club Membership Card.

Our range of material includes: ★ *Upwards of 5,000 Commonwealth and Foreign sets at discount prices* ★ *Thematic cross-reference to identify* **BIRDS** *sets at a glance* ★ *All major themes well represented* ★ *Commemoratives – sets and year sets* ★ *First Day Covers, ordinary and special handstamped* ★ *Presentation Packs* ★ *Missing Phosphors* ★ *Gutter Pairs* ★ *Definitives, singles, sets and FDC's* ★ *Offers from all reigns* ★ *Missing Colours* ★ *Inverted watermarks* ★ *PHQ cards, mint and special handstamped* ★ *Booklets* ★ *Regionals and FDC's* ★ *Postage Dues* ★ *High Values* ★ *Varieties* ★ *Machins.*

An offer you can't refuse is FREE membership with no obligation, simply by writing to:

Stanley
Gibbons
Collectors
Club

Parkside, Christchurch Road,
RINGWOOD, Hampshire.
BH24 3SH. England.

IMPORTANT MESSAGE TO THEMATIC STAMP COLLECTORS!

You know how important it is to have the very lastest Stanley Gibbons Thematic Catalogues with their listings of all the new issues, up to date information on earlier stamps and of course prices accurately set by experts with their finger on the pulse of the current international stamp market.

If you would like us to notify you of the next edition all you have to do is complete the form below and post it to:

> **The Advance Information Service,**
> **Stanley Gibbons Publications Ltd.,**
> **5 Parkside, Christchurch Road,**
> **Ringwood, Hampshire BH24 3SH.**

For similar information on other SG thematic catalogues please indicate title of interest on the form.

ADVANCE INFORMATION WITHOUT OBLIGATION

To: The Advance Information Service,
    Stanley Gibbons Publications Ltd.,
    5 Parkside, Christchurch Road,
    Ringwood, Hampshire BH24 3SH.

Please notify me of publication dates of new editions

of ....

Name: ....

Address: ....

....

....